THE BIOCYCLE GUIDE
TO
YARD WASTE COMPOSTING

Edited By The Staff Of

BioCycle

Journal of Waste Recycling

The JG Press, Inc.
Emmaus, Pennsylvania

The JG Press, Inc.
Emmaus, Pennsylvania

Printed on recycled paper in the United States of America.
ISBN 0-932424-10-4
Second Printing

7116

Contents

Introduction

THE MOST LOGICAL FIRST STEP

T O PARAPHRASE the historic event of 20 years ago when astronauts landed on the moon, yard waste composting can be considered one small step for green debris, one huge step for solid waste management. Mankind will surely benefit from the steady increase in well-managed programs.

As states and communities explore approaches to diverting solid waste from landfills and incinerators, one material that has come under increasing scrutiny is yard waste. The reason for this interest is obvious. Yard waste ranks right behind paper as the second largest component in the nation's solid waste stream. If you want to move away from disposal toward utilization, yard waste is a logical material to target.

Diverting such materials as leaves, grass clippings and tree trimmings affects citizens, haulers, officials, consultants, planners, researchers, landfill owners, soil conditioner suppliers, equipment manufacturers, private sector initiatives, regulatory decisions, as well as local and state laws. That's not an insignificant contribution in a society seeking to alter its throwaway mentality!

In the name of good housekeeping, millions of Americans rake leaves into piles and place them in many millions of plastic bags. Collection crews haul them off to landfills where — until a short time ago — they were indiscriminately buried along with "all the other garbage." So much for good housekeeping. When yard waste composting programs are initiated, the public begins to understand what source separation and organic recycling are all about. The education and citizen participation that underlie all effective recycling and composting programs are well underway. Backyard composting of everyday materials as landscape trimmings, weeds, salad leftovers and yard residues, etc. takes on new significance. Along with being the age-old sensible practice of savvy gardeners, the backyard compost heap is a growing (or shrinking) symbol of *waste reduction*. And waste reduction is a key strategy in municipal waste management.

The home kitchen and garage (or wherever "trash containers" are stored) also have a new look. "Biowaste" containers for household organics make it easy to separate materials that can be included with yard waste. Statistics from a community in the Federal Republic of Germany show that 42 percent of the household refuse was collected via the "biowaste" containers. Increasingly, municipalities in the United States are also planning programs that combine food wastes with yard waste composting programs. The end product from biowaste composting programs is a highly-accepted soil conditioner.

For haulers and landfill owners, collection of yard waste and transport to a composting site involves new contracts, new schedules, special equipment, crew training, and potentially, management of the compost site. The entire process is a far cry from the traditional disposal role for both private and public curbside collection services. Synchronizing yard waste collection with recyclables such as glass, newspaper, metals and plastics — instituting a pay-by-bag collection fee for nonrecyclables — marketing processed materials — all aspects have introduced new variables for entrepreneurial and environmental management.

Elected officials, consultants, planners, researchers in the solid waste management field are all key players in yard waste composting. Making a decision to ban landfilling of leaves and yard waste may not be as tough politically as raising taxes or siting a new incinerator. But it has great impact, leading to a continuing set of initiatives that range from equipment purchases, facility construction and market development.

Officials in Seattle, Washington spent two years shaping a vision of its waste management future and came up with an ambitious goal of recycling and composting 60 percent of its generated waste by 1998. Development of a waste-to-energy plant was set aside to give citizens a chance to show how much recycling can be done, and because of uncertainties about future regulation of ash disposal.

Seattle conducted a comprehensive waste stream analysis, collecting samples monthly for a year from both commercial and residential waste to ensure an accurate record of seasonal trends. The most effective waste reduction strategy has been the variable can rate structure which gives residents a financial incentive to reduce the amount of garbage they throw away. Residents must pay for the amount of garbage they produce. As they reduce the amount set out, they are rewarded by a cheaper garbage bill.

In October, 1988, the Seattle City Council mandated that yard waste be separated from garbage. To handle this yard waste, the city has begun a three-pronged yard waste management strategy of backyard composting, curbside yard waste collection and expansion of the transfer station "clean green" collection program.

More than $500,000 was budgeted to get the backyard composting program underway, with 75 percent coming from the Washington Department of Ecology. The equivalent of six full-time trainers were assigned to reach 6,000 residents, providing in-home instruction on composting techniques.

On January 1, 1989, as part of new garbage collection contracts, Seattle began curbside collection of yard waste from all city residences. For a fee of $2 per month, as many as 20 cans, bags or bundles of yard waste will be collected. Yard waste is collected on the same day as garbage using a one-person rear-load truck.

The yard waste is hauled to a new composting facility on 26 acres near the landfill. The facility is designated to process 30,000 tons annually, but with additional equipment could accommodate more. The yard waste is shredded by a tub grinder, screened and piled in windrows to compost. The finished compost will be sold as a soil amendment or landfill cover.

The yard waste composting program is an integral part of Seattle's plan to achieve a 60 percent recycling rate.

As the pages of this book illustrate beyond doubt, yard waste composting is meaningful . . . is economical . . . is environmentally correct . . . and it's **doable**. There is no reason to delay . . . to be tentative with programs . . . to bury ourselves or our communities in a doom-and-gloom attitude about being buried in waste. The full scope of the policies, the public participation, the entrepreneurial opportunities, the soil conservation benefits from nutrient recycling, the entire sense of relevance generated by aggressive adoption and implementation of yard waste composting — all become evident as you read on.

Jerome Goldstein
Editor, *BioCycle*
October, 1989

Section
I

PLANNING YARD WASTE UTILIZATION PROGRAMS

1

SYSTEMATIC SHIFT FROM THE LANDFILL

IT IS NOT by accident or luck that The Greater Cleveland Ecological Association has from the beginning enjoyed success with its leaf composting program. Ten years ago, the city took a long, cool look at the horrendous volume of leaves going into the landfill, and went about making a change in a systematic way.

With money from the George Gund Foundation and the Cleveland Foundation, Ed Janesz of the Cuyahoga County (Ohio) Cooperative Extension Service was hired to do a feasibility study on the practicality of composting the leaves instead of landfilling them. "The study indicated that composting would indeed be practical, especially with the rising cost of landfill fees," says Janesz. The study paved the way for another grant, this one for $34,000, from the Gund Foundation to get the composting program started. There was one catch: the effort had to be self-supporting after one year. "That was going to be a little tricky," Janesz recalls, "since we knew from our study it was going to take two years to make saleable compost."

Nevertheless, the Greater Cleveland Ecological Association, as it was called, was established as a non-profit corporation, and Janesz was hired as Executive Director. He was assisted by 14 board members, chosen for their clout in local government, their contacts with the news media, and their experience in public relations. The first pressing need was to find some leaves that had been stockpiled in the past season or earlier, so that they could be turned into compost to sell the first year in keeping with the foundation's stipulation to be self supporting in that length of time. Such stockpiled leaves were found, especially at Cleveland's Warrensville Workhouse, where three communities had been piling leaves. Acreage at this site subsequently was offered by the city to the Association as a permanent composting site. Other sites were offered by local governments, public works departments and private companies. The town of Shaker Heights, for example, gave land at its restricted landfill; the city of Lakewood authorized eight acres of its land, and the Cleveland Electric Illuminating Company offered 15 acres which brought in three more communities. "There are 62 communities altogether in Cuyahoga County that we hope someday to serve," says Janesz. "We are at full field capacity right now, with five sites averaging about 8 to 10 acres in size, serving 15 communities. But things are breaking for us. Communities are now calling us and wanting to know how to get involved in the program."

To get in on the action, a community pays a one-time $1500 membership fee up front. The community's public service department in charge of the leaves hauls them to the nearest composting site at its expense, and pledges at least 200 hours of in-kind labor and equipment annually to windrow the leaves, turn them, load customer trucks, and maintain sites. "We pro-rate the in-kind labor charge to the size of the community," explains Janesz. "A bigger city having more leaves will have to donate more labor and equipment time than a smaller city with fewer leaves. We do not own any equipment. The communities have the equipment anyway and by taking turns at the composting sites, no particular community's equipment is tied up too much. It is a very, very cooperative venture, but it works because everyone benefits. We estimate we receive about a half million dollars in in-kind services which is still far less cost to the communities than landfilling which with the new law (Ohio law 592) will soon rise 30 percent up to around $10 a yard. We're taking in about 250,000 cu. yds. of leaves. I expect every community is saving at least $55,000 right now, and usually more than that."

"Since we joined the program in 1982, every aspect of our community has benefitted from this composting effort," says Robert Kleinweber, Lakewood Public Works Director. "It saves us money on landfill costs, it converts a waste product into a valuable resource and citizens can use the compost to beautify home grounds. It's the ideal form of soil ecology. It returns to the earth what has been removed."

What Janesz does, with the help of a part time secretary, a part time bookkeeper, seasonal supervisors at the composting sites, and hard work from board members, is act as coordinator of composting activities and, perhaps more important, as a marketer of the finished product. "I do the scheduling—whose leaves are going where, whose equipment and labor are on duty on what days, and when the sites are open for customers. We have a garden writer from the *Cleveland Plain Dealer* who is very good at getting out information on when compost is available. More and more I'm selling compost. I guess I'm really a broker."

BEST MARKETING METHODS

Experience has taught him the three best ways to market the finished product are:

1. "**Bag and bushel** program," as Janesz calls it. Small scale gardeners bring their own containers and pay 75¢ per generous bushel. This market is open five months, April through June, and September-October. An attendant at the gate acts as salesperson.

2. **Bulk Load Pickup.** "We load the customer's truck and charge $13 per cu. yd."

3. **Home delivery.** Surprisingly, perhaps, this market is the most popular, taking 60 percent to 70 percent of the compost sold. The Association contracts with Three-Z-Inc. to do the hauling. Three-Z, a local dealer in topsoil with a large fleet of trucks, is now vigorously getting into composting activities. "Again, I'm coordinator," says Janesz. "We take the requests for home delivery, and schedule the deliveries according to when front end loaders are available for loading. I pass the orders on to Three-Z. Home delivery is available spring, summer and fall, four days a week. Minimum residential sale is 2 cu. yds., maximum, 10 cu. yds. We charge $50.10 for 2 cu. yds. of regular grade, and $178.30 for 10 cu. yds, including delivery charge and taxes. For out-of-county delivery, there's an added $20 charge. The trucks hold 10 yds. By using a split gate to divide the truck bed, two deliveries, say of 5 yds each, can be hauled at once, greatly saving delivery costs. Semi truckloads delivered to landscapers and commercial

growers are sold at a discount to encourage the use of composted materials on lawns and in potting medium for nursery stock.

"I think part of the popularity of home delivery, aside from its convenience, is that we have a good publicity program. We try to do 30 to 40 publicity stints a year, as we call them, on TV shows, in the *Cleveland Plain Dealer* and the *Akron Beacon Journal*, plus messages in lots of newsletters, all pushing the ecological benefits of the compost. It's beautiful black stuff, and lots of times the truck drivers say that a neighbor will see a load and want some too. In fact, we have flyers that the truck drivers can pass out in situations like this."

"Regular" grade compost is all run through a shredder which the city owns and the Association uses in return for providing the city's parks and urban forest departments with 600 to 700 cu. yds. of compost for landscaping, beautification programs and a garden program for low income residents. But in an effort to develop new markets, Janesz and Three-Z are working together on a more refined compost that is sold in bags at nursery stores. Compost for this market is run through Three-Z's vibrating screen, turning it into an even finer, more granular material. This compost is then loaded on semis and hauled to P.V.P. Industries, a bagging plant in North Bloomfield, Ohio. "We don't see it after that. It is packaged into 40 lb. bags that we designed and sold for $3.39 in a radius of 200 miles of Cleveland. That's about $1.50 for us. The distributor ups that 18 percent, and the retailer has to jack it up more to make his profit. The competition's tough and so far we haven't made much money at it. We are looking for ways to take over the distribution and retailing ourselves."

But an interesting side development has resulted from the effort to sell fine grade, bagged compost. When large-scale gardeners see it in stores, they want to know if they can buy it in quantity, especially for top-dressing lawns and for mulch around flower beds and ornamentals. "So we are exploring the possibilities," says Janesz. "We think we can offer fine grade at a cost of $231.25 delivered or as little as 2 cu. yds. for $65.35. We'll see how that goes."

LOW TECH OPERATION

Janesz describes his compost making as a low tech operation. "We learned we didn't need to employ expensive windrowing equipment. We take only unbagged leaves as they are brought to us although we encourage communities to use vacuum-type pickup systems. It's cheaper and the impeller cracks the surface of the leaves which partially shreds the leaves, so breakdown is faster and therefore cheaper too. Secondly, vacuumed leaves take up less space." When the leaves arrive at a composting site, they are first stockpiled, especially in dry weather. "We may wait until mid-November to windrow them, after rains have brought moisture up to 40-60 percent by weight. When we can squeeze a little moisture out of a handful of leaves, then we know they are wet enough. Windrowing is done with front end loaders, the rows about 25 ft. wide at the base, 15 feet high, and 200 to 300 feet long. We've learned loaders on tracks are much better than those on rubber tires because the latter mire in the mud too much. Ideally it would be nice to have concrete pads to work on."

The first windrowing of the stockpiled leaves also acts as the first aeration. A second aeration or turning is done in the spring, a third in late summer and a final one in fall. The following spring, the compost is ready to shred and sell. "We use 3-ft. thermometer probes to determine when to turn the windrows. When temperature inside the windrows drops below 100 degrees F, we know oxygen is depleted and we turn immediately. The only time we've experienced odors is in the first turning in spring. We wait for the wind to subside or shift away from the residential areas before doing this turning," says Janesz.

LEAF COLLECTING SERVICE

One factor that has slowed expansion of the composting operation to some communities is that they collect leaves in plastic bags. "There is no way we can handle separating the bags from the leaves and so we have no choice but to turn these communities down," says Janesz. So he and the people at Three-Z have put their heads together and are preparing for another giant step forward, as landfill fees escalate. They plan to start a leaf collecting service. Three-Z with the trucks and know-how already in place may be able to offer the service at less cost than it would pay communities to gear up for their own collection machinery. "The association would act as the intermediary and pro-

vide free dump sites," says Janesz. "We plan to have all the information on computer, including curb miles, population, tree density, and so forth. We can go through a bidding process and compete with the landfill system. We'll be able to offer a flat fee for a one year contract or up to five. And it will still be a win situation for everyone while adding to the life of the landfills.

Another key to the Association's success, not to be overlooked, is that it has a good product and makes sure everyone knows that it has. "We can't sell compost as a fertilizer because nutrient value varies greatly and is not high, compared to commercial fertilizers, but it is a wonderful soil conditioner," says Janesz. He ticks off the advantages: the compost has an almost neutral pH, from 6.9 to 7.2, which is perfect except for acid-loving plants. It has a liming effect as well as a conditioning effect which makes it just right for the area's tight clay soils that tend to be acid. The compost increases the soil's cation exchange capacity, its ability to hold nutrients. So the fertilizer value it does have, plus any added, will be held on the root zone longer rather than go into groundwater. And even though the NPK value of the leaves is low compared to a commercial fertilizer, the nutrients are released only slowly from the humus to the plants. Annual applications tend to build up reserves of nutrients, so fertilizing effect is greater than NPK content indicates.

The gardeners know this, and a touch of Janesz' computer proves it. After four years, the reorder rate is 70 percent. That is very good and indicates a happy future for the Greater Cleveland Ecological Association. "I hope so," quips Janesz. "I badly need to hire an assistant or two."

The 250,000 cu. yds. of leaves composted last year made 20,000 cu. yds. of finished compost, with only 3 percent waste residue to go to the landfill. "Gross sales amounted to about $200,000 last year," says Janesz, "enough to keep us in the black."

TENFOLD INCREASE IN PROGRAMS

COMPOSTING is the most doable way to dramatically reduce the waste stream," says Wayne Koser of the Michigan Department of Natural Resource's Waste Management Division. In his role as a traveling adviser/ombudsman for recycling organic wastes in Michigan, Koser is keenly aware of operations at the 100 leaf and yard waste composting sites in Michigan. Each place has its own personality, its own operational features reflecting public or private management, collection methods, kind of site available, degree of mechanization and funding, and the expansion envisioned.

For a state like Michigan, expansion of yardwaste composting is critical since its Solid Waste Policy announced in 1989 establishes a range of 8 to 12 percent as an attainable goal for composting. "The state should assist in implementation . . . by providing land for us in composting projects and by providing funds where necessary for capital costs," notes the policy report. Of the 32,000 tpd of waste generated in Michigan, 3,200 tpd can be composted. The 100 sites are now estimated to be composting 300 tpd.

How does a state increase composting 10-fold in the next few years? Michigan's strategy is to use a combination of legislative initiatives, increased funding for demonstration projects, more intensive advisory efforts and public support. "The public in Michigan is eager and willing to move into composting and recycling," says David Dempsey, environmental advisor to the Governor. "We can exceed the goals in the state policy."

Anticipating the support of state legislative leaders in both parties, like Rep. Jim Kosteva and Sen. Vernon Ehlers, there is growing confidence that legislation will be passed banning yard waste from landfills beginning in 1993. Kosteva eventually would like to see a prohibition against landfilling all compostable wastes.

Along with the impact of new legislation is the incentive that comes from up to $10 million for funding demonstration projects that will show applicability of composting to rural and urban communities. The Quality of Life Bonding Proposal includes a total of $60 million to combat solid waste problems — specifically naming recycling and composting of MSW; Expanding markets for recycled materials; Waste reduction and household hazardous waste collection centers.

Wayne Koser of DNR hopes that a variety of demonstration projects will be funded in the next year or two. He continues his travels throughout the state, into the Upper Peninsula, where MSW co-composting is planned on Mackinaw Island and where the towns of Houghton and Hancock have already begun a project that composts both yard waste and commercial food waste.

"The idea," Koser emphasizes, "is to show the components of successful programs, that the composting approach does work as an important part of solid waste management. Any state that thinks it will move successful programs without financial incentives will run into difficulties. That's why we're providing seed money for projects — to show examples of each phase — screening, shredding, windrowing, marketing for communities large and small."

Michigan has set a goal of 10 percent composting based solely on redirecting a substantial portion of its leaf and yard waste from landfills. "That's a conservative figure," says Dave Dempsey. "We can do better once we get the program rolling."

THE BIOCYCLE GUIDE TO YARD WASTE COMPOSTING

Sums up Wayne Koser as he calculates the huge amount of agricultural residues from the state's fruit and vegetable processing plants: "The more compost projects that operate, the more materials that can be plugged into these projects."

GUIDEBOOK FOR MICHIGAN COMMUNITIES

As part of its educational support effort, Michigan's DNR — with money from The Clean Michigan Fund — published a *Yard Waste Composting Guidebook* for the state's communities. Along with describing methods for collection and composting, the guidebook included appendices such as the following:

Budget Worksheet for Compost Program Costs — Labor, Land, Site Improvement, Equipment, Buildings, and other direct costs (i.e., insurance, education, etc.). A corresponding worksheet covered revenues and credits, listing avoided costs for tipping fees and transport; Credits for topsoil use of compost; no-burn ordinance for counties and municipalities — "No person shall ignite or allow open burning unless permission has been issued." Further references to this useful guide appear in future chapters.

IMPACT OF A STATEWIDE INCENTIVE PROGRAM

The "Clean Michigan Fund" program, created by the state to help communities solve some pressing local environmental problems, provided grants for a number of leaf composting projects beginning in 1986. Following is a review of its impact on some towns in Michigan based on interviews one year after the awarding of the grants:

"Excellent cooperation from the people," says Jacob Montgomery in the village of East Tawas. "Very pleased," echoes Cliff Mulder, assistant to the city manager in Portage. "We more than doubled the amount of leaves picked up last year to nearly 12,000 cubic yards."

In Marquette, officials were equally enthusiastic. "We thought if 40 to 50 percent of the residents responded, we'd have a worthwhile program, but over 90 percent cooperated. We were inundated with leaves," says William Niepoth. Direct mail campaigns aided the participation rate. "Instead of newspaper blurbs, we notified people on their water bills," says Niepoth. Portage officials mailed a brochure with map, showing times leaf pickup would be done in each neighborhood.

East Tawas originally planned to buy a small dozer with its grant money but decided at the last minute to buy a front-end loader instead. "It mixes and turns the leaves better," says Montgomery.

"Since our site is a mile or so out of town, I'd have needed a trailer to haul the dozer anyway."

A village of about 2,600 people, East Tawas picks up the leaves bagged until it can afford something else. "It doesn't take us too long to knock the bags apart. It's a good job for the men when there's nothing else to do," says Montgomery. "Some folks haul their own leaves to the site. Our town lies right next to Tawas City, and there's a lot of rivalry between the two towns. Tawas City sort of snickered when we started leaf composting. Now they want a place to haul leaves too."

Marquette used its grant for a leaf vacuum, a model L400A Super Vac. "We ran into a problem of a very wet fall," says Niepoth. "Wet leaves don't suck up too fast. We found the most efficient method was to use a four-man crew — one driving, one operating the vac, and two raking the leaves into it. You have to hold the bell nozzle off the pavement a little to get a good strong airflow, and keep the exhaust vent open on the receiver box on the truck. The machine would plug occasionally on the wet leaves, but it took only about 15 minutes to take it apart and unplug it. We're satisfied. We'd like to get a second one now."

Despite the wet weather which cancelled a second collection sweep in the city, Niepoth thinks the effort was well worth it. "Very conservatively, we saved $30,000 not having to haul those 6,000 cubic yards to the landfill," he points out. Marquette's landfill is 160 miles away.

Portage elected to stay with its front-end loader for leaf collection with residents living in non-curbed neighborhoods having to bag their leaves. "We decided against a vacuum pickup because we feel it is less effective on wet leaves than using a front-end loader. But the latter, we learned, requires some manual raking. We also built a special chute on the back of the compactor trucks to facilitate loading. Too many leaves dribble out the back without the chute," says Mulder. To remedy both problems, officials are planning to use any further grant money they've applied for to buy a Claw attachment for the front-end loader.

The two jaws of the Claw open to a spread of about 8 feet and can scrape up leaves gently without harm to the uncurbed shoulder of the street, pinching together many more leaves than the scoop on the front-end loader. "This, plus using compactor trucks rather than ordinary dump trucks, will make the job even more efficient," says Mulder. "We get 6 to 7 yards on the compactors but only 1 or 2 yards on a dump truck."

Mulder calculates that already Portage has reduced the cost of handling leaves from about nine dollars to about five dollars a yard. "That still may sound high to some," he says, "but we want *all* the costs: wages, maintenance, computer use, direct mail expense, and so forth."

LOCAL, REGIONAL AND STATE POLICIES

OVER the past several years, there has been an explosion of legislation at the state level that in some way affects yard waste recycling in general. As states have begun to pass comprehensive recycling legislation, one provision that is being seen more frequently is the outright ban of recyclable materials from landfills and incinerators. Many of the first bans usually deal with yard waste. For instance, New Jersey banned leaves generated in the fall from all but composting facilities. Wisconsin banned all yard waste from disposal facilities. By fall, 1989, nine states had legislation that banned at least part of the yard waste stream from disposal facilities. Three states — Connecticut, New Jersey and Pennsylvania — have banned leaves; four states (Florida, Illinois, Minnesota, Iowa, North Carolina and Wisconsin) have banned all yard waste.

The prohibition mandates have led a number of county governments in those states to restrict disposal of yard waste prior to the date set by the state legislation. In Wisconsin, both Dane and Eau Claire Counties have passed ordinances restricting the disposal of yard waste and Sauk and Juneau Counties are considering similar measures. Broome County, New York banned leaves from its landfill in 1986 after developing an alternative composting facility at the County's landfill site.

A less drastic approach used to encourage yard waste composting is to allow those facilities to be permitted and operate under less stringent regulations than other types of solid waste processing facilities. Most states that take a less stringent approach do so because they view yard waste as a resource rather than a waste, in much the same manner that source separated paper, glass and metal are viewed as a resource. Many

state regulatory agencies also believe that the potential for environmental problems at yard waste composting facilities is much lower than at mixed waste composting facilities and other waste processing systems.

States have devised a number of strategies in their efforts to allow yard waste composting facilities to operate under less restrictive guidelines. For instance, in Michigan, yard waste that is source separated and utilized is not considered a solid waste and thus not regulated by the Department of Natural Resources. While the solid waste laws of the state do not apply if the facility violates regulations concerning air emissions, odors, groundwater contamination, etc., appropriate action can be taken under those statutes.

In Wisconsin, the degree of regulation of yard waste composting projects varies with the size of the project. Systems sized to handle less than 50 cubic yards of material annually are not regulated. Projects handling 50 cubic yards to 20,000 cubic yards are governed by a set of guidelines based primarily on site considerations and performance standards. Projects over 20,000 cubic yards in size are subject to a formal permitting process. Pennsylvania recently passed solid waste management regulations that exempt leaf composting sites from regulation if a facility follows the guidelines established by the Department of Environment Resources.

New Jersey retains perhaps the most control over projects without requiring a complex permitting procedure. Its Department of Environmental Resources requires that all leaf composting projects be permitted regardless of size, but the permitting requirements are considerably streamlined in comparison to the procedures for other solid waste processing projects. Even though leaf composting projects do not require sophisticated modeling and engineering drawings as part of the permitting procedures, it is not unusual for the process to take a year or more to complete.

An example of how states can adjust policies to allow the development of yard waste composting took place in New Jersey last year. Faced with the prospect of more than 100 municipalities with no place to take their leaves, Governor Thomas Kean signed emergency rules and amendments that exempt leaf composting sites from normal permitting requirements, allow the state to grant temporary permits for large vegetative composting facilities and allow municipalities to mulch leaves on agricultural or horticultural lands. New Jersey's Mandatory Recycling Law provided that municipalities could not dispose of leaves in landfills during the fall of the year and that those leaves must go to a permitted "composting" facility. Unfortunately, when leaf season came around, 35 percent of the state's municipalities were without permitted composting facilities, due in large part to a backlog of 40+ permit applications awaiting review by the Department of Environmental Protection. The emergency rules were needed to provide sufficient capacity for this year's leaves.

The emergency rules had three parts. The first, allows the state to grant a Temporary Certificate of Authority to Operate (TCAO) for facilities that accept 20,000 cubic yards or more of leaves or accept any amount of vegetative waste other than leaves. The TCAO is good for one year, at which time the facility must have a standard permit to continue to operate. The second part of the rules allows sites which accept less than 20,000 cy of leaves to submit an abbreviated permit package that must be reviewed and acted on within ten days. Those facilities must also follow the operating standards outlined in the order.

The final part of the rules allows municipalities to mulch leaves or agricultural or horticultural lands as long as the mulching is completed pursuant to the guidelines in the rules.

In Minnesota, Carver and Dakota counties have instituted yard waste bans at landfills. In the month directly following such a ban in Dakota County, 25 percent more yard waste was delivered to the compost site than in the highest previous month. The law in Carver County, effective Jan. 1, 1990, specifies that "leaves, grass, prunings, and garden waste cannot be collected with mixed municipal waste if that waste is going to be disposed of or processed in the metro area."

(The topic of state and regional regulations is discussed in more detail in a subsequent section.)

KEY STEPS FOR PROGRAM SUCCESS

A
S PART of its efforts to improve the planning process for municipal leaf composting, the Massachusetts Division of Solid Waste Management prepared a paper on issues to address and steps to consider. "Composting can be a low-effort, cost-effective and environmentally sound way to dispose of your community's leaves," notes the Massachusetts report, "but composting is not simply piling up leaves and letting them decompose. It is a complex, controlled process requiring advance planning."

Following are the specific steps cited in the planning process:

● **Determine the volume of leaves you want to compost.**

Your volume of leaves will help determine what size and type of operation is needed and how much compost you can make available to an interested end-user.

● **Figure out how you will collect the leaves.**

There are three basic methods of collecting leaves for composting: a drop-off system at the local landfill or transfer station, curbside collection in bags or barrels, or bulk collection, in which leaves are scooped, raked, swept or vacuumed directly off the street.

● **Evaluate different composting methods.**

There are two basic levels of technology for leaf composting. The more low-effort method is windrow composting, in which leaves are laid down in elongated piles, watered, and aerated periodically by turning. In static pile or forced aeration composting, the leaf piles are aerated by a fan or blower and perforated pipes, and turning is not required.

● **Choose a site.**

Windrow composting generally requires about one acre of land for every 6,000 cubic yards of delivered leaves. Static pile composting requires less space, about one acre per 12,000 cubic yards of leaves.

● **Assess what equipment you have or will need.**

The basic equipment needed depends on your method. Static pile systems require a pipe system and air blowers to aerate the compost pile. Windrow systems require manual turning or turning equipment such as a front-end loader, or a special windrow machine.

Screening and shredding of the leaves before and/or after composting is an optional step for both systems.

● **Determine one or more end-users for compost.**

As a general rule, the higher the quality of the compost, the easier it will be to find end users. In-town applications, such as municipal parks, recreation areas and roadsides, landfills, or residents' lawns and flower gardens, will minimize the need for marketing.

● **Secure regulatory approvals and permits.**

The necessary site approvals and permits vary widely throughout the country. In most cases, the plan should include: a schematic layout of the site; a listing of equipment and personnel with their qualifications (and/or what training they will receive); an explanation of the composting process; the monitoring techniques for both the process and the end-product; provisions for control of odors and leachate from the compost piles; and a contingency plan if compost operation ceases.

● **Alert and educate residents about your plan.**

An ongoing public education program will help maintain long-term interest and participation. While composting is still in the planning stages, consider holding public meetings and/or distributing materials to explain its economic and environmental benefits and alleviate concerns about its effects on the neighboring community.

● **Develop a protocol for monitoring the composting operation.**

In order to maintain an efficient operation and develop a safe, attractive product, you should regularly record the volume of incoming leaves, the temperature of the piles, and any odors.

● **Devise a system for tracking costs and benefits.**

Records showing the economic benefits that composting provides your community will help justify the renewed costs of next year's budget. Benefits may be expressed in the form of avoided "tipping fees;" the volume of landfill space conserved; avoided transportation costs; money saved through not having to buy compost; or any actual revenues received from sale of the compost.

Benefits include not only monetary factors, but environmental benefits, such as land conservation and revitalization of soils, which may not be quantifiable.

AN EXAMPLE OF STATE ENCOURAGEMENT

Allen J. Dusault Jr.

A FEW YEARS AGO, less than a handful of municipalities in Massachusettes composted their leaf and yard waste. By Fall, 1989, there are over 80 municipal compost operations. We hope to double that number by the end of next year and have nearly all municipalities, which now dispose of leaves, composting them by 1993.

Interest in composting in Massachusetts is stimulated primarily by economics. Tipping fees at commercial disposal facilities currently range from $60-$100/ton. However, even with such high tipping fees many municipalities have been reluctant to initiate a leaf and yard waste compost program without outside encouragement. Our role is to provide such encouragement.

We have found that the most powerful tool in developing municipal composting operations has been our technical assistance program. The technical assistance program is made up of three distinct but complementary components.

The first is a series of hands-on workshops we hold throughout the state every year detailing how to site, design and operate a municipal compost operation. The workshops include a slide presentationtion and lecture on planning, operating and trouble-shooting a composting facility. This is followed by a demonstration at an operational facility which allows municipal officials to see and talk to those who have set up successful operations.

A second component of our technical assistance program is our packet of guidance materials which details the mechanics of setting up and running a leaf and yard waste composting facility. This information packet is sent to interested municipalities and contains all the information necessary for local DPW directors to set up a low technology, cost effective composting operation.

A third component involves field work and includes site visits to prospective and operating facilities. During these visits, we help municipal officials evaluate and select an appropriate compost site, ensure regulatory compliance, reinforce the benefits of composting over disposal and help troubleshoot at problem facilities. These visits also entail a good deal of public relations and confidence building, both of which are essential aspects to a successful program.

In addition to our technical assistance program, the Massachusetts legislature has appropriated $7 million for compost grants to municipalities. Grant awards are made to three categories of municipal facilities—leaf and yard waste, woodwaste processing and municipal solid waste (MSW) compost operations. Awards range from $5,000 to $300,000 per municipality. For leaf and yard waste composting facilities, eligible cost includes site design and preparation, collection equipment, windrow turning, screeners and shredders, compost analysis, public education, etc. Funding for each item is provided at either 50 or 90 percent depending on the nature of the reimbursable item.

Last fiscal year, we awarded nearly $1 million dollars in compost grants to municipalities. Over $600,000 went to 21 municipalities for leaf and yard waste facilities. Five municipalities received the remainder for MSW feasibility studies. Massachusetts fiscal situation makes it unlikely that we will continue the grants program this year but we hope to continue the following fiscal year.

REQUIREMENTS EASED

Another factor that has contributed to the development of municipal compost facilities has been the easing of regulatory requirements for leaf and yard waste facilities. The Department has exempted municipal compost operations from solid waste facility designation, avoiding the problems attendant to permitting solid waste facilities. In its place, we use a registration procedure and site inspections to ensure proper siting, design and operations and prevent adverse environmental impacts. Although it was difficult to convince state regulators to use this approach, it has worked well and helped expedite development of new leaf composting facilities.

Despite our success to date in getting new municipal composting facilities up and running, less than one quarter of Massachusetts municipalities are composting their leaf and yard waste. The reason for this are varied but four major obstacles stand out.

The first is apathy or disinterest on the part of some municipalities, irrespective of economic considerations. Often times, unless forced or prodded to change existing practices, the current practices remain in place.

A second factor inhibiting the development of new facilities is uncertainty by municipalities about the cost of initiating and operating a leaf compost operation. Most municipal officials don't have an understanding of what capital equipment cost or operating expenses are involved. Even where municipalities are operating leaf composting facilities on a small scale, they are often afraid to expand their program because to do so entails moving into a residential collection program where accurate cost information is hard to find.

A third obstacle impeding the development of leaf and yard waste composting relates to provision of specific types of disposal contracts. Some municipalities have signed long-term contracts with haulers or disposal facilities for a fixed tipping fee that is irrespective of the quantity of waste delivered. Under these circumstances there are no economic incentives to divert leaf and yard waste from disposal.

In other situations, a municipality may have been one of the first communities to sign up with a waste to energy plant, and pay a very low tipping fee as a result. Where a town is paying $15, $20 or even $25 per ton for disposal, there is arguably little economic incentive to divert their compostable waste from the incinerator.

The last major obstacle is the invisibility of high disposal costs not paid directly by residents. This invisibility results in a lack of political pressure to reform waste management practices.

NEW INITIATIVES

In recognition of the above obstacles to further expansion of municipal leaf and yard waste composting, we are embarking on a new set of initiatives.

First, to overcome inertia of habit and disinterest on the part of some municipalities, Massachusetts will be implementing a ban prohibiting the disposal of leaves in landfills and incinerators. This will be a broad rule affecting all disposal facilities and is intended to serve as a catalyst for changing existing practices.

To address the problem of cost uncertainties surrounding leaf and yard waste composting, we have recently developed a cost effectiveness worksheet designed for municipal officials to use in determining what their composting operation should look like. Specific cost figures are given for different component costs. The worksheet then allows interested communities to custom tailor their operation calculating cost advantage depending on tipping fees, technology, available equipment, labor costs etc. under different collection and operational scenarios. With such a worksheet, we hope to demonstrate the economic advantage composting offers over incineration and landfill disposal.

To address the problem presented by contracts that offer little or no incentive for waste diversion, we are pushing the large commercial disposal facilities to set up leaf and yard composting systems. By composting rather than disposing of bulky leaf and yard waste they not only save on landfill space but also generate a cover material that costs little to produce.

We are also supplementing these initiatives with a backyard compost program. We have designed our own backyard composting brochure and will be actively promoting this through recycling committees and local programs.

In combination, the above initiatives should significantly reduce and eventually eliminate the large volume of leaf and yard waste now going for disposal, saving municipalities money and ensuring more environmentally sound waste management practices.

Allen Dusault is in the Division of Solid Waste of the Massachusetts Department of Environmental Protection in Boston.

Section
II

COLLECTION — EVALUATING OPTIONS AND METHODS

6

ANALYSIS OF
COLLECTION PROGRAMS

WHILE yard debris is a big target, the material is not as easily managed as one might expect. The problems with yard debris begin even with classifying it. Yard waste is not homogeneous, but rather made up of grass, leaves and woody material. Additionally, the composition varies probably more than any other material in the stream. In some locations, yard waste is a mere 10 to 15 percent of the solid waste stream, while in other areas yard waste accounts for upwards of 40 percent of the municipal solid waste. Beyond even these wide variations, the composition changes widely from community to community and from season to season.

These problems of quantification, not withstanding, a material that makes up even only 10 percent of a community's solid waste stream is an awfully inviting target in this age of landfill diversion. It is such an inviting target that to date four states, Florida, Illinois, Minnesota and Wisconsin and numerous counties and municipalities have passed legislation that will ban the disposal of all types of yard waste at landfills and incinerators. It's likely that many more will follow suit.

In July, 1989, *BioCycle* surveyed communities throughout the U.S. that are separately collecting a full range of yard waste. The intent of the survey was not to fully analyze the entire yard waste collection and processing program, but to generate baseline information on only the collection of yard waste.

COLLECTION METHODS

Presently, there are two principal methods that communities utilize to collect yard debris sep-

arately throughout the year. Either the material is collected in some form of container (a bag, box or can) set out by the homeowners or it's collected loose with the aid of front end loader equipped with a special pincher attachment commonly referred to as a "Claw."

Of the two methods, loose collection has the longest record of use, with several programs studied, including Columbia, SC and Sacramento, CA, providing separate collection since the 1950's or before. With loose collection, homeowners transport any yard debris to the street in front of the home and place it in a pile. The collection team consists of a front end loader, with attachment, and at a minimum, one regular garbage packer truck. In a few programs, two or three packers are used in conjunction with a loader, so that the loader is constantly filling trucks as they shuttle back and forth to the disposal area. To clean the streets after the bulk of material is loaded most programs utilize a street sweeper.

Separate collection of yard debris throughout the entire growing season with containers is a relatively new endeavor, the oldest program found in the survey, Gladstone, OR, began separate collection in 1984. Collection is really straightforward, with the yard debris placed at the curb in either bags or plastic containers. In most programs, a separate packer truck is routed to collect the material. However, in Islip, NY, trash collectors, private and municipal, return to their routes after collecting trash to remove the yard debris.

There are several types of containers that are used. In some programs, including Barrington, IL and Huntington Woods, MI, containers are distributed to householders. Those two programs use 90 and 30 gallon containers respectively. At a pilot program in Montgomery County, MD, 60 gallon containers are being tried.

Several programs, including Urbana, IL and North St. Paul, MN utilize biodegradable plastic bags for the collection, as does a program established by Able Sanitation of Grandville, MI. In all of these programs, the bags are sold in local retail stores at a price that includes the cost of collection and composting yard waste.

While the two methods described above provide the collector with a uniform container to handle, it comes at the cost of either establishing the distribution network or the expense of providing the containers. Some programs surveyed, including Islip, NY and Gladstone and Oregon City, OR, have opted to allow residents to place the yard debris in any container available and take the responsibility of removing the material either while doing the collection or at the processing site.

Collecting yard debris can be problematic because of the tremendous variation in volume throughout the year. In many areas, the fall leaf season produces the largest amount of material. To deal with the volume collected then, communities use a variety of methods. For instance, Sacramento, CA and Barrington, IL increase the number of crews on the streets while Columbia, SC adds six leaf vacuums. In Huntington Woods, MI, the city not only adds three leaf vacuums in the fall, but also runs a separate brush chipping program throughout the year.

PROGRAM STRUCTURE

Institutionally, year round yard waste collection programs are being developed in much the same way as curbside recycling programs. While most municipalities surveyed have taken on the responsibility of developing the separate collection, the actual work is more often as not done by a private firm under contract. In most cases, yard waste collection has been developed as part of the larger solid waste collection contract, with the work performed by the community's regular solid waste collector. However, in several programs where a community is serviced by several haulers, such as North St. Paul, MN and Urbana, IL, separate contracts were developed with a single hauler to provide the yard waste collection.

A different approach was taken in Islip, NY, where 16 private haulers and a municipal authority all collect garbage. According to Elizabeth Gallagher, Commissioner of Environmental Conservation, each of the haulers, including the authority, is responsible for providing a separate collection for yard debris. In addition to Islip providing a partial municipal collection, three other municipalities surveyed, Columbia, SC, and Modesto and Sacramento, CA, operate programs with municipal crews.

While most year-round programs are municipally-sponsored, at least one company, Able Sanitation of Grandville, MI, has developed its own yard waste collection system without municipal support. In May 1989, Able began to require all 17,000 of its customers to purchase and use special biodegradable plastic bags for collection of yard waste. Brian Vander Ark, Able's Recycling Coordinator, estimates that at least 5,000 customers are regularly using the bags.

Although Able mandates that its customers participate in the separate collection, of the programs surveyed only Islip has mandated separate collection. The remaining municipalities all rely on

TABLE 1:
Collection Characteristics

Community	Frequency	Same Day As Trash	Collection Season	Participation
Barrington, IL	Weekly	No	9 Mo	Voluntary
Columbia, SC	Weekly	No	12 Mo	Voluntary
Davis, CA	Weekly	Yes	12 Mo	Voluntary
Gladstone, OR	Weekly	Yes	12 Mo	Voluntary
Huntington Woods, MI	Weekly	No	6 Mo	Voluntary
Islip, NY	Weekly	Yes	12 Mo	Mandatory
Modesto, CA	Monthly	No	12 Mo	Voluntary
N. St. Paul, MN	Weekly	No	9 Mo	Mandatory
Oregon City, OR	Weekly	Yes	12 Mo	Voluntary
Sacramento, CA	Weekly	No	12 Mo	Voluntary
Urbana, IL	Weekly	No	9 Mo	Voluntary
Woodland, CA	Weekly	No	12 Mo	Voluntary

voluntary cooperation of residents. A look at the estimated participation figures shown on Table 2, reveals that even with voluntary cooperation, participation is remarkably high. Of the nine programs that could estimate participation, four claimed rates above 90 percent and two others had rates of 70 percent or more. The two programs whose participation don't reach 50 percent, North St. Paul, MN and Urbana, IL are the programs that were established in communities where several private haulers collect the garbage, allowing residents easy access to an alternative collection method.

COLLECTION SEASON AND MATERIAL VARIATION

In designing a yard waste collection program, perhaps the most fundamental factor is the length of the growing season. In the more temperate states like California, Oregon, South Carolina, Georgia, Florida, Texas and Arizona, the collection season may last all 12 months of the year. However, as you move north and the growing season shortens, the collection season can be correspondingly shortened. This correlation of growing season with collection season is evident in the survey results, as programs in Columbia, SC, Davis, Modesto, and Sacramento, CA, and Gladstone and Oregon City, OR all collect yard waste year round. The four programs in the upper midwest have collection seasons ranging from 6 to 9 months, curtailing collections over the winter months. Islip, NY claims to collect yard waste on a year round basis, but whether much material is actually generated over the winter is questionable.

Another important consideration in the growing season is the variation in amount and type of material collected. Programs experience the heaviest flow of material during leaf fall, with the second biggest season being the spring when people begin to garden after the winter months. In many areas, the summer months, when temperatures get hot and moisture is scarce, the flow on yard waste generally falls below that of these peak periods.

In northern parts of the country, winter is not prime yard waste season, but in more moderate climates that may not be true. In Sacramento, CA, from November through April the yard waste collection averages more than 6,000 tons monthly. During the remainder of the year, the average is less than 5,000 tons monthly.

Another important consideration in developing a yard debris program is the type of material that will actually be collected. While some rule of thumb estimates show that as much as 75 percent of yard waste is grass, with leaves in the 20 to 25 percent range and brush between 5 and 10 percent, as all rules of thumb go those numbers can be misleading. For instance, in Urbana's program, Jim Darling, the Public Works Director, estimates that 50 percent of the yard waste collected is brush, with 35 percent leaves and only 15 percent grass. Leaves only account for 6 to 7 percent of the yard waste collected in Davis' program.

COLLECTION FREQUENCY

Of the programs surveyed, all that collect a full range of yard waste collect the material on a weekly basis. Only Modesto, CA, which recently converted from collecting all yard waste to collect-

TABLE 2:
General Program Characteristics

Community	Population	Households Served	Start-Up Date	Materials Collected	Participation
Barrington, IL	10,000	3,200	6/88	G, L, B	96%
Columbia, SC	100,000	29,000	1950s	G, L	95%
Davis, CA	44,000	10,000	1972	G, L, B	70-80%
Gladstone, OR	9,600	3,800	1984	G, L, B	95%
Huntington Woods, MI	6,900	2,500	5/89	G, L, B	50%
Islip, NY	306,000	78,000	9/88	G, L, B	N/A
Modesto, CA	137,000	35-40,000	1/89	B	N/A
N. St. Paul, MN	12,500	3,500	4/89	G, L	30-40%
Oregon City, OR	14,500	5,800	1986	G, L, B	95%
Sacramento, CA	339,000	100,000	1950s	G, L, B	85-90%
Urbana, IL	38,000	7,500	Fall, 88	G, L, B	30-35%
Woodland, CA	35,000	10,000	1979	G, L, B	85%

G = Grass   L = Leaves   B = Brush

ing brush only, has a monthly schedule. While weekly collection appears to be the direction most programs are headed, in a pilot program, San Jose, CA is investigating both weekly and monthly collection, and although the sections of town that are receiving weekly collection are outperforming the monthly areas, Neal Van Keuren, who heads the effort, would like to explore the possibilities in collecting yard waste every two weeks.

In collecting recyclables at the curb, common wisdom tells us that having the collection on the same day as regular trash collection helps to increase participation. However, the results of the survey suggest that this is not the case with yard waste collection. In fact the majority of programs don't collect on trash collection day. This contradiction may be explained by the fact that yard waste is generated differently than most trash, with the material usually collected from the yard at one point in time, not periodically throughout the week.

PROGRAM OPERATIONS - CREWS AND EQUIPMENT

As explained previously, the equipment used to collect yard waste in a year round program, with the exception of the "Claw" or pincher, is generally standard trash collection equipment. This fact alone makes the entry into yard waste collection relatively easy for communities or private haulers. Because standard trash collection is utilized, with containerized collections crew size generally parallels that which has traditionally been used in the

area with trash collection. From Table 3, it's apparent that most containerized collection is accomplished using either one or two people to a crew, with only Islip having larger crew sizes.

With a loose collection program, a crew must have at least two workers, with one person operating the front end loader and the other driving the packer truck. All of the loose collection programs surveyed used a two person crew, except for Columbia, SC. In Columbia's case, a minimum of 5 people make up a crew, the standard front end loader and packer truck operators, along with two laborers used to sweep the street and consolidate piles, and an extra packer truck operator.

PROGRAM OPERATIONS— ROUTE SIZING

From the information BioCycle was able to obtain, generalizing about the relative efficiency of the collection is difficult. Only one of the ongoing full-scale programs was able to provide information on the number of stops a crew made on individual collection days. In Columbia, SC crews regularly pick up material from 50 to 75 percent of the homes on each route (yard waste routes in Columbia average 1550 homes each) and in Barrington, it's estimated that 80 percent of each route (approximately 800 homes in each route) sets out weekly. Additionally, in San Jose, CA where a loose collection is used, the set out rate is averaging between 500 and 650 homes per week for four collection days.

The total route size of the programs surveyed

TABLE 3:
Yard Waste Separation Results

Community	Total MSW (Tons)	Yard Waste Collected (Tons)	Percentage Separated
Barrington, IL	N/A	N/A	—
Columbia, SC	87,000	35,000	40%
Davis, CA	42,000	6,000	14%
Gladstone, OR	N/A	4,800	—
Huntington Woods, MI	5,000	1,000[1]	20%
Islip, NY	390,000	75-80,000[1]	19-20%
Modesto, CA	120,000	6,000[1,2]	5%
N. St. Paul, MN	N/A	N/A	—
Oregon City, OR	N/A	7,200	—
Sacramento, CA	250,000	66,000	26%
Urbana, IL	40,000	2,000	5%
Woodland, CA	N/A	12,000	—

1 = Estimated Annual Tonnage
2 = Brush Only

varies greatly. For loose collection of a full range of yard waste, the range is from Sacramento's 1000 households per route to Davis' 2500 household per route. Containerized collections exhibit an equally wide range of route sizes, from Islip's 700 to 800 households to North St. Paul's 3500 households per route.

PROGRAM COSTS

The information on the cost of the programs surveyed was sketchy, with most of the data available relating to householder costs. In North St. Paul, MN, residents pay $.30 per bag (with the county contributing another $.20 per bag). The Urbana, IL program costs residents $.50 per bag and $2.50 for every bundle of brush and the Able Sanitation program costs its customers $1.00 per bag.

Two programs estimate costs on a household basis. The Barrington, IL program costs residents $1.25 per household per month for collection only. In Davis, CA the entire program, including composting leaves, costs residents $3.97 per household per month.

In terms of municipal costs, Urbana pays its contractor $8.25 per compacted cubic yard for the collection and the Public Works Department estimates that it costs approximately $3.00 per cubic

yard to process and compost the yard waste. Sacramento, CA puts its costs of yard waste collection at $80 per ton.

YARD WASTE COLLECTION POTENTIAL AND RESULTS

Yard debris is probably the least studied of all major components in the municipal waste stream, but in many communities it makes up the largest single component in that stream. Take the case of Columbia, SC. According to Jim Bonner, Columbia's Sanitation Supervisor, his crews collect approximately 35,000 tons of yard debris from the city's 29,000 households annually. All other residential and commercial collection accounts for only 52,000 tons annually. In other words, of Columbia's 87,000 tons of municipal solid waste, at a minimum, a staggering 40 percent is yard waste.

In addition to Columbia, Sacramento's solid waste stream is approximately 40 percent yard waste, but in Sacramento's case, the program only captures about 26 percent of the yard waste through the separate collection. While none of the other programs surveyed reach these levels, the results they are achieving are still impressive. Islip estimates that it is capturing close to 20 percent of its 390,000 tons of municipal solid waste through

TABLE 4:
Program Operations

Community	Crew Type	Size	Equipment Type	#	Container/ Loose	Route #	Size
Barrington, IL	Contract	2	Packer	4[1]	90 Gallon	4	800
Columbia, SC	Municipal	5	Claw[2]	5[3]	Loose	20	1550
Davis, CA	Contract	2	Claw	1	Loose	4	2500
Gladstone, OR	Contract	1-2	Packer	1[4]	Misc.	5	N/A
H-ton Woods, MI	Contract	2	Packer	1-2[5]	30 Gallon	1-2	1250-2500
Islip, NY	Municipal/ Contract	3	Packer	100	Misc.	100	700-800
Modesto, CA	Municipal	2	Claw	6	Loose	60	600-700
N. St. Paul, MN	Contract	2	Packer	1	Biodegradable Plastic Bags	5	1500
Oregon City, OR	Contract	1-2	Packer	1[4]	Misc.	4	N/A
Sacramento, CA	Municipal	2	Claw	21-24	Loose	105	1000
Urbana, IL	Contract	2	Packer	1[6]	Biodegradable Plastic Bags	5	1500
Woodland, CA	Contract	2	Claw	2	Loose	10	1000

1 = Increased to 5 units in the fall
2 = All claw equipment also uses a packer to transport material
3 = Also uses 6 leaf vacuums in fall
4 = 2 trucks used during the peak season April-September
5 = Also uses a chipper crew for brush and 3 leaf vacuums in the fall
6 = Also uses a pickup during peak seasons

its yard waste program. Huntington Woods has a similar estimate. Davis, CA yard waste collection is approximately 14 percent of all its municipal solid waste. Even in Urbana, IL, where the separate collection only accounts for 5 percent of the municipal solid waste, the county yard waste composting site is capturing 10 to 12 percent, because private haulers that are not involved in the separate collection are removing yard debris on their own to save money on their landfill tipping fees. Finally, Modesto, CA, is separating 5 percent of its municipal solid waste stream and it is collecting only brush.

These numbers speak for themselves, the diversion possibilities associated with yard waste are great, but collecting yard waste separately does not make that potential a reality. Of the programs surveyed, four (Columbia, SC, Davis, CA, Sacramento, CA and Woodland, CA) compost only a portion, primarily leaves, of the material collected.

Separate collection of all yard waste throughout the year is an issue that is just emerging. As state legislation that requires diversion of all yard waste from landfills and incinerators kicks in and other states follow suit, communities that have full programs and others like Lincoln, NB, Montgomery County, MD and San Jose, CA that are doing pilot programs will be providing valuable information to all those that follow.

7

CHARACTERISTICS OF COLLECTION METHODS

Mark D. Selby

PUBLIC and private yard waste collection efforts throughout the country range from citizen dropoff to curbside programs. Table 1 qualitatively compares five curbside collection methods using these criteria: Convenience to residential generator; Ease of implementation; Effectiveness; Capital cost; Operating and maintenance costs; Operational problems; Labor and Noise.

The principal factor used when selecting a yard waste collection system is the availability of existing collection equipment such as compaction vehicles, dump trucks, front-end loaders, skid loaders and vacuum equipment. But solid waste officials should define the short-and-long term yard waste landfill objectives prior to selecting a collection program and making equipment purchases. Factors to consider include:

● Sanitary landfill abatement level required;

● Waste streams of interest—such as incorporating all yard wastes and selected biodegradable waste streams into the program (e.g., municipal and commercial sludges, food wastes, various grades of waste paper); and

● Seasonality and frequency of curbside pickup for the organized collection program.

The following briefly describes commonly used yard waste curbside collection methods. A citizen drop-off option is also discussed which could supplement or replace the curbside collection program during late fall or winter months.

Mechanical Claw-Truck

Generators place grass clippings, leaves, and brush into loose piles about one foot from the curb. The pincer bucket or mechanical claw attached to a small front-end loader is used to pick up the material. Yard waste is placed directly into a rear-loading packer truck, a roll-off, or dump-truck which transports it to a compost site. Transportation costs are minimized when compaction equipment is used.

Vacuum Leaf Collector-Truck

Generators pile unbagged leaves near their curb or street. A collection crew picks up the leaves using either a Vac-all or Super vac unit which blows the leaves into a support transportation vehicle or collection bin. If a collection bin is used, a filled bin is placed onto the transport vehicle and replaced with an empty unit. Material is then transported to the compost site. Vacuum equipment will grind up and compact yard waste which can hasten the rate of biological decomposition while decreasing transportation costs.

Packer Trucks and Dump Trucks

There are several variations to this general method. In one, generators place their collected leaves or grass clippings inside plastic bags. A hauler empties the contents of each plastic bag directly into a rear-loading packer truck. The hauler returns each empty bag to the generator and transports the "clean" load of grass clippings and leaves to a compost site. A "bag free" yard waste stream significantly minimizes centralized compost facility operating expenses. In the second, homeowners place collected yard waste inside plastic bags. A hauler picks up and places each bag directly into a packer truck. Every load is transported and deposited at a compost site where each plastic bag is opened, yard waste emptied, and the bag disposed separately. Finally, generators place their leaves or grass clippings inside biodegradable bags. A hauler collects the bags and transports them to a compost site where they are placed into windrows.

Front-End Loader-Dump Truck

Generators rake their yard waste into the street. A front-end loader scoops up the material and places it into a dump truck for transport to a compost site. This method is essentially identical to the previous one with the exception of how the leaves are placed into the transportation vehicle. Yard waste is not compacted using this method and it may also result in higher transportation costs when compared to packer trucks.

Citizen Dropoff

This alternative puts the burden on the generator to either transport the yard waste to an acceptable location or process the yard waste at the point of generation by backyard composting or mulching. Dropoff sites will not attract high residential participation rates compared to curbside collection programs. Use of a citizen dropoff program in place of organized collection during peri-

ods of low yard waste generation should be considered. The private transportation of yard waste to dropoff sites involves an increase in the number of vehicle trips during the year with associated increases in noise, dust, and exhaust emissions. The trade-off between the positive environmental impacts of composting over landfilling yard waste, and the negative environmental impacts associated with additional vehicle trips has not been studied; however, the positive impacts are judged to outweigh the negative impacts. A continuous public education program is required to maintain a high general public participation rate. The finished compost product is usually given away to residents who participate in the program.

COLLECTION IMPEDIMENTS

Separately collecting yard waste can pose a unique set of problems to a community. The type of problems encountered depends on the collection method. Representatives from communities using the mechanical claw, vacuum leaf collector, and front-end loader/dump-truck methods have indicated the following operational difficulties: blowing yard waste; cars driving over yard waste; auto-

TABLE 1.
Characteristics of Yard Waste Collection Methods

	Mechanical Claw-Truck[1]	Vacuum Leaf Collector-Truck[1]	Packer Truck[2]	Dump Truck[2]	Front-end Loader-Dump Truck
Convenience to Residential Generator	Excellent	Excellent	Very Good	Very Good	Very Good
Ease of Implementation[3]	Easy	Easy	Easy	Easy	Easy
Effectiveness	Moderately Efficient[4]	Very Efficient[5]	Very Efficient[5]	Very Efficient[5]	Moderately Efficient[4]
Capital Cost[6]	High	High	Moderate	Low	High
O&M Cost[7]	Moderate	High	Low	Low	Moderate
Operational Problems	Low	High	Moderate	Low	Low
Labor	Low-Moderate	Low-Moderate	Low	Low	Low-Moderate
Noise	Moderate	Potentially High	Moderate	Low	Moderate

[1]Usually used for seasonal collection.
[2]Used for weekly collection.
[3]Includes a public education program.
[4]Capture rate is approximately 90%.
[5]Capture rate is approximately 100%.
[6]Assumes new equipment is purchased; although use of existing equipment is very likely.
[7]Cost comparison made per collection activity. Refer to footnotes 1 and 2.

mobile catalytic convertors starting leaves on fire; vehicles parked on top of yard waste; sewer drain blockage and sticks, rocks, glass, and oil contaminating "clean" leaves.

Individuals in communities which use the packer and dump truck methods have noted the following problems during collection: trash placed in bags; plastic bags falling apart; crew members injuring themselves lifting heavy bags; and increased labor requirements to open plastic bags. Two problems common to all collection methods include: homeowners not following proper directions and vandalism of bags placed at the curb.

CALCULATIONS

The costing methods differ for each community and are dependent on the following variables: local labor rates, equipment used, frequency of collection, equipment rates, equipment maintenance, insurance, fuel, and financing mechanisms.

Accurate and reliable yard waste collection cost information reflecting existing programs is difficult to obtain. For example, most Public Works Directors determine labor and equipment rates but do not calculate specific maintenance, insurance or debt service expenses associated with the collection effort. Annual collection costs were derived from a limited survey of existing collection operations in California, New Jersey, and Minnesota. In 1986, the costs ranged from $9.00 per ton of yard waste collected using a packer truck to $80 per ton using a vacuum leaf collection truck. Based upon previous DPRA collection studies, a cost of $60 to $80 per ton is common. This cost range includes the use of new equipment, municipal labor, and equipment depreciation. The range would include the use of new compaction vehicles, vacuum trucks, or front-end loaders.

The following equipment information is given to aid the solid waste officer during initial planning and can be used to "ball park" yard waste collection cost.

Front-end loader. Late-1988 retail price varies from $80,000 to $150,000 delivered. The suggested pricing is for a mid-size front-end loader with a 2 to 4½ cubic yard general purpose bucket. If the loader is dedicated to the yard waste collection and processing programs, the front-end loader should be supplied with an oversized bucket designed for loose, light materials.

Mechanical Claw. The retail price varies between $7,000 to $11,000. This is an optional piece of equipment which would attach to the front-end loader lift assembly.

Packer Truck. Late-1988 retail price for a 25 cubic yard rear loading packer truck ranges between $75,000 and $95,000. The price reflects a truck with a 900 to 1,000 pound per cubic yard compaction capability. Reconditioned, used equipment can be purchased at a 20 to 50 percent savings when compared to the retail price range.

Dump Truck. Late-1988 retail price varies from $55,000 to $75,000. The price assumes a 4 to 6 cubic yard hydraulic tip box, 200 hp diesel engine, and single axle drive train.

Vacuum Collection Truck. Late-1988 retail price varies between $90,000 to $130,000. The capital cost assumes an 8 to 12 cubic yard unit mounted on a truck chassis with a 250 hp diesel engine and a tandem rear-end drive assembly.

Mark Selby is a Project Engineer with DRPA, Inc. of St. Paul, Minnesota.

8

COMPOSTABLES AT CURBSIDE

Peter J. Matsukis

THE VILLAGE of Barrington, Illinois, a suburb of approximately 10,000 people, located 35 miles northwest of Chicago, started a comprehensive curbside/composting program June 6, 1988. After 10 weeks, results showed a 90 to 95 percent participation rate, which is diverting 40 percent of its waste from the landfill. They demonstrate the point that if you do integrate a curbside compost collection along with a glass/can/paper curbside program, you can divert 35 percent or more of your waste from the landfill.

In January, 1987, the League of Women Voters for the northwestern suburban area of Chicago approached the Village Board about considering a curbside recycling program. Following the League's initiative, an Ad Hoc Recycling Committee was formed to study the feasibility of a curbside system, and how it could be best integrated with a twice a week garbage pickup.

A comprehensive analysis was done of other programs in such places as Seattle, San Jose and Oak Lawn, Illinois.

In order to have an effective curbside recycling program, the committee included composting yard waste made up 25 to 30 percent of Barrington's residential waste stream per year. The Village Board, along with the Recycling Committee, decided to incorporate a Curbside Recycling/Composting program by integrating it within the twice a week pick up system.

The village distributed 3,000 90-gallon containers for the collection of composting materials, and 3,000 sets of stackable recycling containers for the glass, aluminum and paper. Although photodegradable bags were originally used for excess yard waste, it was found that they weren't decomposing rapidly enough. The village has since switched to paper leaf bags. The theory is that spending the money to initiate the program now will offset higher tipping fee increases in the upcoming years.

On Mondays, Laidlaw picks up the compost and the recycling materials. To collect the yard waste, Laidlaw utilizes four semi-automated rear packer trucks to cover the village's 3300 households. The set-out rate for collection of the yard waste is approximately 70 percent, thus each truck averages in the neighborhood of 575 stops per collection day. The amount collected ranges from 100 cy to 175 cy per week.

The yard waste goes to a farm that the village has subleased, and the Barrington Public Works Department monitors the yard waste and turns it at least once a week to continue the compost process. Glass, aluminum and newspaper are taken to a transfer site located in town where they are dropped off in cement bins. The Public Works Department then distributes the materials from the cement bins to awaiting roll-off trailers that various recycling vendors have provided. The village markets all materials recycled and receives all money from the sale.

The village did do an extensive four-month education campaign in which three newsletters and a brochure were sent out explaining what the program was, why the village was undertaking such a program, and how it would benefit the Barrington residents in the long run. The village also had open public discussions in which residents were asked to come to voice their opinions about the Recycling Program. Initial results were that most of the village was in favor of the program and that the consensus was to go ahead with the program.

Peter Matsukis was formerly Recycling Coordinator for the Village of Barrington and currently works for Laidlaw Waste Systems.

9

COST COMPARISON
OF COLLECTION METHODS

Lori Segall and Ron Smith

A COMPARISON of three different methods of leaf collection in Bristol, Connecticut (pop. 60,000) was made during an eight-week period from mid-October to early December, 1988. The city was divided into four zones for bulk collection of leaves. Residents raked leaves to the curb on specific weeks, depending on the zone of the city. Each zone received bulk pick-up services twice during the leaf collection period. Bag collection services were provided on the same day as the regular trash pick up, or eight times during the collection period.

Two bulk collection methods and one bag collection method were evaluated during this study. Bulk pick up was accomplished by trailer type leaf vacuums, with associated boxes mounted on the back of dump trucks, and front-end loader collection, with dump trucks. The third collection method evaluated was pick up of biodegradable leaf bags, loaded into packer trucks. These bags were made available free to residents wishing to bag their leaves.

● **Vacuum collection:** The vacuum truck crew consisted of three workers, two rakers and a driver. The driver advanced slowly while the two rakers pushed leaves toward the vacuum hose. When the leaf box was full, the vacuum apparatus was detached and the truck driven to the compost site to deposit leaves. Collection would resume when the truck returned and the vacuum was re-attached.

● **Front-end loader collection:** Front-end loader crews consisted of six workers; one loader operator, two rakers, and three dump truck drivers. Rakers aided the loader operator in picking up the leaves which were dumped into a dump truck.

When that truck was full it drove to the compost site and the next empty truck took its place.

● **Bag collection:** Bag collection crews often consisted only of one driver and one laborer at the back. Two laborers were occasionally employed for heavier volume routes. The driver often helped at large set-outs of bags. Leaf collection personnel were instructed to collect only special biodegradable bags with leaves. When the City ran out of bags to distribute, set-outs of regular trash bags with leaves were allowed, and collection personnel were instructed to open the bags at the curb and dump only leaves into the packer.

Bag collection crews were extremely efficient. A two-person crew on a 25 cubic yard packer routinely collected at least 20 tons per ten-hour day.

BULK DENSITIES

The bulk density of the leaves varied depending on the type of leaves, moisture content and method of collection. There is a wide range of reported values from various collection programs. The bulk densities of the collected leaves in Bristol is on the lower end of this range due to the high percentage of oak leaves and the relative lack of rain during the 1988 leaf collection period. Bulk densities are reported in Table 1.

The bulk density for dump trucks of 128 pounds per cubic yard most accurately reflects the value for loose leaves. This value, used to estimate the total volume of loose leaves taken at the compost site before grinding, yields 59,000 cubic yards. As much as one-half of that volume was deposited and compacted to some degree. After

TABLE 1:
BULK DENSITIES

	Leaf Vacuum Box	Dump Truck Load	Packer Trucks[1] R-4 = R-7
Average Weight of Leaves	2,200 lbs	1,000 lbs	12,000-20,000 lbs
Dimensions of Container	8.5×6×5' 9.44 cubic yards	10×7×3' 7.78 cubic yards	25 cubic yards
Bulk Density	259 lbs per cubic yard[2]	128 lbs per cubic yard	480-800 lbs per cubic yard

Notes:
1. Because of the different packing capacities of the two most commonly used packer trucks, a range was given.
2. Leaf boxes were not filled to capacity due to back pressure on the vacuum line when the boxes filled up. The volume of boxes was set at 8.5 cubic yards for these calculations.

---

grinding, the volume could be estimated at 30,000 cubic yards.

CALCULATION OF COLLECTION COSTS PER TON

The cost of each leaf collection method was calculated by adding the labor costs (hourly wages of each worker times the number of hours worked, excluding benefits), estimated equipment operational costs (excluding amortization), extra equipment rental costs, and cost of bag plus labor costs for distribution. These costs were divided by the number of tons collected by each method.

For vacuum collection, cost was $106.33/ton.

For the front-end loader, cost was $95.80/ton. For the bag method, cost was $55.28/ton. (This figure accounts for purchase price of bags and associated distribution costs.)

It is clear that bag collection is much more cost-effective than bulk collection. This is not surprising when it is known that a good packer truck can collect 20 tons of leaves in a day with only two people. A team of three dump truck drivers, one front-end loader operator, and two laborers will collect an average of 15 tons of leaves per day.

Lori Segall is with E&A Consultants; Ron Smith is with the Bristol Dept. of Public Works.

10

VOLUNTARY APPROACH AND PUBLIC EDUCATION

Carter Kuehn

IN SPRING, 1986, the Crow Wing County (Minnesota) Board of Commissioners approved the establishment of a Leaf Composting Program. Basic incentives included the need to save space at the county landfill, reduce operational costs, save wear and tear on machinery, and create a usable compost product.

The haulers happily agreed not to pick up any yard or tree wastes, making the program mandatory for county residents. The county nursery and landfill as well as the Paul Bunyan Arboretum served as collection points where citizens could bring vegetative material. Each site varied in materials handling methods. The Arboretum, which received the most leaves and yard waste, windrowed compostables and the highway department turned the windrows twice a year when its machinery was in the area.

The final compost product is used as a soil conditioner. County residents who deposit leaves at the Arboretum are given a ticket to cash in for finished compost.

Letters were sent to each of the six major cities in Crow Wing County, and after a personal visit, each council approved the program. It included the voluntary cooperation of service clubs and scouts to pick up yard waste for the elderly and handicapped, who simply placed materials at curbside for pickup and deposit at the closest collection point. Finally, after city approval, the County Board sanctioned a mandatory leaf composting program.

Leaves fell very early due to unseasonably warm weather, forcing a rush to publicize the program. Senior citizens voiced their displeasure about being grouped with the handicapped when requesting help in the form of special collections. County commissioners and city officials received a barrage of phone calls from disgruntled citizens who felt haulers should pick up the leaves.

As a result, the program went back to being voluntary. Haulers were directed to pick up leaves upon request. All other aspects of the program remained intact.

The program is still in effect on a voluntary basis. During the key periods of early spring and fall, press releases and radio announcements go out reminding the public of the locations and times open for each collection point. Leaflet information on how and why to compost leaves and yard waste is distributed to all city halls and county offices.

It's estimated that between five and 10 percent of our residents use one of the three collection sites. During 1988, approximately 8,000 cubic yards of leaves were collected—nearly three times what was collected in 1986.

Although increased participation can be largely attributed to burning bans, I like to think that the public is also more familiar with the program and the need for it. For all its problems, the program now represents a new no-cost proposition to the county, keeps most leaves and yard waste out of county landfills, and serves as a continuing education program for the public regarding solid waste management.

Carter Kuehn serves as Solid Waste Officer for Crow Wing County, headquartered in Brainerd, Minnesota.

CURBSIDE COLLECTION OF GRASS CLIPPINGS

Lillian Dean and Mark Wollenweber

HUNTINGTON WOODS, Michigan is a small residential suburb (pop. 6,300) in Oakland County, about two miles north of Detroit. Because of rising disposal costs, the large percentage of grass clippings during spring and summer, and the environmental advantages of composting, the City proposed a pilot project in spring, 1988 for collection of grass clippings.

From a municipal public works standpoint, grass clippings collection and composting raise the following concerns: 1. Grass clippings are difficult to successfully compost because of the need to control odors; 2. Plastic bags, typically used by households for grass clippings, inhibit the composting process; debagging at the compost site is too time consuming to be useful; and 3. A special pickup is required to separate grass clippings from the solid waste stream.

The potential benefits from grass composting, however, are also clear. During spring and early summer months, yard wastes (especially grass) account for 20 percent - 30 percent or more of the residential waste stream in communities such as Huntington Woods. For instance, in Huntington Woods, approximately 26 percent of its residential waste is yard waste. Of the City's 5,000 tons generated annually, approximately 800 tons (16 percent) is leaves, 400 tons (8 percent) is grass and 120 tons (2 percent) is woody material.

To address the concerns and demonstrate ways to take advantage of composting benefits, Huntington Woods initiated a grass clippings collection pilot project in 1988. The pilot project was undertaken in cooperation with the Southeastern Oakland County Incinerator Authority (responsi-ble for composting of the grass) and with financial assistance from the Clean Michigan Fund.

For a 16 week period, a special once/week curbside collection of grass clippings was implemented. Half of the participants received plastic bins and half plastic bags to use for grass clippings. Following the curbside collection, grass clippings were transported to the compost site at the landfill.

The pilot project has demonstrated that curbside collection of grass clippings is feasible from an operational standpoint. The use of 20-gallon plastic bins (rather than plastic bags) is acceptable to many residents, since bins are easy to fill, can be reused, and save the cost of numerous bags.

PROJECT PURPOSE

Project objectives included the following: 1. To identify the most effective method for curbside collection of grass clippings; 2. To examine the feasibility of curbside grass clippings collection as a public service from the standpoint of residents, the City, and the Southeastern Oakland County Incinerator Authority; and 3. To document quantities of grass clippings generated during peak spring and summer months.

The pilot area offered a useful mix of large and smaller yards and a cross-section of Huntington Woods residents. The boundaries of the pilot area were determined by the regular garbage pickup routes. To solicit participation, residents were sent a letter from the City Manager, a project fact sheet, and a return postcard. Follow-up telephone calls were made to nonrespondents (an essential step) and a second letter was sent to persons who still could not be reached. Out of the 459 households in the pilot area, the following responses were received:

• **Yes, willing to participate:** 269 households (59 percent of total)

• **No response/unable to reach:** 77 households (16 percent of total)

• **No, not able to participate:** 113 households (25 percent of total)

Reasons for not participating included the following: 14 percent—lawn service; 4 percent—compost grass in the yard; 3 percent—use a mulching lawn mower; 3 percent—no reason given; 1 percent—Other (e.g., not interested; moving; no grass).

The pilot project was divided into two areas for the purpose of testing relative advantages and disadvantages of moderate-sized bins vs. bags for curbside pickup. Participants in the northern half of the pilot area received bins, while participants in the southern half received bags. All residents were informed that grass clippings collection would take place on Friday, the day of their regular trash pickup.

Blue plastic bags (30-gallon) were purchased in quantity from a local supplier for the pilot.

Depending on the size of the yard, either one, two or three bins were delivered to each participating household with a list of instructions. A few extra plastic bags were also provided to handle weeks when grass was rapidly growing. Small-moderate sized lots in the "bag" section of the pilot area received 50 bags for the 16 week pilot project. Households with large lots received 80 bags.

The City's regular solid waste contractor agreed to provide the special grass collection service. A special pickup in the northwest area of the city on Friday, the same day as regular trash pickup, was scheduled. The price paid by Huntington Woods was a per stop fee of 67 cents/household, calculated as if all households in the pilot project area used the service. Although this fee allocation was agreed upon for the pilot project time period, research shows that special recycling/composting collections by contractors are typically paid for on a user charge basis. In other words, the per stop fee is paid only for the households actually using the service.

Laidlaw Waste Systems staff recommended and carried out the following operational procedure: 1. A regular packer truck (driver plus one worker) was used to complete the curbside grass collection prior to the regular refuse pickup; 2. Bins of grass were emptied into the truck; 3. Plastic bags of grass were slit with a pocket knife at the curbside and emptied into the truck. Empty plastic bags would then be put into the regular trash containers.

From an operational standpoint, the process worked well. Bins and bags were readily emptied into the truck and plastic bags were not left to fly around the neighborhood. The problem of debagging grass at the compost site was avoided.

The grass pickup route in Huntington Woods was completed in about one hour. Following a weighing at the incinerator site, the grass was transported by Laidlaw to the compost site at the landfill. Because of the relatively small amount of grass collected through the Huntington Woods pilot project, mixing grass with leaves was not undertaken last summer. Plans are being made, however, to dedicate a portion of the compost site specifically for leaf and grass composting in the future. Several municipalities, in addition to Huntington Woods, joined the program in 1989.

RESULTS AND EVALUATIONS

The reaction and experience of participants to the grass collection pilot project was documented through a two-page questionnaire, answered by 47 percent of the participating residents. Without a doubt, the grass clippings collection program piloted by Huntington Woods is a very popular city service. Of the persons responding, 82 percent consider grass clippings collection and composting to be either an important or very important public service. The reasons for the program, especially environmental benefits and reuse of organic materials, are understood by many.

A major question for the pilot project was the acceptance of plastic bins as compared with regular plastic bags. Of the persons using bins for grass clippings, 73 percent prefer the use of bins. Factors influencing the preference for bins include ease of filling, convenient size, and the permanence of the container. Since most households use plastic bags for grass clippings on a regular basis, this high response was surprising. Odors were mentioned as a problem by only 9 residents, and it is believed that many solved this problem by simply washing out the bins or lining them with plastic bags (with the edge of the bag pulled over the rim of the bin).

Of the persons using plastic bags only (without the experience of bins), 64 percent prefer bags. An additional 25 percent have no preference.

Grass collection with regular trash on Friday is preferred by 63 percent of the respondents. An additional 17 percent would prefer a special Monday pickup, while 20 percent have no preference. If a special Monday collection for grass clippings were offered, however, 79 percent would use the service.

Although 60 percent of the pilot area residents

participated in the project, it is estimated that only half of this number (30 percent of the total area) placed grass clippings on the curb each week. This fluctuation is common in recycling and composting programs, and reflects the fact that families may be out-of-town, forget about recycling, etc.

The use of the 20-gallon bins proved extremely feasible. The 20-gallon size could be easily lifted and emptied, even when filled with grass. Laidlaw reported no problems with the use of the bins and indeed strongly preferred them to bags.

During a normal summer, four tons of grass clippings might be expected as a maximum. On an average, over a 16-week period, two to three tons of grass would be expected.

The cost-effectiveness of curbside grass clippings collection will be greatly improved if either of the following changes takes place:

a. SOCIA could provide composting services at no charge to municipalities in order to encourage special grass and leaf collection. Hennepin County and Ramsey County in Minnesota, for example, provide free compost sites for use by municipalities within the county. In contrast, a significant fee is charged for the use of other county solid waste disposal facilities.

b. If the tipping fee for municipal solid waste rises significantly but the price for composting remains the same, yard waste collection and composting will become more cost-effective.

Lillian Dean is Recycling Education Coordinator and Mark Wollenweber is City Manager for Huntington Woods, Michigan.

12

BIODEGRADABLE BAGS FOR YARD WASTE

Gene Hanlon and Gary Brandt

LINCOLN, NEBRASKA has established a yard waste collection and composting demonstration project utilizing the newly-developed cornstarch biodegradable additive for polyethylene trash bags. Although the city does not face a solid waste crisis as in other communities, the recent siting and construction of a new 200 acre landfill, which has taken four years to implement, has led to a keen interest in extending its life as long as possible.

The Mayor's Landfill Operations and Alternatives Task Force recommended a special collection and subsequent composting of yard waste as one step. The task force estimated that over 25,000 tons of grass clippings and leaves could be collected from April 1st through November 30th and add six years to the life of the landfill.

In analyzing various approaches for the collection of yard waste, the city was interested in eliminating the costly process of separating plastic bags from the compost pile. It considered the use of 90 gallon containers or the biodegradable cornstarch trash bags. The latter was chosen because less capital cost would be required and the fact that existing collection equipment would not have to be modified. In addition, the Nebraska Corn Development, Utilization and Marketing Board was interested in finding alternative uses for corn products and agreed to fund a portion of the project, if the cornstarch bags were used.

A demonstration project was established by working with three of Lincoln's independent waste haulers and selecting three representative areas in the city for a separate collection of yard wastes. The three neighborhood areas chosen included: (1) an older portion of the city with small lots and

large trees; (2) a newer area with large lots and very small trees; and (3) an area with a mixture of large and small lots with mature trees. A total of 1,300 households are within the demonstration project areas.

Since Lincoln has twice a week collection of garbage, a third separate pickup was added to collect yard waste. The haulers are paid $28.40 per ton to collect the yard waste.

SURVEY OF HOUSEHOLDS

Prior to the start of the project, a survey was mailed to each household to determine the number of households having yard waste and their support in using cornstarch biodegradable bags. There was a 39 percent response to the survey. Table 1 summarizes the current practices in handling homeowners' yard waste. Roughly 74 percent of the responding households leave yard waste for the garbage haulers to collect sometime during the growing season. Twelve percent of the respondents have a lawn service haul away their grass while an equal amount mulch or compost their yard waste. A little over one percent of the homeowners do not collect their grass clippings when they mow.

Not all of the homeowners that have yard waste leave it for the garbage hauler in the same week. For example, during the month of June, an average of 42 percent of the households actually had yard waste to be picked up for the special collection. The dry weather in the Plain States has reduced the volume of grass collected. Close to 80 tons of grass was collected from the participating households during the first month. The average weight of grass collected for the month was 272 pounds per participating household.

In addition to collecting yard waste from homes in the demonstration area, all yard waste taken to the landfill by small vehicles and lawn service companies is diverted to the composting site. Over 280 tons of material were collected during the month of June, 1988.

All of the 360 tons of material is currently being stockpiled in windrows at the composting site on the city's old landfill. In August, the city rented equipment to shred the cornstarch bags and yard waste it has received. A portion of this material will be mixed with sewage sludge so that the city will have some finished compost by the spring of next year. In addition to yard waste and sewage sludge, the city plans to experiment mixing various portions of pen waste from Nebraska's State Fair Park, wood chips and leaves later this fall.

The city would like to keep its composting

TABLE 1
Summary of Current Practices in Handling Yard Waste by Project Participants

# of Households	Percent	
7	1.4	Don't collect clippings
60	11.8	Lawn service cuts grass and hauls away
63	12.4	Mulch or compost yard waste
130	25.5	TOTAL households that don't have yard waste for garbage hauler.
50	9.8	Sometimes leave yard waste for garbage hauler, sometimes mulch or compost
11	2.2	Lawn service cuts grass and leaves at curb for garbage hauler
315	61.9	Homeowner mows, leaves at curb for garbage hauler
376	73.8	TOTAL households that have yard waste for garbage hauler at some point during growing season
3	0.6	Don't know
509	100.0	TOTAL

costs low; thus, it is utilizing a relatively "low-tech" approach to composting. The windrows containing sewage sludge will be turned at least twice a week while the turning frequency for the windrows containing grass and leaves will depend upon the pile temperature.

Finished compost will be divided into thirds. One third of the product will go to homeowners that participated in the demonstration project, another third will be used in a test area as a soil amendment on the old landfill, and the remaining third will be given to local landscapers and professional gardeners to evaluate its commercial value and applications.

Overall project cost is estimated to be $75,000. Funding for the project came from the City of Lincoln, the Nebraska Corn Development Utilization & Marketing Board, and the Nebraska Department of Environmental Control. The purpose of the demonstration project is to determine the feasibility of a citywide collection program. If successful, the project will be expanded next year. Thus far, the demonstration project has gone quite well. Only 17 households out of 962 that have yard waste for the hauler have chosen not to participate. Of those participating, 3 to 5 percent of households are using conventional trash bags rather than the bright yellow, cornstarch bags.

CORNSTARCH BAGS

The cornstarch bags have a 33 gallon capacity. Their strength and performance is quite good. Steve Hatten, President of the Lincoln Solid Waste Management Association, has commented that the bags are stronger than most of the traditional polyethylene bags available in a store. Although this strength is useful from the collection side of the project, it could lead to a longer decomposition period.

Traditional plastic takes anywhere from 4 to 400 years to decompose. Promoters of the cornstarch bags say that they will degrade within 18 months or 6 years depending on how they are handled. The bags utilized in the Lincoln project contain a cornstarch biodegradable additive amounting to 6 percent of the bags composition. In addition, the bags contain varying amounts of a photodegradable chemical and a pro-oxidant chemical which makes the bag more susceptible to oxygen and heat decomposition. In an active compost pile, it is estimated that these bags will degrade within the 18 month period.

Even though the city is only stockpiling the grass clippings that it has collected so far, temperatures in the windrow have remained at about 140°F. After five weeks, the pile was opened and bags of grass clippings were removed. The cornstarch bags appeared to have lost some of their strength and tore easily while removing them from the pile. Portions of the bright yellow bags had also turned a brownish color. Samples of the bags are currently being evaluated by the University of Nebraska—Lincoln regarding any loss in the bags' tensile strength.

Some concern has been expressed regarding the possible release of residual chemicals from the degradation of the cornstarch/polyethylene bags. In order to assess this, funds have been set aside to conduct a priority pollutant test of the finished compost. This test will scan the finished compost for concentrations of toxic chemicals. It is anticipated that the testing could play a significant role in determining the marketability of the finished compost and the cornstarch bags.

Gene Hanlon is Recycling Coordinator and Gary Brandt is Utilities Coordinator for Nebraska's capital city of Lincoln.

13

RESEARCH ON DEGRADABLE BAGS

IN 1988, the officials in charge of the yard waste composting project for the Region of Durham (located near Toronto, Ontario) thought they had found the solution to the messy problem associated with debagging leaves. Rather than use standard plastic bags for a pilot leaf collection and composting project, the Region made cornstarch-based degradable plastic bags available for the collection.

"Our supplier told us the bags would degrade in three months," explained Elaine Collis, who heads the composting program. Unfortunately, while the bags had lost some of their strength, even in May they were still holding up and holding leaves. "We finally had to go into the piles and remove the bags by hand," remarked Collis.

If yard waste is collected in regular plastic bags, at some point in the process those bags have to be removed. Most of the options for removing the bags are expensive and time consuming. The promise of degradable plastic bags, not worrying about removing the bags, is almost too good to be true in those situations. But as the problems in the Region of Durham illustrate, a few questions need to be answered.

WHAT QUESTIONS?

While in applications like yard waste composting there appears to be great potential for the use of degradable plastic bags, a number of questions have also begun to appear. First, and most basic, is the issue encountered by the Region of Durham. How long does it take for degradable bags to break down in the compost pile?

If a bag degrades at a rate that corresponds with the rate of decomposition of the yard waste, then from a yard waste compost manager's point of view, it has solved the pesky debagging problem. However, if the bags take appreciably longer than it takes to compost the yard waste, the manager has problems similar to those posed by use of regular plastic bags.

The type of problems encountered depend upon the composting system used. For instance, if whole bags are piled in windrows and turned with only a front end loader, the composting rate will be retarded if the bags don't readily degrade. The yard waste will sit in the bags without the essential ingredients for composting. In fact, many involved in yard waste composting suggest that even when degradable bags are used, some means of breaking the bags open is appropriate.

Even in programs where the degradable bags are run through a pre-processing shredder, or a windrow turning machine that rips the bags open, if the residues of the plastic don't degrade along with the yard waste and remain visible, a final screening will be needed to produce a marketable product just like with regular plastic bags. In short, why spend the extra money for a degradable plastic if its performance during the composting process does not enhance the operation and the product?

Another major question about degradable plastics is what they become when they degrade. One manufacturer's promotional material states that, "full degradation leaves only a fine powder which is absorbed by the environment." Little research has been conducted into the effect of this fine powder in the environment. According to Dr. Susan Mooney of the U.S. Environmental Protection Agency, who heads the EPA's look at degradable plastics, "In aquatic environments, there may be problems with animals ingesting the fine plastic particles. On land, the question is what happens when fine plastic particles are incorporated into the soil or possibly inhaled. Are there any environmental or health effects?"

"The size of the plastics fragments resulting from degradation" is also identified in a report of the U.S. General Accounting Office, *Degradable Plastics: Standards, Research and Development*, as a safety-related issue along with the "potential toxicity of chemicals leaching from degradable plastics." Some in the plastics industry also voice those concerns. Speaking at a 1987 conference on Degradable Plastics sponsored by the Society of the Plastics Industry, Regina Johnson of Dow Chemical Company noted that "Degradation products of degradable materials are not well characterized, so their toxicity and environmental effects are unknown."

Most people who have examined the toxicity issue believe that it's not the polyethylene molecules that could cause potential problems, but rather additives such as pigments used to color the bags, inks used for the printing on the bags and stabilizers that keep the plastic in one piece while the bags are in use.

The toxins of concern to most are heavy metals that include lead, cadmium, nickel and cobalt used in the additives. In 1988, the city of Lincoln, Nebraska started using yellow-colored degradable plastic bags in their yard waste collection pilot program. When the city ran tests on the compost this year, samples showed trace amounts of cadmium. According to Gene Hanlon, who heads the project, the source of the cadmium was the yellow bags. "Cadmium was part of the pigment used to color the bags."

If additives using heavy metals are used, the concern is that those metals could pose long term effects on the environment and health if they leach into the groundwater or are taken up by plants and then consumed by humans and/or animals.

INDUSTRY'S ANSWERS

While questions about using degradable plastic bags in yard waste composting projects exist, the degradable plastic industry believes that it has the answers to most, if not all, of the questions. Take, for instance, the concern about the rate of degradation. When degradable plastic bags were first introduced, most companies claimed that the bags would degrade to a size that was indistinguishable within three to five years. That length of time certainly isn't appropriate for composting. However, now the two principal suppliers of the degradable additive — Archer Daniels Midland (ADM) and St. Lawrence Starch Co. — have introduced formulations that offer a much quicker action than the standard formulations. These two companies supply the additive, the active ingredients of which include starch and oxidizing agents, that is used by the bag manufacturers in producing the degradable bags.

"Last year, the standard formulation we used just didn't perform well in composting applications," explains Tim Shiveley, ADM's National Sales Manager. In the spring of 1989, ADM put together a new formulation designed to degrade at a much faster rate in a composting pile.

According to Dr. George Poppe, who heads ADM's degradable plastic research work, bags using the new degradable additive should break down to pieces of one millimeter, or less, within six months and should be unnoticeable in the compost at the end of one year. "We souped up the catalysts used to encourage the degradation process considerably," says Dr. Poppe.

St. Lawrence started selling a formulation, Ecostar Plus, for composting last year and reports from users are that the bags using it perform well in yard waste compost projects. One user of Ecostar Plus, Petoskey Plastics, has sampled a number of projects and according to Jim Craig is "seeing the plastic break down to dime-size pieces in six months or less." Ecostar Plus is an adaptation of the original Ecostar formulation. According to Peter Campbell, St. Lawrence's Project Engineer, Ecostar Plus was the culmination of research done in Europe that looked at various combinations of starch and photosensitive additives. "The final formulation includes 10 percent starch and an iron salt additive," remarks Campbell. "We believe the plastic bags will be unidentifiable as a plastic within 12 months of being placed in a yard waste composting windrow."

While some programs, like the Region of Durham's, are experiencing trouble with bags not living up to manufacturer's claims, at least one manufacturer believes that the fault lies more with the operators of the compost facilities than the bags. "Many municipalities simply don't know the proper way to make compost," maintains Charlie Armistead of Manchester Packaging. "They pile the yard waste up and only turn it every six or eight months. Then they wonder why the bags and the yard waste haven't broken down."

PRODUCTS AFTER BREAKDOWN

While it appears that in a short period of time, the producers of degrading additives have been able to cut the time required to make the plastic in a composting project "unidentifiable," there remains the question of into what the plastic degrades. Most of the manufacturers of the degradable bags and the degrading additives maintain that the plastic will break down into CO_2 and water, or those two products and a humic material. "In an active microbial setting, the plastics should break completely down within three to four years," contends Dr. Poppe. Likewise, Peter Campbell of St. Lawrence believes that plastic will break down completely, but "we haven't tested long enough to know exactly how long the process will take. St. Lawrence is conducting those tests now."

What causes these polymers to degrade into CO_2, water and humic material in the process is the fact that the polymer chains, which have a very high molecular weight, are broken into smaller and smaller pieces until finally when they reach between 500 and 3000 molecular weight, microorganisms can metabolize the material. While some degrading technologies can break the plastics down to these low levels at least one researcher, Dr. Michael Cole, of the University of Illinois isn't sure if all systems can reach molecular weights as low as 500. "The literature on this subject isn't conclusive," notes Dr. Cole.

Even if the plastic does not completely degrade, or if it takes three to five years, or as long as 50 years as some suggest, will the resulting material be harmful? Many in the degradable plastics field think not. "Polyethylene is a very stable material," says Mr. Armistead of Manchester Packaging. "It's not going to cause problems in the compost."

Dr. Richard Wool of the University of Illinois' Degradable Plastics Institute goes a step further. "It may be over-designing to try and degrade plastics into CO_2 and water, when they are used in compost projects," says Dr. Wool. "In fact, although I don't want to overstate the case, polyethylene particles may enhance the compost by adding structure to it."

The final issue is that of toxins being released when the bags degrade. Most scientists in the field believe that toxins should not be used as additives. Ramani Narayan of Purdue University who heads the Environmentally Degradable Plastics Subcommittee of ASTM states that "toxic materials should be avoided when manufacturing degradable plastic bags." Lyle Schwartz of the National Institute of Standards and Technology believes there are alternatives to toxic coloring agents and inks that can overcome any potential problems. Those sentiments are echoed by Dr. Michael Tempesta of the University of Missouri. "We concluded early on in our research that manufacturers should not use heavy metals when they were producing composting bags," relates Dr. Tempesta.

Apparently the degradable additive manufacturers agree, because they have made an effort to keep toxins from being put into the bags. "In our technical literature, we tell our customers that toxic pigments containing lead, cadmium and the like, should not be used in producing bags," declares Peter Campbell of St. Lawrence Starch. "Likewise we want to see the bag manufacturers using non-toxic inks in any printing that is done."

Many of the bag manufacturers, particularly those that produce a composting bag, have followed this advice. For the most part, compost bag manufacturers are now marketing either clear or opaque bags that require no heavy metal pigments and use either carbon black-based or vegetable-based inks. "Clear bags make a lot of sense," states Jim Craig of Petoskey. "Not only don't you have to worry about heavy metals, but the clear bags help collectors identify yard waste for pick up and allow for visual inspection of the contents."

The other potential source of heavy metals in degradable plastic bags are photodegradation catalysts, particularly nickel and iron. While these materials are indeed heavy metals, some in the industry maintain they are present in such low concentrations that they cause no harm. For instance, research at Iowa State University showed the 50 year loading of nickel on agricultural land from one formulation was just over 1 percent of the EPA's proposed nickel level from sewage sludge applications.

DEGRADABLE PLASTIC BAG RESEARCH

Whether the questions that surround the use of degradable plastic are valid or not, asking them has spawned a bevy of research projects that are attempting to answer them one way or another. Unfortunately, at this juncture, most of the research and tests that relate to composting is ongoing and won't be completed for several months. Several places where tests on the performance of the bags are currently being conducted include Lincoln, Nebraska; Urbana and Chicago, Illinois; and Composting Concepts' project in Minnesota. Michigan's Department of Natural Resources also plans tests in the near future at a number of sites throughout that state.

While most of the research and tests have not been completed, one thing becoming clear is that the degradable formulators are improving their products to the point where the bags are breaking down at a rate conducive to composting. According to Tom Waffen, manager at the Southeast Oakland County (Michigan) Resource Recovery Authority's yard waste project, Petoskey bags put in the piles in April had become brittle within six to eight weeks and were easily broken open. "These bags are breaking down quite nicely," states Mr. Waffen. Similar sentiments about the bags are expressed by John Maroney of Composting Concepts. "We're very pleased with the Polar Plastic bags. They are breaking down at a rate that should make them unidentifiable in less than a year."

This year's tests in Lincoln follow up some rudimentary testing in 1988 that turned up the cadmium in trace amounts. That cadmium was believed to have come from yellow bags. "This year we're using clear bags," notes Gene Hanlon. According to Hanlon, tests will be conducted on the strength and degradation rate of the bags and the leachate will be analyzed for heavy metals content.

"Last year when we did our testing, there was virtually no loss of strength in the bags," notes Dr. Wilfred Hanna of the University of Nebraska, who heads up the research team. "The six percent ADM formulation (not ADM's new composting formulation) that we are testing this year is showing some loss of strength, but it's a slow process." In addition to performing strength tests and tests on the leachate, Dr. Hanna's team is also doing microbiological studies to determine how the microbes on the surface of the bags change over time.

Two independent tests are being conducted at Urbana's yard waste composting site. In one research project, Drs. Michael Cole and Karen Leonis of the University of Illinois are studying the degradation rates and loss of strength in three types of bags — the bags produced by Petoskey and Manchester and a third type that utilizes a photo-degradation process, the Plastigone technology developed by Ideamasters. Dr. Richard Wool is also conducting degradation rate experiments at Urbana testing an expanded number of degradable plastic films.

In addition, projects planned by Michigan DNR will include a full range of toxicity tests.

"We'll be sampling a number of programs that have utilized several different types of bags," reports Wayne Koser, DNR's Composting Specialist. "The tests will be conducted on both compost piles that include the degradable bags as well as those that had yard waste brought in by other methods. We want to be sure of these bags before we give them a clean bill of health." Similarly, Minnesota's Pollution Control Agency and its Department of Agriculture are testing the degradable bags at Composting Concepts for much the same reason.

In addition to the independent experiments, many companies involved in producing degradable bags are also conducting tests of their own. Petosky Plastics is doing a series of toxicology tests looking at both final compost products. Tests are also being done on the bags alone. Other companies that have or are sponsoring toxicology tests include Manchester Packaging, Ideamasters and St. Lawrence. St. Lawrence is also running tests to determine exactly into what the bags degrade.

While these and other tests may not answer all questions relating to using degradable bags in yard waste composting projects they certainly will add to the limited amount of information available at this point. Already the research has moved the industry away from using heavy metals in pigments and inks, as well as helping to improve breakdown of the bags.

For their part, a private yard waste collector or municipality intent on using degradable bags should make sure the bags it purchases are designed specifically for composting and produced without heavy metals in pigments and inks.

14

EVALUATION OF PAPER BAGS

Ken Schwindt, Timmi Nalepa and Glenn W. Munson

A PILOT PROGRAM to evaluate the merits of using biodegradable paper refuse sacks for municipal collection and composting of leaves was undertaken in fall, 1987 by the Department of Highways of Brookhaven Township, New York. The two purposes were: (1) to compare effectiveness of leaf composting in windrows made of loose leaves, leaves in plastic bags, and leaves in recyclable paper bags; and (2) to assess the tradeoffs in using recyclable paper bags rather than plastic bags.

Based on a 1986-87 analysis, an estimated 200,000 cubic yards (approximately 35,000 tons) of leaves are collected in Brookhaven annually. Eight towns and villages within Brookhaven Township collect their own solid waste, including leaves, through municipal departments or private contractors. The Highway Department collects leaves and brush along the remaining 1,600 miles of roads. In the past, a substantial amount of leaves were collected loose using vacuum pickup or payloaders and dump trucks, but loose collection is being discouraged. The majority of leaves are put in 30-gallon plastic bags by homeowners who pile them at curbside for pickup.

Brookhaven Township has four solid waste sites. The principal site is an 80-acre double-lined sanitary landfill which receives all solid waste other than leaves, brush and recyclable materials. A smaller site accepts recyclable materials, brush, and leaves collected in plastic bags. Here, brush and woody materials are chipped for mulching use. Bagged leaves are composted in windrows for 18 to 24 months, then shredded before being used. Shreds and pieces of the nondegradable plastic make this process highly inefficient.

A third disposal site, the Holtsville Ecology Site, accepts only loose leaves or leaves collected in recyclable paper bags. These are also made into windrows for composting, with finished compost being used for highway and municipal landscaping. Compost is also available here for use by Brookhaven residents in their yards, gardens and indoor plantings. The composting test reported here was conducted at the Holtsville Ecology Site.

A fourth site, the Pine Road Holding Yard, is a 10-acre site used to hold leaf windrows until they can be transferred to Holtsville. It is strategically located in the north half of the township to cut down on travel time to Holtsville during the busy leaf collection season.

The 145-acre Holtsville Ecology Site was once a town dump, then a State-operated openpit burning dump, then a sanitary landfill until it reached its limits and was covered with a final layer of sand and soil, and formed into hills and plateaus. New York State abandoned plans to operate it as a park in 1975, and the Brookhaven Highway Department took it over in 1979 for its growing Ecology Division.

COMPOSTING SINCE 1970

Brookhaven began composting leaves in 1970 and today uses a windrow composting technique. Payloaders build windrows approximately 20′ at the base and 10′ high. The length of the windrows depends on the available space, but is commonly as long as 300′. Windrows are made throughout fall and early winter, since residents rake yards from October into December.

During the second summer, after windrows

have completely decomposed, the finished compost is put through a shredder before it is used. Compost which began as loose leaves shreds easily. Compost made from plastic-bagged leaves, however, is problematic. Although the bags have torn and ripped apart, pieces and shreds of nondegradable plastic remain mixed throughout the piles. This requires the use of extra personnel to manually remove the pieces of plastic from the compost as it exits the shredder. An additional downside is that larger pieces twine around axles in the shredding box causing the machine to jam, and the shredder must be run at half speed to help overcome this problem. Shredding plastic bag windrows is five to six times more costly than windrows made of loose leaves.

A study made in 1985 by the Department of Agricultural Economics and Marketing at Rutgers University calculated the retail value of leaf compost to be $7.40 per ton[1] of original leaf volume, based on a leaf-to-compost yield ratio of 5:1. At this rate, Brookhaven's annual compost production would be worth over $259,000 as a cash crop. Although no in-depth economic analysis is available, we believe this evaluation would represent upwards of 75% of the composting costs.

Brookhaven produces approximately 40,000 cubic yards (7,000 tons) of organic compost annually, calculated on the basis of 20 percent original volume (weight). With our 20th "harvest" in 1991, Brookhaven will have generated approximately 140,000 tons of leaf compost.

The compost is used as a soil additive and mulch for highway, park and other municipal landscaping projects, and has been highly beneficial in revegetating and developing the Holtsville Site. Compost is mixed with peat moss in the potting soil mixture used in the Holtsville greenhouses. The majority of this compost, however, has been made available free to homeowners.

PAPER BAGS

In the fall of 1987, the Highway Department purchased 400,000 biodegradable paper Ecolobags from Dano Enterprises, in Plainview, New York. Through public information channels, we offered free Ecolobags to residents who would pick them up from a half-dozen Highway Department yards throughout the town. Municipal and private haulers were asked to deliver the filled paper bags to the Holtsville Site.

Although paper refuse bags have been available for at least two decades, drawing some public attention in the early 70s during the initial environmental movement, their major use has been for industrial purposes. The public is not familiar with these bags and they are not generally available in supermarkets, garden centers and other retail outlets as yet.

The Ecolobag used in this project is a heavy-duty, weather-resistant folded paper bag made of two plies of 50 pound kraft paper, using a waterproof, nontoxic adhesive throughout. It has a 16" × 12" square bottom and stands a waist-high 35 inches. It is self-standing. It has a 30-gallon capacity, equal to the standard home trash can plastic liner.

Although both are rated at a 30-gallon capacity, the Ecolobag holds 1½ to 2 times the leaves of a 30-gallon plastic bag. Holtsville personnel found they could usually empty the leaf contents of two plastic bags into one Ecolobag with energetic compacting.

REACTIONS OF HOMEOWNERS AND DEPARTMENT PERSONNEL

Nearly all the 400,000 paper bags picked up by residents, found their way back to Holtsville, mostly from pickup by Highway Department crews, or by other haulers. Throughout the fall, residents brought them to the Ecology Site in their cars or pickup trucks, most often taking finished compost with them for their own gardening use. Although we did not conduct a written survey, the staff was able to ask two or three dozen residents why they had made an effort to use the Ecolobags and what they thought of them.

Many said they had used the paper bags for environmental reasons, not surprising since all were familiar with Holtsville and used its compost or recreation facilities. Some pointed out that the bags had been free. When asked what they liked and disliked about the paper bags, the advantages most often cited were: the bag's strength; bags don't puncture and tear like plastic bags; bags are self-standing; they fill through a top opening, while leaves must be swept or raked into partly filled plastic bags; the waist-high opening saves bending over; water-resistance.

Unfavorable comments centered around bag closure and size. Several users said they found the bag difficult to close and wished there were some kind of built-in system for closing the bags easily and securely. Most users closed the bags as they would a grocery bag, by creasing in the sides and folding the top down two or three times. This method of closing the bag works fairly well, especially if the bag isn't crammed full to the top, but some users said the bag's thickness made it difficult to fold shut. A good many users said that stapling the top made closing easy and secure.

Some users thought the bag was too small, and estimated its capacity to be less than 30-gallon plastic bags. They found it hard to believe that we'd been able to dump the leaves from 1½ to 2 plastic bags into one Ecolobag.

The consensus on paper bags among highway

crews was "no problem." Some of the crew did notice specific advantages in the paper bags which made handling easier and more efficient. It's not uncommon for plastic bags to split open and spill their contents when picked up at the curb. When this happens, the crew has to stop to clean up the spill. If the bagged leaves were unusually wet and had been left inside the bag for a long enough time, they produced an especially rotten and unpleasant smell.

POTENTIAL PLASTIC ALTERNATIVE

This project was designed to look at collecting, composting and shredding recyclable paper bags, and to investigate their potential as an alternative to plastic bags for municipal leaf collection and composting. The project has yielded specific answers to some of our questions and provided a better understanding of factors involved if a switch to paper bags were to be seriously considered or eventually required by environmental legislation.

Composted paper bags can be shredded as quickly and inexpensively as composted loose leaves. The shredder does not have to be run at half-speed and extra personnel aren't required to remove bag material, as is the case with plastic bags. This represents an important savings, although an analysis of the specific savings has not been made.

Curbside collection of paper bags is somewhat more convenient and efficient than collecting plastic bags. Collection crews are favorably disposed towards paper bags. Homeowners find paper bags convenient to use, but cite closing as less convenient than plastic bags.

Although we found that paper bags can hold the leaf contents of upwards of 1½ 30-gallon plastic bags if reasonable effort is made to compact leaves during filling, homeowners perceive the paper bags to be smaller than plastic bags. It is unreasonable to expect homeowners, especially older residents, to compact leaves so firmly that curbside paper bags will hold the volume of two plastic bags, even though we have proven this capability.

ECONOMIC FACTORS

Recent bids submitted by bag suppliers to Brookhaven Township show that recyclable paper bags cost $0.29 apiece, approximately 61 percent more than plastic bags, which cost $0.18 each. Based on price comparison alone, few consumers would choose the paper bags at a retail store. Yet our project has shown this off-the-shelf price discrepancy doesn't take into account other important considerations which may not be apparent to the homeowner. For example, if homeowners filled paper bags with leaves equivalent to those held in 1½ plastic bags, the useful value of plastic bags to paper bags would be $0.27 to $0.29. Paper bags would be only 7 percent more expensive than plastic bags.

Another critical economic factor, one not easily discernible by homeowners, is the savings realized at the shredding step in our composting program. A detailed analysis of the additional cost to shred and remove plastic from composted leaves has not been made. But clearly the extra time and personnel required to shred plastic windrows is not insignificant. Our conclusion is that biodegradable paper refuse sacks are a cost-effective and environmentally sound alternative to plastic bags for use in municipal collection and composting of leaves.

Ken Schwindt is Ecology Project Supervisor at the Holtsville Ecology Center; Timmi Nalepa is Education Coordinator; and Glenn Munson is Project Consultant.

15

SEPARATE COLLECTION OF VEGETABLE - FRUIT - YARD WASTE

Femke Reijenga

AS PART of the Dutch Waste Act, primary emphasis has been placed on minimization with the second priority being reuse. The policy on household wastes has been increasingly directed to separate collection of compostable waste. The collection and composting of this waste (in the Netherlands called vegetable, fruit and yard—VFY) now comprises an essential part of Dutch waste management.

Analysis shows that about half of household waste here consists of VFY waste. The compost of separately collected materials has a purity of more than 95 percent, and the heavy metal contents are very low. There is a market for clean compost in the Netherlands. But the most important argument is the overwhelming success of experiments in many towns and villages.

In 1984, the Dutch government started the first experiments with VFY waste. Since 1985, many regions volunteered to take part in the trials. In 1987, the results of the town of Purmerend convinced many municipalities and sanitation departments about the advantages. The city of Apeldoorn (55,000 households) was the first to introduce separate collection and composting on a permanent basis for the entire city.

● **Preconditions**

The Waste Act and the Provincial Waste Programs give no legal impediments for introduction of separate collection and composting. The PWPs even can mandate municipalities to separate compostable wastes. Provinces should determine necessary capacity of facilities including composting plants. Provinces have the instruments to make plans and guidelines, and arrange regional projects.

● **Participation**

In most projects, participation is voluntary, and there proved to be no specific characteristics determining participation. In rural areas, separate collection is easiest to do. Almost all households (90 percent) participate, and much yard waste is generated. Therefore, bins or containers should be large enough (but not too large to make handling excessive). Two-week collection frequency is effective. In one week, the VFY waste is collected; in the other week, the other (mixed) waste. In the low-rise districts in urban areas, the collection is also without problems. Bins or containers should not be too large because of limited space in kitchens and gardens. In districts with apartment buildings, problems can arise because of lack of space in flats. In the Netherlands, about 30 percent of the population live in flats, but most move often, eventually to low rise houses. Collection is not advised for city center areas.

● **Information Campaign**

Educational campaigns have been very effective. A municipality introducing separate collection of VFY waste on a permanent basis should budget DFl 2 (about $1) a household a year for the information campaign (including materials). Activities can include instruction for personnel involved via reports and conferences; letters, leaflets, calendars, etc. to households; educational programs and exhibits for schools. Campaigns should begin a few months before collection start-up and continue for three months after.

In most projects, households received a small bucket to use in the kitchen. This bucket is not necessary but might be helpful. Each household will need a special container for the VFY waste. Some towns tried to introduce plastic bags, but these bags gave serious trouble in the processing of the compost and the households could not put their (large) yard waste in the bags.

Various kinds of buckets, bins and containers can be used for the VFY waste. Important for the collection is the frequency as well. To assure a good participation, the frequency must be high enough. Municipalities should choose the collection method that fits their specific character. Separate collection does not have to be expensive.

Collection costs for the duobin-system (once a week) or the 240 litre container system—once in two weeks—will increase about 15 percent (or about Dfl 20 a ton). In some areas with a high incineration tariff, these extra costs will be less than the savings from the (lesser) incineration of waste. In other areas, the separate collection will mean a small increase in the total collection and disposal price.

In all the projects in rural and urban areas, about 40 percent of the household waste is collected separately as VFY waste. The waste reduction in districts with only apartment buildings and flats is almost 20 percent. In low rise districts, every household has (an average of) 7 kilograms VFY waste a week. In flats, this is about 4 kilograms a week.

The purity of the VFY waste, according the separation rule is 95 percent. Most of the 5 percent "pollution" consists of paper. This can be composted and will not harm the quality of the compost.

VFY waste includes leftovers and trimmings of vegetables, fruit; coffee grounds and filters; animal manure, grass, straw, leaves, small cuttings, garden residues, etc.

REMAINING HOUSEHOLD WASTE

While VFY composting can reduce total household waste by 30 to 40 percent, there still remains a disposal problem for the remainder. Paper and cardboard comprise 35 percent of that balance, plastics about 10—15 percent, glass 7 percent, and about 5 percent metals. For these components, recycling possibilities are available. The next steps to reduce the waste stream will concern improvements in collection and processing efforts.

CURBSIDE COLLECTION OF ORGANICS IN CANADIAN COMMUNITIES

Two Ontario communities—the cities of Guelph and Mississauga—have developed pilot curbside collections of household organic waste (kitchen and yard waste). Initially, according to environmental officials in Ontario, both municipalities concentrated on the collection end of the process, testing different containers for use by householders to evaluate quantity and quality of materials recovered. For food waste collection in Mississauga, all 1,200 households received kitchen catchers, rigid plastic containers that can be mounted on a cupboard door along with plastic liner bags. For the collection of yard waste, the city provided large, clear plastic bags, along with instructions to bundle thick branches separately.

For the third step which involved bulking the food and yard waste before placement for collection, the households were subdivided into three areas. Each area tested a different type of container—large, plastic bags with a drawstring closure, and 10 and 17 gallon rigid containers.

Data from the first four months of the program showed that organic materials constitute 22 percent of the total amount of garbage and organics collected, according to Pat McFarlane, managing editor of *Ontario Recycling Update*. When this is combined with the materials recovered through the city's Blue Box program—glass, cans, mixed plastics (rigid and film), newspaper and phone books—31 percent of the residential waste stream is being captured. Seventy-six percent of the households in the pilot area are participating in the program, with approximately 9.8 kg of organics being collected per household per week.

Guelph in its pilot composting program tested variations of the European wet/dry system. Like the Mississauga program, the 600 participating households were subdivided into three areas. The first group of 200 homes used two containers, a 120 liter container for wet waste and a 240 liter container for dry waste (recyclable and non recyclable). A second group of homes separated waste into a wet stream and a dry stream, but unlike the first group, they had a special container for the dry stream. The third group separated their waste into three streams: wet, dry and recyclables. Household organics were collected in a modified side loading packer truck with an automatic lift.

One conclusion of our surveys of households is: Because of separate VFY collection, more people are interested in other separate collections.

The separate collection and composting of VFY waste needs many adaptations and changes within the sanitation departments of municipalities. But these changes are possible, and the costs for this new waste disposal can compete with the costs of the present disposal methods.

Femke Reijenga, a social scientist, is a researcher with the Interfaculty Department of Environmental Science (IVAM) of the University of Amsterdam.

Section
III

SITE SELECTION, REGULATIONS AND PERMITS

16

SITING THE FACILITY

IN THE LAST few years, as yard waste composting facilities have rapidly increased in number and size, more states have established guidelines for siting facilities. The first state to issue a leaf composting manual and include siting criteria was New Jersey in 1985. Prepared by Peter Strom and Melvin Finstein of Rutgers University, the manual included these points:

Site selection should take into account nearness to residences and streams, prevailing winds, traffic patterns, travel distance and its effect on equipment and labor costs.

A minimum of one acre per 3,000-3,500 cubic yards of leaves collected is required for the actual composting operation. This assumes the use of low-level technology, and is in addition to the requirement for a buffer zone. A buffer zone is required between site activities and neighboring land use to minimize possible odor, noise, dust and visual impacts. It would seem prudent to provide at least 50 feet between the composting operation and the property line. At least 150 feet should be allowed between composting activities and any sensitive neighboring land use areas.

State regulations generally do not allow siting in a flood plain and caution against steep slopes. "Windrows should run up and down rather than across slopes to allow leachate and runoff to move between piles, rather than through them" advise Strom and Finstein.

In its guidelines for leaf composting facilities issued in June, 1988, the Pennsylvania Department of Environmental Resources outlines the areas where leaf composting facilities are *not* allowed. These areas are: (1) In any wetlands; (2)

Within one-quarter mile upgradient and within 300 feet downgradient of any private or public water source; (3) Within 300 feet measured horizontally from any occupied dwelling unless the current owner thereof has provided a written waiver consenting to any leaf composting activities closer than 300 feet. The waiver shall be knowingly made and separate from a deed unless the deed contains an explicit waiver from the current owner; (4) A minimum 50 feet buffer area must be maintained between the property boundary and any active composting pile or windrow, processing area, curing or storage areas.

In January, 1989, Connecticut issued a leaf composting guide, prepared by the state's Cooperative Extension Service, that provided this data on facility siting:

Area Requirements: Processing sites — A good leaf volume estimate can be made from records of the number of truck loads of leaves hauled. For this purpose, one ton of leaves is taken to be the equivalent of approximately four cubic yards of leaves. (See Table 1 for calculating weight, volume and bag count data.) In the absence of such information, a leaf volume of six percent of the total annual solid waste volume can be used. Space requirements vary according to the composting method, ranging from 3,500 to 12,000 cubic yards of leaves per acre. For example, a suggested guideline for a windrow and turn facility is one acre for each 6,000 cubic yards of leaves. Additional space is required for compost storage and buffer areas.

Compost Storage Area — For the windrow and turn method, the storage area for finished compost should be an additional 15 percent the size of the windrow composting area. Compost will need to be kept in the storage area for a minimum of one month while it cures.

A minimum of five feet should be maintained between the base of the deposited leaves and the maximum high water table or bedrock. (This recommendation is based upon the current Connecticut practice for siting solid waste land disposal facilities but may be modified in accordance with specific site conditions such as soil permeability and hydrologic setting.)

Composting Pad — This is the surface where composting occurs. It should be constructed of well-drained materials and be designed for heavy equipment use in all seasons. To prevent ruts from forming, a paved surface can be used as a pad.

Water — A source of water is needed for wetting the leaves, and provision must be made for fire protection. Where a water source such as a pond or a hydrant is not available, a water tank vehicle can be used. For very dry leaves, approximately 45 gallons of water are required for each cubic yard of leaves. For large operations, an onsite water source may be necessary.

To provide an overview of site selection and preparation criteria, here is the material under that heading in the Michigan Department of Natural Resources manual on yard waste:

Potential areas for compost sites will be determined by facility size, hauling convenience, drainage, and proximity to residences and other sensitive land uses. Some communities with widely dispersed residential areas may choose to establish several sites to reduce transport costs. Others will centralize operations by providing a single site.

● **Location:** A centralized area with access over hard-surface, non-crowded, non-residential roads is preferred. Sites adjacent to cemeteries, parks, runway buffers at airports, fallow farm fields, golf courses, and buffer areas of old landfills might provide suitable locations.

TABLE 1.
Weight, Volume and Bag Count Data

Description	Data*
A. Bagged or loose leaves in a compactor truck:	
(1) Actual count based on one full load of 31 cu yd, weighing 14,525 lb and containing 1,550 bags (Springfield, MA; 1987, reported by Macy)	50.0 bags/cu yd; 468.5 lb/cu yd;
(2) Average by truckload based on truck capacity without adjustment for partially filled loads:	
a. Averaged over 1,745,380 lb (Springfield, MA 1987, reported by Macy)	414 lb/cu yd
b. Averaged over 1,413,010 lb (Waterbury, CT, 1987, from town records)	555 lb/cu yd
(3) A general estimate (reported by Derr)	450 lb/cu yd
B. Loose leaves collected with vacuum equipment and blown into a leaf box:	
(1) Average by truckload based on truck capacity without adjustment for partially filled loads:	
a. Averaged over approximately 150 loads, Scarsdale, NY (reported by Rice)	190 lb/cu yd
(2) A general estimate (reported by Derr)	350 lb/cu yd
C. Loose leaves loaded into an open truck with a front end loader:	
(1) Average by truckload based on truck capacity without adjustment for partially filled loads:	
a. Averaged over 13 loads (Springfield, MA, 1987, reported by Macy)	371 lb/cu yd
(2) A general estimate (reported by Derr)	250 lb/cu yd
D. Bagged leaves in an open truck:	
(1) Based on 9.37 lb/bag and an assumed average bag volume of 25 gallons (3.34 cu ft/bag)	75.7 lb/cu yd

*These estimates reflect a variety of measurement techniques, moisture conditions, and degrees of compaction and are presented here as a general guide. (From Connecticut Leaf Composting prepared by The Conn. Cooperative Extension Service).

● **Wetland/Flood Plain:** A compost site should not be located in wetlands or on a flood plain. Having compost windrows wash away in a flood is not a desirable scenario. Flood hazard maps can be obtained from local Soil Conservation Service offices. Standing water must not be allowed to collect around compost windrows because anaerobic conditions can quickly develop, causing odor, and a slower rate of decomposition. Standing water also makes operations difficult; ruts form if the site is muddy and equipment will get bogged down.

● **Regulatory/Permit Requirements:** Public Act 641: Leaf and yard waste composting sites in Michigan currently do not require a permit under Public Act 641, the Solid Waste Management Act. Sites must, however, meet established criteria to protect the environment. If, for example, air or water quality standards are not upheld, the State of Michigan has the authority to regulate operations to ensure compliance. In the future, all compost sites may well be required to register with the State and have an *active* program to rotate the incoming yard waste, meaning that leaves shall not accumulate more than three years. This action will prevent "leaf dump sites" that, by definition, are not composting programs.

● **Permit Coordination:** The Department of Natural Resources has developed a Permit Coordination form. It is designed so that if the answer is "yes" to any of 15 questions, a permit may be required. Phone numbers and the appropriate division are given for each item, as in the following example.
Yes or No: "Does the project involve the discharge of any type of wastewater to a storm sewer, drain, lake, stream, or other surface water? Permits, Surface Water Quality Division, 517-373-8088." Other questions pertain to groundwater, wetlands, air quality; location in state parks, forests, or game areas; enrollment in farmland and open space preservation areas, hazardous waste storage, and other environmental concerns.

One goal of the State of Michigan is to divert as large a volume of yard waste from landfills as possible in an environmentally acceptable manner. Composting of these source-separated materials is one way to accomplish this. By providing information on how to develop a sound composting program and by keeping the requirements for permits to a minimum, the programs can move forward rapidly.

● **Consistency With County Solid Waste Management Plans:** A composting facility falls in the domain of county solid waste management plans, and it is important to work with the planning committees in addressing any requirements they may stipulate. Size and locations for composting sites may be influenced by possibilities for shared use by one or more governmental units, so coordination with such planning bodies is important. The communication that occurs during this coordination process may lead to agreements for shared or contractual use of specialized composting equipment, thus reducing the total amount of space and equipment cost required for the actual composting operation.

● **Operations Area:** Windrow and access aisles for aerobic composting require a minimum of one acre per 3,500-5,000 cubic yards of leaves. Additional space is needed to provide adequate room for equipment storage, an all-weather staging pad for depositing incoming materials, and areas for curing and stockpiling compost. A structure for storing tools and monitoring equipment can also provide space for an office. A five-acre site should provide an adequate area for composting 14,000-20,000 cubic yards of incoming leaves and yard waste, allowing about one acre for the staging, curing, and storage areas.

● **Buffer Zone/Setbacks:** Buffer zone requirements in addition to the operations area should provide a minimum of 500 feet (more if possible) between active compost operations and residences, with a 50 foot setback from compost windrow edges. Curing piles can be placed so as to create a berm around the perimeter of the site to serve as a visual and sound barrier.

● **Percolation:** The need for the soil to provide sufficient stability for heavy equipment must be balanced by the ability of the surface to drain off excessive rainwater. Natural soils should have a high enough percolation rate to move water away quickly so that standing ponds of water are avoided. A paved surface makes vehicle access and equipment operation easier and provides a firm base for operating front-end loaders. These advantages can be outweighed by the difficulties in managing runoff.

● **Water Table:** Flooding of a compost site is an avoidable disaster and will cause anaerobic conditions if the windrows sit in standing water. High water tables increase the chance of ponding water and such conditions must be avoided. With greater depth to groundwater, more filtration of the leachate is likely to take place, lessening the possibility of groundwater pollution. Soil surveys providing information on soil types, percolation rates, and depth to ground water are available from the Soil Conservation Service.

● **Public Acceptance:** Consideration must be given to citizen concerns in choosing a composting site. Noise and vibration from heavy equipment, dust, possible odors, and visual impacts are problems that may arouse public outcry. However, a composting site can be made visually attractive with berming, fencing, and orderly, well-maintained windrows. By seeking citizen participation in the siting process, municipalities can access and stimulate their interest, address their concerns, and hopefully obtain support. If given the opportunity, many citizens will develop a sense of ownership and pride in a well-run composting program. Active citizen involvement can be expected to increase participation, both for dropping off properly prepared materials and for picking up finished compost.

One way to reduce possible citizen opposition to a composting site is to locate it at or near an existing or closed landfill, transfer station, or sewage treatment plant where acceptance of waste processing activities already exists. Careful consideration should be given if you plan to locate a compost site on a closed landfill because operations can damage the clay closure cover. Communities are strongly urged to check with the local DNR Public Act 641 representative for prior written approval of a specific site.

SITE PREPARATION

Once the composting site has been chosen, local zoning and health ordinances addressed, the public adequately consulted, traffic patterns identified, surface and groundwater issues resolved, and the sources of yard waste committed, preparation of the site can begin.

● **Slope:** Site preparation begins with grading. The area should have an adequate drainage pattern for run-off as well as protection from stormwater run-on. Level areas should be given a minimum of 1-2 percent slope to avoid ponding. Drainage swales should be marked to keep organic material from being deposited into drainage areas.

● **Roads:** The primary access road should be graveled, if not paved. Permanent roads to the staging and unloading areas should be built and maintained. Drainage along roadways should be established, including culverts where necessary. The degree of slope and area of drainage should be designed around the hydraulic overload generated from a 100 year storm, usually a seven inch rainfall over 24-hour period.

The aisles and access points of the compost windrows should be designed parallel to the angle of slope or fall line. These aisles should not be graveled since the location of windrows will change frequently and the gravel will invariably be lost in the turning process. Wood chips are often used for the base of composting roads and work effectively, although they can be difficult to grade and may contaminate the compost.

Access roads should provide for a circular pattern for entering and exiting to keep traffic congestion to a minimum. Adequate turning and dumping areas are essential. The purpose is to allow for the easiest possible drop-off of materials while avoiding the problems of stuck equipment. An all-weather location will ensure the likelihood of the site's fullest use.

● **Water:** Unless the site uses a system where precipitation is the only source of water to the windrows, provisions should be made for watering the windrows. Sources of water include city services, wells, surface water pumping, and trucking. A water service that produces a net of 30 gallons per minute is sufficient to supply six garden-size hoses simultaneously. A series of spigots should be located conveniently around the site, adequately protected from equipment damage.

● **Security and Safety:** The site should be fenced and the gate locked unless access is limited due to natural geographic barriers. A facility identification sign, "Keep Out" signs, and "No Dumping" signs are recommended. There should be a telephone and a two-way radio system for the site operator. Provisions for a second operator, a type of "buddy system", is a good safety practice. The office building should include a toilet, drinking water, electricity, heat, and air conditioning.

The guidance document issued by the Massachusetts Division of Solid Waste Management for area requirements stresses that consideration should be given to the space that will be required for maneuvering equipment at the site. At least a 20 foot zone should be allowed around the compost area for this purpose, and additional space provided for the turn around of any delivery trucks, and for the drop off of bagged leaves.

Adequate space must also be allocated for the on-site storage of finished compost, which is approximately 25 percent of the original volume of the leaves.

At minimal technology facilities, 8,000 to 16,000 cubic yards of organic waste can be composted per acre. (For leaves a cubic yard is roughly equivalent to 500 pounds or 1/4 ton). This includes 20 feet between windrows for equipment maneuvering. Operators must plan for 3 to 5 years on-site residence of leaf and yard waste until the compost process is complete.

At low-level technology facilities, 4,000 to 8,000 cubic yards of organic waste can be composted per acre, or about one-half that of the minimal technology facility. This also includes 20 feet between windrows for equipment maneuvering. On-site residence of 10 to 12 months, from deposit of the leaves to curing, should be expected for complete composting. The curing process takes place from six to eight months after the leaves have been deposited at the site. The composted leaves are moved to the curing area, allowing adequate room for composting a new year's supply of leaves.

High-level technology operations require somewhat less area per cubic yard than low-level technology facilities with an on-site residence time of less than 10 months.

17

PERMITTING THE FACILITY

MOST STATES recognize that yard waste composting facilities do not pose the potential environmental hazards that exist with other solid waste management facilities. Therefore many state regulatory agencies have set up permitting procedures for yard waste composting that expedite the process so facility managers need not submit as much technical data; or facilities under a certain size are treated less stringently because of less environmental impact. Some states have different permit requirements depending upon whether the site will compost only leaves or grass and other yard wastes (more stringent for grass clippings due to potential odor problems or nitrogen leachate.)

Before describing specific state permitting procedures in detail, here is a capsule summary to indicate the range of policies:

● **Connecticut**—No public hearing required; state recommends building at permitted, operating landfills, thereby requiring only a minor permit amendment which does not require public notice or 30-day comment period.

● **New Jersey**—Because of insufficient compost facility capability to meet state's needs by ban date, emergency regulations were passed in October, 1988 that made leaf composting facilities (less than 20,000 cubic yards per year) exempt from Solid Waste Facility permitting if requirements of new rules are met; Vegetative waste facilities (i.e., a facility which accepts more vegetative waste than leaves or accepts less than 20,000 cubic yards of leaves) could apply for a "temporary certificate of authority to operate" for one year; leaf mulching operations (direct application and disking of leaves into agricultural land) are exempted.

● **Pennsylvania**—Leaf composting facilities are exempt from MSW composting permit requirements. However, they must not accept grass and must follow state guidelines.

● **Washington**—Permit is required by state health department, however, requirements are that all compost must leave facility within five years, and 50 percent must "turn over" every two years. Permit mainly requires that "minimum functional standards" be met.

● **Wisconsin**—Facilities less than 50 cubic yards per year are exempt from any Department of Natural Resource regulations; 5,000—20,000 cubic yards require only a simple two-page report; above 20,000 cubic yards need a yard waste processing license from DNR.

● **Massachusetts**—All facilities must operate according to Department of Environmental Protection guidance document. Facilities composting only source-separated leaves are not required to obtain a "site assignment"; Facilities processing more than 50,000 cubic yards per year must obtain "plan approval" from DEP.

● **Michigan**—Currently no permit is required for yard waste composting facilities. However, they must meet established criteria to protect the environment. If air or water quality standards are not upheld, state has authority to regulate operations to ensure compliance.

● **New York**—Facilities receiving less than 3,000 cubic yards per year are exempted from permitting; more than 3,000, a permit is required.

PERMITTING PROCESS THAT PROMOTES COMPOSTING

The 1988 Guidelines for Leaf Composting Facilities issued by the Pennsylvania Department of Environmental Resources were established "to promote leaf composting in the Commmonwealth while providing an appropriate level of protection to human health and the environment. . . . Improper operation will be treated in the same manner as health or environmental problems at other solid waste management facilities."

Under the category of "General Requirements," the Pennsylvania DER Guidelines include the following:

(A) Each person or municipality that operates a leaf composting facility shall comply with the operating requirements set forth in these guidelines.

(B) Each person or municipality that proposes to operate a leaf composting facility without obtaining a composting facility permit from the Department shall notify the Department with the following information:

(1) Sponsoring municipality (where applicable).

(2) Responsible official/contact person.

(3) Facility location, including identification of the site on a U.S.G.S. 7.5′ topographic map.

(4) A general site plan for the facility indicating the following: Access road and gate location in relation to the nearest public road; Tipping area; Processing area including location of compost piles or windrows; Curing or storage areas; surface water controls.

(5) An operational narrative describing: Collection methods to be employed; Methods to be utilized in constructing compost piles or windrows, including equipment; Proposed dimensions of compost piles or windrows; Source of supplemental water to maintain an optimal 50 percent moisture content of compost piles or windrows; Proposed turning frequency, including method for determining that frequency; Proposed duration of composting process, including curing or storage time, and the term of compost distribution; Distribution plan for the finished compost; Residue disposal plan including the location of disposal site(s); Provisions for emergency response; Public information and education program.

(6) Volume of material processed during the previous year.

ILLINOIS BANS LEAVES FROM LANDFILLS

In the introductory paragraph to its permit re-quirements, the Illinois Department of Energy and Natural Resources explains that the Illinois General Assembly passed three bills affecting the future of yard waste disposal because "diversion programs play an important role in minimizing waste going into landfills." The bills include provisions which:

(1) Beginning September 1, 1989, prohibit sanitary landfills from accepting for final disposal truckloads composed primarily of leaves; and which, beginning July 1, 1990: (2) ban the disposal of yard waste at landfills unless the waste is to be composted; (3) prohibit persons from knowingly putting landscape waste into a container intended for collection or disposal at a landfill, unless such container is biodegradable; and (4) prohibit conducting a landscape waste composting operation without an Illinois Environmental Protection Agency permit. Requirements for obtaining these permits follow:

● **The Permit Requirements** as specified in Public Act 85-1429 include: a legal description of the site; a topographic map of site of the scale 200 feet/inch or larger; a description of the operation, including the area served; an estimate of the volume of materials to be processed, documentation that the location of the facility: has a setback of at least 200 feet from any potable water supply well; is outside the boundary of the 10-year floodplain; minimizes the incompatability of the character of the surrounding area including at least a 200-foot setback from any residence.

● **Design** of the facility should: not be within 5 feet of the water table; provide for adequate control runoff from the site and management of any leachate that is generated on the site.

● **Operation** of a compost facility shall include: appropriate dust and odor control measures; limitations on operation hours; appropriate noise control measures for shredding, chipping and similar equipment operation; management procedures for containment or disposal of non-compostable wastes; description of procedures to be used if operation closes; recordkeeping sufficient to document amount of materials received, composted and otherwise managed; submittal of a written annual statement to IEPA on or before April 1; of each year which includes an estimate of amount of materials, in tons, received for composting.

Permit application reviews may take up to 90 days before a permit is issued. Permits must be renewed every three years.

EXPEDITED PERMITTING
IN CONNECTICUT

Siting the "urgent need for leaf composting facilities," the Connecticut Department of Environmental Protection set forth an expedited permitting procedure for uncontested applications. "A properly run leaf composting facility should represent no serious threat to environmental quality," notes the DEP. The expedited permitting procedure is described as follows:

● **New Facilities**—Need Permit to Construct and Operate

1. Applicant uses an engineer to prepare site plans and application in accordance with DEP Composting Guidelines and the Leaf Composting Manual.

2. Application and supporting documents received by DEP Solid Waste Management Unit (SWMU) and reviewed for completeness. DEP also notifies chief elected official of receipt of application in accordance with Sec. 22a-208(a)(b) C.G.S.

3. Applicant completes application by providing requested data to SWMU.

4. DEP staff makes permitting recommendation to the Commissioner.

5. DEP staff prepares and applicant publishes a public notice of intent to issue a permit. A 30-day public comment period follows.

If a petition with 25 signatures is received or other substantial public comment, a public hearing may need to be scheduled at this point.

6. If no substantial public comment occurs, the Commissioner issues the Solid Waste Permit to Construct and Operate with appropriate site specific conditions. The applicant may then begin site preparation. The operation may begin after the prepared site is inspected by DEP staff.

Other local approvals, such as inland wetlands permits or planning and zoning permits, may be needed.

● **Compost Areas**—To be located at existing permitted Solid Waste Facilities.

Where suitable vacant area exists, the SWMU recommends that leaf composting facilities be located at existing permitted Solid Waste Facilities, particularly landfills. The environmental impacts will be minimal, public acceptance should be better, and the permit process can be streamlined.

Leaf composting facilities at landfills can be approved by the SWMU as a minor permit amendment to the existing facility permit to construct, as per Sec. 22a-209-4(f) R.C.S.A. The permit process would be identical to that previously described for a new facility except that no public notice or 30 day comment period is required.

18

ANALYSIS OF STATE REGULATIONS

WHILE STATES are doing what they can to encourage yard waste composting, many jurisdictions recognize that although yard waste composting facilities are less likely to cause environmental problems than other types of solid waste processing facilities, there are still potential problems, particularly with odors and water quality, which must be controlled.

Over the last several years, the states that have been most active in encouraging yard waste composting have also developed approaches to regulating their siting and operation. In general, the approach that most of these states have taken is to streamline the yard waste composting permitting requirements and limit the regulation of the operations. As one regulator noted, "many states are relying more on education and guidance than regulation" to ensure that the facilities don't cause problems.

There are a number of different avenues states are taking to monitor and control yard waste composting facilities. Short of allowing facilities to be developed and operated without restrictions, the approach Connecticut has chosen is probably the least restrictive. In July of 1989, Connecticut Public Act 7472 eliminated permit requirements for all leaf composting facilities. Rather than permit the facilities, Connecticut now only requires that project sponsors register with the Department of Environmental Protection (DEP) prior to developing a program. In place of regulations, the DEP has developed siting and operational guidelines which can be used by operators to help ensure that the facilities don't cause problems. The DEP believes that if the guidelines are followed the chance of a problem occurring at a leaf composting site will be minimized.

While Connecticut's guidelines don't have the "force of law," guidelines in at least two other states, Massachusetts and Pennsylvania, do work in place of regulations in controlling the siting and operation of yard waste facilities.

In Massachusetts, when a yard waste project sponsor registers a facility, it must agree in writing to follow the guidelines developed by the Department of Environmental Protection. In Pennsylvania's case, Municipal Solid Waste regulations (Chapter 75) don't contain leaf composting regulations but do require that "A person or municipality that operates a leaf composting facility shall comply with the Department's leaf composting guidelines."

Two other states that forgo permits for yard waste composting facilities are Maine and Minnesota. In these states, yard waste composting facilities are developed using a "permit by rule" approach. Basically, this means that facilities don't go through a formal permit review process, but developers must follow the state regulations in siting and operating a facility. (Maine's permit by rule applies only to those facilities that have a capacity of less than 6,000 cubic yards.) In both cases, the states also require that facilities be registered with the respective environmental agencies prior to beginning operation.

The final approach, used in states such as Illinois, New York and Washington, has been to develop both permit requirements and yard waste composting regulations, (or in the case of Illinois, a law which regulates siting and operations). Even in this approach, the states have put in place systems that don't require the rigorous permitting and operating regulations used for most solid waste facilities.

In developing these various approaches, state

regulators have had to temper the desire to expedite the development of the yard waste composting infrastructure with concerns about potential environmental problems. These concerns have led the regulators to limit the use of expedited permitting to rather narrowly defined areas. For instance, states have not reduced the permit requirements for yard waste if it is to be combined with other types of organic material, such as sewage sludge and food waste. In fact, in Connecticut, New Jersey and Pennsylvania, these reduced requirements apply only to leaf composting; projects that combined leaves with grass are subject to stricter requirements.

Another way states have confined their application is to limit the size of projects to which they apply. In Maine's pending yard waste composting regulations, the permit by rule provisions apply only to those facilities with a capacity of 6,000 cubic yards or less. In New Jersey the permit exemption is for leaf composting facilities containing less than 20,000 cubic yards. And in Wisconsin, the yard waste regulations apply to sites with a capacity of less than 20,000 cubic yards.

SITING REQUIREMENTS

In developing yard waste composting facilities, the principal environmental concerns, water quality and odors, are reflected in the siting criteria most states have adopted. In general, the approach states have taken is to separate the facilities from, as one composting specialist says, "sensitive odor receptors" (i.e, noses) to help prevent odor complaints. To protect water quality in the area around the facility, many guidelines and regulations utilize setbacks to help keep runoff and leachate from entering either ground or surface water. Additionally, states often restrict the placement of facilities in sensitive areas such as flood plains and wetlands.

As with the permitting requirements, states have taken divergent approaches to developing siting criteria. In terms of requiring separation distances between the actual composting or storage areas and residences, occupied dwellings, and property lines, which are used to mitigate odor problems, and between surface water, drinking water sources, high water table and bedrock, which

TABLE 1:
General Requirements For Yard Waste Composting Facilities

State	Material Covered	Permit Required	Size Limit	Siting Regs/ Guidelines	Registration Required	Regulation ID.
Connecticut	Leaves	No	None	None	Yes	
Florida (Pending)	All	Yes	None	Regulations[1]		
Illinois	All	Yes	None	Law	No	EPA 21r
Maine (Pending)	All	No[2] Yes	<6,000CY >6,000CY	Regulations Regulations	Yes	
Massachusetts	All	No	None	Guidelines	Yes	
Minnesota	All	No[2]	None	Regulations	Yes	MN 7035.2835
New Jersey	Leaves	No	<20,000CY	Regulations	Yes	NJAC 7:26-1.11
New York	All	Yes[3]	None	Regulations	No	6 NYCRR Part 360-5.4.5.5
Pennsylvania	All, Except Leaves	No	None	Guidelines	Yes	
Washington	All	Yes	None	Regulations	No	
Wisconsin	All	Yes[4]	<20,000CY	Regulations	No	NR 502

[1]Facilities under 3,000 cubic yards only have to register to obtain permit; [2]Permit by rule
[3]Facilities accepting less than 3,000 CY/year don't require permits; [4] facilities accepting less than 50 CY/year don't require permits

TABLE 2:
Yard Waste Facility Siting Standards

State	Restrictions From:		Minimum Separation Distance To:					
	Flood Plain	Wetlands	Dwellings	Property Line	Surface Water	Drinking Water	High Water Table	Bed Rock
Connecticut	No specific siting standards							
Florida	Yes	Yes	No	No	200'	No	No	No
Illinois	Yes 10 Year Flood	Yes	200'	No	No	200'	5'	No
Maine	Yes 100 Year Flood	Yes	500'	100'	300'	300'	24"	40"
Massachusetts	Yes	Yes	No	No	No	No	4'	5'
Minnesota	Yes 100 Year Flood	Yes	No	No	No	No	No	No
New Jersey	Yes	Yes	150'	50'	No	No	No	2'
New York	Yes	Yes	200'	50'	200'	200'	2'	2'
Pennsylvania	No	Yes	300'	50'	No	300' to 1/4 mile	No	No
Washington	No	Yes	No	No	No	No	No	No
Wisconsin	Yes	Yes	No	No	1000' (Lake)	1200'	No	No

TABLE 3:
Yard Waste Facility Design and Operation Requirements

State	Maximum Capacity (CY/AC)	Windrow Size	Orientation	Grade	Minimum Turning Frequency	Annual Report Required	Controls Required For:				Access Control	Visual Screening
							Leachate	Dust	Odor	Noise		
Connecticut	No	No	No	No	No	Yes						
Florida	No	No	No	(1)	1/yr	Yes	No	No	No	No	No	No
Illinois	No	No	No	No	No	Yes	Yes	Yes	Yes	Yes	Yes	Yes
Maine	No	No	No	1-4%			Yes	Yes	Yes	Yes	No	No
				(1)	4/yr	Yes	Yes	No	No	No	No	No
Massachusetts	5000	No	Parallel	2-5%	No	Yes	Yes	Yes	Yes	Yes	Yes	No
Minnesota	No	No	No	No	Periodic		Yes	No	No	No	No	No
					(2)	Yes	Yes	Yes	Yes	Yes	Yes	Yes
New Jersey	3500	6'High 14'Wide (Maximum)	Perpendicular	(1)	3/yr (3)	Yes						
							Yes	Yes	Yes	Yes	Yes	No
New York	No	No	No	No	No	Yes	Yes	Yes	Yes	Yes	Yes	No
Pennsylvania	3000	6'-8'High 12'-16'Wide	Perpendicular	1%	2/yr	Yes						
							No	No	No	No	No	No
Washington	No	No	No	No	No	Yes	Yes	No	No	No	No	No
Wisconsin	No	No	No	No	No	Yes						

(1) Must prevent ponding; (2) must be capable of maintaining temperature and controlling pathogens; (3) within 2nd month; within the 4th to 6th month; within the 10th month

are used to protect water quality, some states have chosen to adopt specific distances while others prefer to review facilities on more of a case-by-case basis.

For instance, Minnesota and Wisconsin, both of which have yard waste regulations, have chosen not to include specific separation distances. Maine and New York, on the other hand, have spelled out required separation distances from numerous manmade and natural features.

Even for those states that have developed minimum separation distances, the distances involved can vary greatly between states. In Maine, the pending setback distance to a residence or occupied dwelling is 500 feet, 200 feet greater than Pennsylvania and 350 feet greater than New Jersey, whose setback distance is 150 feet. Similarly, the minimum distance to a drinking water source

in Pennsylvania is 300 feet downgrade from the facility and 1/4 mile upgrade from the facility, while in Illinois and New York the minimum distance is 200 feet in any direction.

With the exception of Pennsylvania all of the states that have developed guidelines (those that have the force of law) or regulations have excluded yard waste composting facilities from being placed in flood plains, and all of them have placed wetlands out of bounds for development. In some instances, such as in Illinois and New York, the restriction on building in a flood plain is not absolute if the facility can be flood proofed.

FACILITY DESIGN AND OPERATING STANDARDS

The specific yard waste facility design requirements that have been adopted by most states are

TABLE 4:
State Bans On Landfilling Yard Waste

State	Date Effective	Yard Waste Banned	Market Development	Compliance
Connecticut	1/1/91	Leaves only	Preferential procurement for recyclables that could include yard waste	Measures under consideration; enforcement possible under solid waste law
Florida	1/1/92 (from lined land-fills only)	Vegetative matter, including stumps & branches	State agencies required to buy compost products when cost-competitive	Via achievement of 30% state recycling goal by 1994; yard waste can represent 15% of the 30% goal
Illinois	7/1/90 (ban on truckloads of leaves by 9/89 repealed)	All landscaping waste, grass, leaves, tree trimmings	State working with Dept. of Transportation on compost use	Enforcement action at landfill
Iowa	1/1/91	Not yet specified	Agencies should give preference to compost use in all land maintenance activities	Unannounced inspections at landfills
Minnesota	1/1/90 for 7 county metro area; 1/1/92 for rest of state	Yard waste, clippings, boughs, etc.	1985 Exec. Order covers state use of compost products; Waste Mngt. Act also requires market development for compost	Enforced at county level
New Jersey	8/89 (Ban extended to year-round vs. only 9/1-12/31)	Leaves only	All public lands must give preferential procurement to compost materials	Provisions available under Solid Waste Mngt. Act to impose fines; enforcement at landfills and transfer stations where permits don't allow acceptance of yard waste
North Carolina	1/1/93	All yard trash	Market evaluation due by 3/91; all state agencies & local govts. required to procure compost when cost-competitive & suitable substitute	
Ohio	1/1/93	Leaves, grass, brush & other woody bits	Assistance being evaluated for all recycled products, including compost	Fines; and need provision for yard waste composting in solid waste mngt. plan to get state approval and funding
Pennsylvania	9/26/90	Leaf waste, inc. leaves, garden residues & tree trimmings but not inc. grass clippings	Preferential consideration to use of compost in maintenance of public lands	Non specific to leaf waste ban but mechanisms are available
Wisconsin	1/1/93 (6 of 72 counties have bans in place)	Leaves, grass, small woody bits under 6"	Communities' responsibility	No state mechanism

concerned primarily with the amount of material processed on the site and the formation and turning of windrows. Additionally, most states have general control requirements for leachate and nuisances such as dust, noise and odor.

Given that there are numerous approaches to composting, the majority of states that have developed facility standards have chosen not to restrict facility operators to fixed capacity, windrow dimensions or turning schedules, but rather allow the operators flexibility in design and operation. Two notable exceptions to this practice occur in New Jersey and Pennsylvania. These two states have established maximum capacity requirements and windrow dimensions, as well as minimum turning frequencies. Both also require operators to orient windrows perpendicular to grade to help minimize runoff.

In terms of facility operations, Maine has probably gone the furthest in the definition of proper procedures. While most states have not established standards for grass composting, Maine's pending regulations prohibit grass from being brought to a facility unless there is a sufficient amount of other material on hand to mix with it. Further, Maine's pending regulations will require that grass be mixed with leaves on a 3 to 1, leaves to grass ratio. "We understand that some composters believe that a 2 to 1 or better ratio is possible," notes Brian Cavanaugh, who is putting together Maine's regulations, "but we prefer to be a bit conservative on the mixing since no one in Maine has much experience with it."

In terms of grading, most states want to ensure that ponding is prevented. Some states also have developed grading parameters. For instance, Maine and Massachusetts, grading ranges are 1 to 4 percent and 2 to 5 percent respectively, while Pennsylvania has a minimum grade of 1 percent.

Since a principal concern about yard waste composting is water quality, it's little wonder that state regulators all specify that operators must develop facilities which control leachate and runoff from the site. In most instances, the standards require that water must be diverted from areas where the yard waste is composting and where the compost is stored. Additionally, the facilities must be constructed to prevent runoff from leaving the site. While exact measures are not spelled out, in some cases, this may require that settling ponds are constructed. While no state requires that compost pads must be constructed, Minnesota's Cathy Berg-Moeger, notes that leachate control requirements "could force some facilities to go with a pad."

Clearly, yard waste composting in the United States is on the rise. With its increased use state regulators are having to develop mechanisms that encourage the practice while also controlling possible environmental problems. To date, with prodding from composting advocates, they have taken that tack. What remains to be seen is if facility operators will be diligent enough to use this freedom or abuse it.

Section
IV

METHODS
AND OPERATIONS

19

TECHNOLOGICAL OPTIONS

IN 1986, P.F. Strom, F.B. Flower, M.H.P. Liu and M.S. Finstein of Rutgers University wrote a report: "Recommended Methods for Municipal Leaf Composting," which described three different levels of technology:

1) Minimal Technology: Leaves are formed immediately into large windrows, e.g. 12 ft. high by 24 ft. wide using a front end loader. Once each year the windrow is turned and reformed. A new windrow is constructed each fall with the new leaves. After three years or sometimes longer, the material in the windrow is stabilized and ready to be used as compost.

The minimal technology is not designed for rapid composting. Much of the pile remains anaerobic for a full year between turnings. Unpleasant odors can be expected prior to the first turning, and serious odors may be released after the first turn. Therefore a leaf composting site using minimal technology should be relatively isolated. The advantage of this approach is that it is extremely inexpensive, with relatively little space required for the actual composting of the leaves. A useable compost is produced, albeit with the potential for serious odor problems during turning.

2) Low-Level Technology: Because the authors of the article were developing methods for leaf composting in New Jersey, which is a densely populated state, they determined that the minimal technology approach was not the most viable. Thus a low-level method was developed to achieve more rapid composting of the leaves under conditions that would not generate offensive odors. In particular, say the authors, this meant having to ensure adequate conditions of moisture content, oxygenation, and temperature within the pile.

Prior to or during initial windrow formation, a minimum moisture content of 50 percent is desired (a rough approximation is about 20 gallons of water to be added per cubic yard of collected leaves). The desired temperature range for composting is 70°F to 140°F, which can be achieved by adjusting pile size. But oxygenation levels can be adversely affected by pile height. To balance the two, the authors recommend starting with moderate size piles—6 ft. high by 12 to 14 ft. wide—then combining two piles after the first burst of microbial activity, which lasts approximately one month.

The piles should be turned in the spring to increase the rate of decomposition and improve destruction of any pathogens or weed seeds. During turning, maximum mixing and "fluffing" is desired. Water can be added if the material is too dry, but this is not necessary if the material was wet enough initially. Additional turnings throughout the summer will further enhance the composting rate and product quality. While much of the material will not be stabilized completely by the end of the summer, the authors point out that the material is fairly well decomposed, has low oxygen demand, and is unlikely to generate unpleasant odors. This material can be put into larger curing piles built around the perimeter of the site. While the piles can be made as large as desired to conserve space, compaction should be avoided. A well stabilized, finished product should be available by the following spring. The authors add that shredding is an optional step, one which improves the physical quality and appearance of the finished compost, making it more acceptable to the public for many uses. The disadvantages to shredding are increased capital and labor costs, as well as a need to dispose of rejects.

3) High Level Technology: Space constraints

and a desire to complete composting in a year led to the development of the high level of technology. It involves forced aeration of the large windrows with blowers. (The authors point out that turning the windrows more frequently with a front-end loader can produce a finished product within a year, however, since the original windrows can be no larger than those of the low-level technology to avoid odor problems, little space is saved). The blowers are controlled by a temperature feedback system to ensure near optimum temperatures in the bulk of the material while maintaining a well-oxygenated condition at the same time. Nitrogen (fertilizer) could be added to further speed decomposition. Adequate pre-wetting of the leaves is a necessity, and after perhaps one month of high rate processing, the blowers could be removed and mechanical turning of the piles would begin. Although the high level technology approach speeds decomposition, the authors recommend a moderate size buffer zone because the incoming leaves may themselves be odorous and these odors may be released during the initial windrow formation and start up.

TECHNOLOGY UPDATE

"We have added one more level of technology," says Strom, "an intermediate level that includes the use of a windrow turning machine. But in New Jersey, the low level technology approach is the most prevalent, although some of the regional and commercial sites are going to the intermediate approach. They do weekly turnings with a turning machine and have a finished product in four to six months. Because they are using the machines, generally the intermediate technology facilities actually need more than the one acre per 3,000 yards of leaves that we recommend because the intermediate pile height has to be five feet or less to accommodate a turning machine. The oversize Scarab, however, can handle higher windrows. The machines give more efficient and better turning, but of course there is also the increased capital cost."

Strom discussed a number of issues, from odor control at leaf composting sites to the primary end uses for the material. His comments are presented below.

● **BioCycle: How complex does leaf composting need to be with regards to monitoring moisture, aeration rates, and temperatures?**

Strom: With regards to moisture, if the leaves are too dry, they won't compost. How important that is depends on the system. If the intermediate or high technology levels are being used, and the operators want to get the compost off the site quickly, moisture content is very important. If you have three years to produce a stable compost, it is not as critical if you get a slow start. The low level

technology usually requires some water addition if composting is to be completed on schedule.

Oxygen, on the other hand, is critical. Odors can close a leaf composting site down just as they can with sludge composting. Oxygen levels are controlled with turning, aeration, and the original pile size. For research purposes, we have a monitoring technique that involves the use of an oxygen meter that can be purchased for about $350. We made our own probe of eighth inch pipe, which routinely is put in the center of the pile—at about 3 foot height and 3 foot depth. The rule of thumb is that we like to see more than five percent oxygen. At five percent, there are not extensive anaerobic zones, although there will be some. With the low level technology, it will dip below that, but the intent is that it will only dip below in small regions for short times.

Maintaining temperatures in a proper range (less than 140°F) is not as critical with leaves as it is with sludge composting because the piles won't heat up as much. And leaf composting is a more forgiving system, with most of the putrescibles being destroyed while achieving certain temperatures. When the piles are turned, they are reinoculated with organisms from the outside that were not killed by the extreme temperatures, but that is not as critical as it is with sludge composting.

● **BioCycle: That brings up the question of pathogen control in leaf composting versus sludge composting. Where do the primary concerns lie?**

Strom: There are pathogens to destroy, but obviously they do differ from the human pathogens in municipal sludge. The two groups you want to destroy are weed seeds and plant pathogens. The major weed seed is acorns because end users don't want oak trees in their flower gardens. The plant pathogens come from diseased vegetative materials, which need to be destroyed. And there is tremendous destructive capabilities with composting —better than disinfection.

● **BioCycle: Odor control is a primary site management concern. What have you learned from the operating experiences of leaf composting sites?**

Strom: We strongly recommend keeping grass clippings out. In the future, we hope they can be incorporated but at present, we want to keep them out. They get mixed in by landscapers or homeowners and some places have tried to compost them in New Jersey. You can mix grass clippings with partially composted leaves (after four to six months). The compost is improved because of the nitrogen in the grass clippings. But the problems are caused before you mix the grass in. It goes anaerobic and begins to stink almost immediately after it gets piled up.

We have done some experiments with a mix of 3:1 of partially composted leaves to grass. We think 2:1 would be effective, but have never tried it. Rutgers will begin research soon on composting grass clippings, but overall, we recommend that leaf composting sites do not accept any clippings in bulk unless they have some special way of handling them.

In general, with regards to odor control, make sure you maintain aerobic conditions so that odors are not generated. That is accomplished by not making the windrows too large and not storing the leaves. Form windrows right away. If you store leaves in large piles, they start composting right away and go anaerobic.

● **BioCycle: What about mixing in yard waste or brush as a bulking agent to help with aerobic conditions?**

Strom: My concern would be how to get the brush out at the end. The wood won't compost, so you would either have to grind the end product or have an outlet for it. This raises a more general point about the term, yard waste composting. Leaves have dramatically different characteristics than grass or wood wastes. Grass, for example, is high in nitrogen and readily degradable. Leaves don't break down as quickly and wood is much slower to decompose. Some towns handle each waste separately, while others mix them together and get good results. The key is to plan out what your end markets are. If you know what you are doing with the final product, it may not matter if it contains wood chips, e.g. if you plan to use it for landfill cover. Homeowners, however, don't generally want wood chips mixed in.

● **BioCycle: What is the advantage, if any, to shredding leaves prior to composting?**

Strom: Pre-shredding speeds up the composting process. This will have an impact on the level of technology being used, because if you increase the rate of composting, you need to increase the rate of oxygen being supplied, either by forced aeration or increased turning. Normally we recommend against pre-shredding.

● **BioCycle: What are the primary end uses for the compost?**

Strom: In New Jersey, the primary uses are as follows: 1. Return to town residents for use; 2. Top soil companies; 3. Nurseries; and 4. Public works and parks departments. Other potential uses include landfill cover and reclamation of waste land. In general, you have broader uses for leaf compost because no public health threat is perceived. Most municipalities are giving it away to residents and charging a nominal fee to bulk users.

● **BioCycle: What is the proper length of time for curing the compost?**

Strom: You really judge the finished product by its appearance. Is the leaf structure gone? Does it have a rich brown color and coffee grinds type texture? The pH also will have reached seven or above by the time the composting is finished.

● **BioCycle: What trends have you seen with regards to the cost of leaf composting and methods of leaf collections?**

Strom: The greatest costs appear to be connected to collection of the leaves. With the actual composting, shredding at the end to produce a clean, uniform product is the greatest expense.

The cost to compost at publicly owned facilities is $2 to $4/cubic yard. Privately owned facilities, which tend to use a higher level of technology, are charging a tipping fee of about $7/cubic yard.

With regards to collection methods, we see a lot of collection in bags. The first year, most sites let the bags in. The second year they don't. Operators have problems with odors and getting the bags open. In one case, the bags acted as a dam, and caused leachate to build up. Also, there are increased manpower requirements to deal with bags. One solution is to have the public works people strip the bags at the street during collection, or to use paper bags.

With bulk collection, there are problems satisfying residents with frequent enough pick ups before leaves start to back up gutters. We also hear of periodic fires started by catalytic converters, or injuries or deaths resulting from children playing in the piles of leaves and getting run over.

● **BioCycle: Have you noticed any problems with toxics in the leaves, or pollution problems at the leaf composting sites?**

Strom: We have done limited testing for lead and the leaves turned up quite clean, although there is some there. With grass, we will be studying the content of pesticides and herbicides. The leachate from leaf composting passes the drinking water standards for lead. We recommend that facilities allow the leachate to percolate through the soil—either vertically or horizontally—before it gets to surface waters. In general, we want to be certain there is some distance between the site and surface water. Therefore a paved site is not as good because the leachate would not be able to go into the soil. We do recommend a paved or gravel access road, however, so trucks don't get stuck. And because leaves have little nitrogen, we don't have to worry about groundwater contamination.

20

GUIDANCE IN
STATE MANUALS

SINCE RUTGERS UNIVERSITY researchers provided a methodology for composting leaves for municipal leaf composting in New Jersey in October, 1985, other states have been offering valuable material in a series of publications. An overview of composting methods, prepared by the University of Connecticut Cooperative Extension Service, categorizes the options as passive leaf piles, windrow and turn, aerated static pile, and in-vessel composting:

● **Passive Leaf Piles:** Leaves are deposited in piles ranging in height from 9 to 20 feet and are left undisturbed for a minimum of two to three years. Leaf piles that are too small (less than 6 feet high) should be combined. An optional measure is to turn and aerate the leaf pile in the early spring or late fall. Although process management is minimal, the leaf piles should be maintained to avoid an unsightly appearance and should be combined after there is a noticeable volume reduction from the initial leaf pile size. Odor may be a problem when these piles are disturbed as anaerobic conditions may exist in the oxygen starved center of the pile, so wind directions should be considered before work on the piles is undertaken. Compost consistency for end use is fair, as it may retain clumps of uncomposted leaves.

● **Windrow and Turn:** Leaves are deposited on a compacted pad to form a triangular shaped windrow measuring 10 to 20 feet at the base with a height of 6 to 12 feet or higher. The windrow can be up to several hundred feet long or as long as the site allows. In this process, the windrows are turned periodically with a front end bucket loader or a special turning machine and water is added as needed. The frequency of windrow turning is determined by the temperature and moisture content of the windrow. Windrows are combined as they shrink in size. The leaves compost through the winter and spring, cure over the summer and are available for end use by the next collection season. The finished compost can be removed from the composting site to make room for incoming leaves. The consistency of compost for end use is good as periodic turning will result in fewer clumps of undecomposed leaves.

Use of specialized windrow-turning machines improves aeration, resulting in shorter time requirements for composting. The turning machine is either self-propelled or machine driven. If machine driven, it is important that the drive method selected be properly matched to the machine.

With windrow-machine turning, the machine selected limits the windrow height to 5 to 7 feet. Windrow width varies from 14 to 18 feet to give a trapezoidal shaped pile.

● **Aerated Static Pile:** The windrow configuration is similar to that described for windrow and turn except that the windrow is stationary (static pile) and has a base of wood chips or some other porous material. Since the leaves are not turned in this process, it is particularly important that non-compostable materials are removed before windrow formation. The leaves are also put through a tub grinder or shredder before forming the windrow. A perforated plastic pipe is placed over or in the base material and air is forced through the pipe into leaves using an air blower. After the windrow is formed, a 4″ - 6″ layer of compost, wood chips, sawdust or an equivalent porous material is placed over the pile to help retain process heat, moisture and odor. In order to manage windrow temperature the air movement is controlled either by a timer switch or manually. Experience with this method for composting leaves is limited. It is generally used in sewage sludge composting.

● **In-vessel Composting:** In-vessel composting encompasses a variety of systems involving mechanical agitation, forced aeration and enclosure within a building. These systems are designed and supplied by consultants or commercial suppliers.

AEROBIC WINDROW COMPOSTING

While its Guidebook for Michigan Communities on Yard Waste Composting describes the range of technologies—including direct land application and sheet composting, the DNR publication believes that aerobic windrow composting best suits their need to handle large volumes efficiently on limited space. The following instructions are given concerning size, formation, turning, combining and incorporating grass clippings:

● **Windrow Size**—Aerobic windrows can be any length, but should be constructed 12 - 14 feet wide at the base and 6 - 8 feet high. The 6 - 8 foot height permits air to penetrate to the interior of the pile, and results in less compaction than occurs in higher piles. Windrows that are at least eight feet tall may be needed to retain heat during Michigan's cold winters.

The key factor in determining windrow size will be the equipment used for pile turning. Front-end loaders can turn windrows of greater heights (8 - 10 feet vs. 4 - 8 feet) than windrow turning machines. Because windrow width is also determined by equipment, final site design should wait until equipment specifications are known. Some leeway is available for establishing windrow height when piles are initially formed because leaves compress and windrows will shrink in size. Smaller windrows should be merged to keep windrows at the optimum height and width. An important point to remember is that piles that are too large turn anaerobic due to compaction.

● **Space Configuration**—The rule of thumb for aerobic windrow composting is that 3,500 - 5,000 lightly compacted cubic yards of incoming leaves requires approximately one acre of land. Aisles between windrows must be of sufficient width to accommodate the equipment to be used. Access aisles should be 14 - 16 feet, or of sufficient width to turn and manipulate the equipment. Some compost turners require eight foot aisles, with 30 feet available at the ends of the windrows.

One method of conserving space that can be utilized with front-end loaders is to form initial windrows in pairs with access aisles in between the pairs. Within the pair, each windrow is separated from the other by one or two feet. Windrows are initially turned from the access aisle. By the time they are turned again, volume is sufficiently reduced to combine the two adjacent windrows into each other.

● **Windrow Formation**—The loader operator layers the material one scoop deep, lengthwise. Although a skid steer loader (Bobcat type) with a 1/2 cubic yard bucket can be used, using an oversized, one-yard bucket will move piles more efficiently if care is taken not to lift the bucket to the point of tipping the loader over. This layer should be watered at a rate of approximately 15 to 25 gallons per cubic yard, or up to five minutes at five gallons per minute - never enough to cause runoff. The cubic yards per linear foot of windrow is essential to calculate before watering. As a rule, a ten foot high windrow will have 1 1/2 cubic yards per foot.

Once the layer is watered, another layer is placed on top with two scoops width wise and watered again. It is critical to water the pile **layer by layer** to provide sufficient moisture evenly through the pile. Attempting to water a pile when it is finished only results in runoff, a dry center, and uneven decomposition. Natural soil bacteria provide microorganisms for composting without inoculation, although adding old compost helps "seed" compost piles. While this may appear to increase material handling and site retention time, it is a good technique for accelerating composting rate and reducing odors. With yard waste, ten percent old compost is suggested as the maximum.

● **Windrow Turning**—Once the initial pile is formed and watered, it can be left for seven days after which it should be turned. Using a front-end loader, the piles are best turned scoop-by-scoop rather than pushed end over end. Scoop-by-scoop turning provides more thorough mixing and keeps the loader tires from driving on the piles and compacting the material. Scoop-by-scoop turning helps ensure that the outer edges of the pile are moved first and placed in the center of the next windrow in order to help mix dry sections with wet material. The operator needs to leave sufficient space on the side of the pile for the next windrow. All piles should be aligned in the same direction, aisle space kept equal, and access areas kept open between windrows.

● **Combining Windrows**—Windrows can be left 10 - 14 days after the initial turning during the first week. At this time, two piles should be able to be merged together to form one new windrow. When this operation is carried out, the loader operator places materials from the other edges in what will become the center of the pile to ensure uniform

TABLE 1:
Leaf Compost Guidance Summary.

Parameter	Method		
	Leaf Pile	Windrow and Turn	Forced Aeration
1. Site information.			
Size: cubic yards leaves/acre	8,000-12,000	3,500-8,000	5,000-10,000
Surface	Earth pad	Earth pad (paved surface acceptable)	Earth or paved
Grade	2% slope (min)	2% slope (min)	2% slope (min)
Drainage			
Subsurface	Moderate	Moderate	Moderate
Surface	Satisfy acceptable water quality criteria for discharge (or contain on site if needed). Divert surface water from piles.	Satisfy acceptable water quality criteria for discharge (or contain on site if needed). Divert surface water from windrows.	Satisfy acceptable water quality criteria for discharge (or contain on site if needed). Divert surface water from aerated windrows.
2. Suggested separation distances (in feet) from compost site.			
To residential and business complexes	200-250'	200-250'	200-250'
From adjacent property line	100'	100'	100'
From a surface water body	100'	100'	100'
From ground surface to bedrock	5'*	5'*	5'*
From ground surface to seasonal high water table (highest seasonal level)	5'*	5'*	5'*
3. Compost process time	2-3 years	Varies with frequency of turning windrows 6-12 months	4-6 months
4. Curing time (following compost process)	Not applicable	1 month (min)	1 month (min)
5. Odor generation	Can be high at time of initial pile disturbance.	Some odor potential when pile is first disturbed; proper management will reduce or eliminate this potential; decreases with pile turning frequency.	Minimal problem if the system is properly designed, installed and operated.

Current State of Connecticut practice followed for siting solid waste land disposal facilities.

TABLE 1:
Leaf Compost Guidance Summary (continued)

Parameter	Method		
	Leaf Pile	Windrow and Turn	Forced Aeration
6. Equipment needs	Front end loader daily during leaf collection period.	Front end loader daily during leaf collection period and when windrows are turned. Three or 4 foot stem type thermometer. For large leaf composting facilities, evaluate the use of specialized mechanical equipment for turning windrows.	Front end loader, tub mill grinder, blower type fan, temperature and timer switch controls, plastic piping (both solid and perforated lengths needed), 3 or 4 foot stem type thermometer. Adequate electrical capacity. Optional leaf shredder.
7. Water supply	Required for fire control and wetting of leaves. Up to 45 gals/cu yd.	Required for fire control, wetting of leaves; can use water hose or a portable water tank source having water spray capability. Up to 45 gals/cu yd. Large operations may require on-site water.	Required for initial wetting of leaves (see windrow) and for fire control. Upto 45 gals/cu yd.
8. Operational	Nothing done to leaf piles; may combine leaf piles after initial pile shrinkage. Maintain height of at least 6 feet.	Combine windrows after pile shrinkage occurs (1 or 2 months after their formation). Turn windrows as indicated by temperature and moisture data.	Blow air through the pile. An organic material such as wood chips, sawdust or compost is used as a pile cover for insulation. The frequency and time of aeration is by timer switch or temperature controlled.
9. Comments	End product quality may limit marketability: shredding will improve appearance.	Acceptable compost quality; screening of compost will give a more uniform product.	The field experiment data available for this application is rather limited. Method has been used successfully where leaves have been composted with sewage sludge (Greenwich, CT).

Current State of Connecticut practice followed for siting solid waste land disposal facilities.
—*Compiled by the University of Connecticut Cooperative Extension Service*

exposure to the high interior temperatures.

The material should have lost at least one third of its original volume due to compaction and settling, especially if it is composed primarily of leaves. The composting material should be warm, if not hot in parts. Dry and wet materials should be mixed and blended, adding water again to dry spots if necessary. By raising the loader bucket as high as possible and having the materials drop through the air, a maximum amount of air is added and clumps are broken. Using a three to five cubic yard loader makes windrow turning work proceed more quickly.

● **Windrow Turning Machines**—When yard waste volume is expected to reach 25,000 or more cubic yards annually, municipalities will find it worthwhile to explore the possibility of purchasing a compost windrow turning machine. Designed specifically for aerating and mixing, these machines can accomplish in hours what will take days for a front-end loader operator to accomplish. Another advantage of such machines is that mats of leaves and grass are broken up, wet and dry materials are mixed, and the rate of composting is greatly enhanced.

Recent experience demonstrates that compost turners can also be used to help remove plastic bags from windrows. As the bags get caught on the tines, the operator and/or laborers remove them. After one or two passes, most of the bags are removed with less labor than is required to debag by other means. For communities that do not collect yard waste in bulk, using a windrow machine provides a means for debagging. Screening of the final product would be required to remove the shreds of plastic that remain in the compost.

● **Grass Clipping Incorporation**—After a community has one or more years of experience with leaf composting, it may wish to incorporate grass clippings into its composting operation. Grass clippings are generated weekly and produced continuously for several months, and residents may bag them or place them in containers. Grass clippings must be managed as soon as they come in to avoid severe odor problems.

Because grass clippings are high in both moisture and nitrogen, they can restore vigorous composting activity to a pile lacking these essential materials. This high moisture and nitrogen content can also cause problems, because grass clippings contained in a plastic bag become odorous very quickly. It will therefore be necessary to debag the grass clippings and incorporate them into existing windrows within one or two days from the time they come in. Use of degradable bags will not eliminate the requirement for debagging because odor problems develop within one or two days; the currently available degradable bags do not begin to break down for several weeks or months.

One method of incorporating grass clippings into existing windrows is to place them alongside a windrow of partially composted leaves that have been turned several times since fall collection. A front-end loader is used to push the top of the windrow over on top of the grass clippings, completely covering and encapsulating them. When a windrow turning/aeration machine is available, grass clippings can be added to existing windrows at a rate not to exceed 25 percent and incorporated directly into the pile, thus taking advantage of the turning, shredding, and mixing action of the machine.

21

USER FEES AND SUPER COMPOSTING

Mitchell Deisch

SINCE THE CLOSING of the Isabella County Landfill in 1987, the cost of refuse disposal for Mt. Pleasant, Michigan has jumped from $1.25/cu. yd. to $8.75/cu. yd. This increase put a tremendous strain on the City's solid waste disposal budget. Therefore, Mt. Pleasant decided to place collection and disposal of refuse on a user fee bag/tag system instead of using a tax-based approach.

Under the old system, residents were limited to six bags of refuse per week. With the user fee system residents can place out as many bags as they want because they pay for the exact amount of service they need. Residents are only required to separate yard waste from general refuse and place it at curbside in a clear bag designated for yard waste.

Refuse bags/tags are priced at 10 for $6.00 and yard waste bags are 10 for $2.50. The prices were set to cover the cost of collection and disposal. Yard waste bags are being delivered directly to the city's compost operation, thus avoiding tipping fees and high transportation costs.

Mt. Pleasant adopted the user fee bag/tag system for several reasons. One primary reason was to make residents aware of the solid waste crisis. Because the cost of refuse collection and disposal was previously buried in property tax bills, residents really did not understand the city's financial predicament.

The second reason was to promote recycling. Isabella County opened a Recycling Center in August, 1987. From August 1987 through May 1989, the Recycling Center diverted approximately 2-3 percent of the county's solid waste stream from being landfilled through recycling. Since Mt. Pleasant implemented the user fee system in June 1989,

participation at the Recycling Center has jumped 50 percent. Along with the participation increase at the Recycling Center, city-contracted waste haulers have also indicated that the amount of waste being placed out has been drastically reduced.

The City's new solid waste ordinance included several sections in the area of code enforcement to help assure the program's success. First, the ordinance was written so enforcement could be directed at either the property owner or renter. Second, since Mt. Pleasant is a college town it has a great number of student rentals and rooming houses, which have always posed a real problem. This problem was solved by defining the term "rooming house" and requiring all houses that fit this definition to provide a 90-gallon containerized cart or commercial dumpster for their tenants. Finally, the ordinance allows the city to issue appearance tickets to residents who are continually in non-compliance with the system or caught illegally dumping their refuse. These appearance tickets can result in fines ranging from $100 to $500. At this time, no appearance tickets have been issued because of the high level of compliance the new program has received.

Mitchell Deisch is an Administrative Intern in the Mt. Pleasant, Michigan Public Works Department.

"SUPER, SUPER" COMPOSTING

That's the way Alan Little at the leaf composting facility in Morristown, New Jersey describes the Morris County operation in its first year. "We're composting 27,000 cubic yards of last year's leaves from seven municipalities, and things have worked out very smoothly," he says. "We bought the biggest Wildcat model made (for about $135,000) to turn the windrows and have been very pleased with its performance. We'll be ready to accept the new crop of leaves on schedule this fall, and have been adding grass clippings to the compost too."

A second facility will soon be opened, with four or five eventually planned. To haul the Wildcat from place to place, workers have converted a conventional trailer into a lowboy by removing the sides, installed permanent tie downs on it, and changed the hitch system so it can be pulled by loader or dump truck. "Essentially, composting becomes a one-man operation," says Little.

New Jersey's new law prohibiting leaf and yard waste from being landfilled, sent municipalities scrambling for ways to meet the requirements. The freeholders of Morris County held meetings, punched numbers, and came up with a program where the county would advance the money for yard waste composting and the municipalities would gradually pay it back at a charge of $4.10 a cu. yd. "That may seem like a high price, but everyone was satisfied. The alternative was a cost of $110 a ton to haul to a transfer station," points out Little. "There's no profit in it for the county, just a break even rate based on land and machinery costs and the average employee salary, and enough more so that at the end of a 10 year cycle we can purchase new equipment." Finished compost is delivered back to residents at $40 per seven yard load. "That pays for the hauling," says Little.

Process-wise, the Morris County facility has found that five feet high and about 10 feet wide is the right size windrow for turning with the Wildcat. "But we had to build larger piles to accommodate all the leaves coming in last fall," says Little. "These larger piles hold the moisture better anyway. Later, after they had shrunk a little, we repiled them with a front-end loader."

Knowing when to turn the windrows is an art, he adds. "Like sailing a boat. You trim the sails to suit conditions. We probe the piles and when temperature gets up to the 140° to 150°F, we 'wildcat' them. It amounts to about every two weeks."

22

ENCLOSED SYSTEMS FOR YARD WASTE COMPOSTING

M. Mayer, H. Hofer and U. Maire

AS MORE LARGE-SCALE projects are planned for communities, it can be expected that some will make use of enclosed systems for composting yard wastes. One such system is now operational in Uzwil, Switzerland, where a local cooperative had managed a combined garbage incineration and composting plant from 1969 to 1984. In 1984, this plant was shut down because compliance with new, more strict regulations regarding emission reduction would have been too expensive. Buhler-Miag purchased the plant and it was placed at the disposal of the Environmental Engineering Department for R & D purposes. The plant was renovated and some new equipment was added to process and compost yard waste. The capacity of the plant is 10 tph. In 1987, approximately 45,000 citizens were served by the plant and the amount of yard waste composted came to 1,200 tons.

The yard waste is discharged into a bunker. A grab crane feeds the Trimalin screw mill. This mill was especially designed for processing yard waste. It is able to process very soft, damp yard waste particles (e.g. long grass) in plastic bags as well as sections of trees and shrubs (e.g. 20 cm dia. and several meters long) by reducing them to optimum size.

The drum sieve separates mainly tough, resilient particles such as plastic bags that were filled with yard waste. It is important that the screw mill is fed with a mixture of damp yard waste and twigs. This assures an optimum mixture of wet waste and bulking material for the subsequent biological decomposition.

The raw compost is then formed into windrows. The water content of the windrow generally comprises 45 to 60 percent at the time decomposition begins. The first phase of the decomposition process is completed outdoors. After a few weeks, each windrow is turned by a special turning machine and moisture is added if necessary. After each windrow has been turned over three times, the material is ready for the final decomposition/drying phase in a covered hangar. Following a few weeks in the hangar, the finished coarse compost is transferred to the fine treatment process.

The coarse compost has a water content of 30 to 35 percent. It also contains a small amount of undesirable particles, such as hand-sized pieces of plastic or stones, which have to be removed. A conveyor feeds the coarse compost into a drum sieve, where the product is screened into three sizes; less than 10 mm, 10 to 50 mm and over 50 mm. The 10 mm product, approximately 60 to 65 percent, is free of any undesirable material and forms the main, high quality end product. The 10 to 50 mm material is separated from plastic and stone particles resulting in wood pieces the size of a finger. This fraction is passed through a hammer mill resulting in a mulch product.

The original mass of material shown is reduced to approx. 38 parts compost and seven parts residue. The balance is moisture and organic losses. Refined compost is sold easily in spring and fall and shortages can occur despite relatively high prices. The 1m^3 compost sells for $25.00, and 1.8 ft^3 bags sell for $3.50.

Large-scale plants (ca. 8000 t/a and up) can basically follow the same design as the smaller plant in Uzwil. In other words: Coarse and fine processing as described above, with two alternatives for the decomposition area. Equipment used in small and large yard waste composting plants is the same as existing equipment currently used in a large number of operating MSW composting plants.

Partially covered area: The primary windrow cross-section is approx. 7.5 m². The windrows are aerated by a forced air system. This method cuts the specific area required by the plant in Uzwil by 50 percent. The pile goes through the decomposition process for several weeks outdoors before the product is moved into a hangar for final decomposition/drying. The windrows are subjected to forced aeration dependent upon their temperature for several weeks and then dried to 30 to 35 percent moisture content. The windrows are turned once a week in order to increase their activity. After that time, the product is ready for the fine treatment.

Composting area with roof or totally enclosed hangar: Experience has shown that the decomposition process should take place under a roof if rainfall substantially exceeds 60 mm/week or 30 mm/day. If organic household waste (kitchen waste) is processed together with yard waste or if the plant location is critical, (unfavorable climate, less than 1000-1500 m distance from surrounding houses), a completely enclosed hangar is generally required in Central Europe. All exhaust air is deodorized by means of biofilters. Extensive calculations regarding climatic conditions have to be completed.

EVALUATING THE FINISHED PRODUCT

Existing regulations in Switzerland regarding waste and effluents covered in the environmental protection law define limits, methods of control, sanitation rules to such an extent that compost derived from waste is excluded from the market if it is of questionable quality. The criteria used for judging the quality of compost include beneficial properties, content of contaminants and degree of fineness.

MARKET POTENTIAL

Experience has shown that good quality composts made from separately collected organic wastes and sold at fair prices generate a high de-

mand. Not only small-scale consumers but mainly professional landscapers are interested in substituting expensive peat moss with compost of at least equal value from Niederuzwil. At the moment, peat moss costs approximately $10 per 6 ft³ packs, whereas the compost costs $25 per 35 ft³.

To take Switzerland as an example, the amount of compost, soil, peat, manure, etc. required for vineyards and fruit and vegetable production alone amounts to approximately 300,000 tons or 790,000 yd³. The total need for Switzerland is approximately 1.3 million yd³. Domestic production covers only about 10 percent of this requirement; the balance is imported.

If all of the organic household waste (yard waste and food waste) were used, the 790,000 yd³ could be supplied domestically. If waste generated by agriculture, forestry and the food industry were to be added, all the demand could basically be met.

BIBLIOGRAPHY

1. Federal Agency for Environmental Protection; Publication on Environmental Protection No. 26, Composting, Bern, June 1984.
2. Obrist, W.; Baccini, P.; Selection Criteria for Compostable Waste. Water, Energy, Air, 78th Edition, Brochure No. 11/12, 1986, Baden.
3. Baccini, P.: Switzerland is well-supplied - How Will it Dispose of its Waste? CHIMIA 41, No. 7 - 8, 1987 Basel, Special Edition.
4. Schiesser, W. et al: Interim Statement on Environmental Protection, NZZ Publishing Co., 1987 Zurich.
5. Federal Agency for Environmental Protection; Publication on Environmental Protection No. 27, Statistics on Waste, Bern, July 1984.
6. Meyer, M: Criteria for Quality of Compost Derived from Domestic Waste. Considering Trophological, Legislative and Global Agricultural Aspects. Technical Report, 1985, Uzwil.

M. Mayer and H. Hofer are with Buhler Brothers Ltd. in Uzwil, Switzerland; U. Maire is with Buhler Inc. in Minneapolis, MN.

23

COORDINATING SITES ON A COUNTY LEVEL

John A. Haas

ONE OF the challenging opportunities for county governments in New Jersey in implementing the state's Mandatory Recycling and Source Separation Act is the development of a countywide system for composting leaves. In the 1987 Law, municipalities were required to provide for the collection of leaves generated in each jurisdiction, but counties were left to identify composting facilities that could be used.

Ocean County is large county, consisting of 50 miles of ocean front and with a year round population of 435,000 people. The county consists of 33 municipalities, ranging from small beach communities to more heavily populated suburban and urban areas. The northern part of the county is made up of oak forest with many large, mature trees and the rest of the county is southern pine-oak forest.

When the Mandatory Recycling Act was passed, eight municipalities in the county had leaf composting operations. Several sites utilized a "low technology" composting method, while others used a leaf mounding and natural decomposition method.

STRUCTURING A COOPERATIVE ARRANGEMENT

In its approach, the county chose to work with existing operations, rather than develop a separate facility to compost the leaves. An Interlocal Services Agreement was arranged with existing facilities, in which the county was obligated to provide the staff and equipment necessary to upgrade leaf processing to meet state standards and accelerate

the decomposition process. In return, those municipalities that had existing composting sites and were interested, agreed to serve as regional sites for other county municipalities.

In January, 1988, the county sent the agreements to seven municipalities with leaf sites. Currently, the county has fully executed agreements with three municipalities.

In developing the program, the county established a waste flow arrangement that provided each of its municipalities with a site to utilize. In all 27 municipalities utilized the county-coordinated sites, while four municipalities operate their own captive sites. The county-coordinated sites serve approximately 80 percent of the county's population.

MUNICIPAL RESPONSIBILITIES

Those municipalities that use a site must bring only acceptable leaves and brush. If the material brought is in plastic bags, it must be removed by the generator. Both the host and the other municipalities in the service area have access to the final compost, with the host having first choice of material.

In this cooperative venture, while the host municipality provides the compost site, the county is responsible for processing the incoming leaves into compost and processing the brush received into chips that are suitable to use as mulch. The county also must remove any compost or mulch that isn't utilized by the municipalities by September 1st of each year, in time for the current year's leaf fall.

In March, 1988, the county went to bid for an equipment package that included a windrow turner, tub grinder, front end loader and compost screen. The entire package, which was designed to be mobile and capable of being transported from site to site, cost $420,000.

Because all of the cooperating sites were being used to compost leaves prior to the agreement, there was a considerable amount of material on each site before the county took over the operation. Although all of those sites had permits, in some cases, the operation of the site and the rate of composting was not sufficient to move material through the location fast enough to handle the quantity of material expected to be received when the site became a regional facility. Our first task was to process all of that material through the Jones Manufacturing "Mighty Giant" tub grinder and form the windrows.

Until the fall of 1988, the county crew, which consists of a supervisor, four equipment operators and two laborers, concentrated on upgrading the sites and turning the existing windrows with a Resource Recovery Systems of Nebraska machine. When the fall leaf season began, initially the leaves were dumped by each municipality's crews directly into rough windrows. As the season reached its peak and the amount of material increased all of the sites used staging areas to unload the leaves and the county crew became responsible for the initial formation of the windrows. While most of the leaves were on site by Christmas, some communities continued to bring leaves into February.

After the majority of the material was on site, the county developed a rotation plan for turning the material and other processing that moved the equipment to the sites about every eight weeks. In all, from October, 1988 through May, 1989, the four county sites handled more than 40,000 cubic yards of leaves and 7,000 cubic yards of brush.

In spring of 1989, the county started to move some of the compost at the sites. During this first season, we produced a fine screened compost for a county golf course and a coarser material for distribution to the municipalities.

In all the county has established a three-pronged approach to marketing the compost, which is provided free to county residents. The primary system is to distribute the material to municipalities so that they can make it available to residents. Almost all the municipalities provide space at their recycling centers or public works yard for this pick up. Additionally, any county resident can pick up material from the county site at Lakeview or at the County's southern recycling center. Because we have such a high concentration of senior citizen communities we also have a special program for those communities to pick up compost for use by seniors in their gardens.

The Ocean County approach of regionalizing existing municipal leaf composting sites has worked for us and it could work in most jurisdictions. In New Jersey, the permit process for a new leaf composting usually takes a minimum of one year to obtain. The Interlocal Service Agreement approach can save time in getting facilities operational. Some of the other advantages include:

1) The leaf compost crew provides a regional service.

2) The equipment required to accelerate the decomposition process is beyond the available funds of many municipalities.

3) All the municipalities in our county have an area they can utilize for leaves and brush.

4) The compost is of a high quality and is in demand.

5) Many of the municipalities are saving disposal fees for a substantial portion of their waste.

John Haas is District Recycling Coordinator in Ocean County, NJ.

24

SOLVING THE PROBLEM OF DEBAGGING LEAVES

ONE OF THE THORNIEST problems associated with yard waste collection and composting is removing the grass or leaves from the bags that hold them. Options for debagging include manual removal of material and mechanical processes. Another way of overcoming the bag problem is to use either biodegradable plastic or paper bags.

While these options are available, each has a separate set of problems. Manual debagging is a slow, labor-intensive process. Mechanical means, while less laborious, are costly in terms of capital expense. The use of paper bags is costly, and there are questions about the residue remaining from biodegradable plastic bags and whether those bags will break down at the composting rate of the yard waste.

MANUAL DEBAGGING

For years the only way yard waste was debagged was through manual processes and it's safe to say these methods are still the predominant approach to debagging. There are two general ways to approach manual debagging; removal of the yard waste at the time the material is collected or removal at the compost site. The Michigan Yard Waste Composting Manual notes at least three techniques for debagging on route, including cutting with a hand held knife, throwing the bag against a cutting edge attached to the compactor hopper and ripping the bag open by hand. Another option is to have residents leave bags at the curb untied. The Michigan manual estimates that it takes approximately twice as long to break open a bag and empty it than it does to simply throw unbroken bags into the compactor hopper.

Manual debagging at the composting site is accomplished in much the same manner as it is on route, with workers either ripping the bags open by hand or by slicing them open with a knife. In some programs, the bagged yard waste is brought in and spread on the ground. Workers then go through the bags ripping them open and removing the yard waste. After the bags are removed, the yard waste is picked up by a front end loader and windrowed. In other programs, the bagged yard waste is dumped from the collection vehicles at a staging area and debagged. The contents of the bags are placed on a conveyor and moved to a storage pile prior to windrowing.

MECHANICAL DEBAGGING

To date, mechanical debagging has only been implemented at the composting site, although at least one firm is reportedly working on a compactor-mounted debagger. One type of mechanical debagging system calls for yard waste to be put through a specially-designed debagger that splices the bags. After the bags are sliced, the material, bags and all, is run through a trommel which separates the yard waste from the bags. A system similar to this, only using a slow speed shredder to replace the special debagger, is used in Islip, New York.

During the initial stages of the Islip program, the debagging/shredding operation consisted of an Iggesund Recycling shredder and a trommel that had been used by the town at its materials recovery facility. Even with this, not-so-appropriate trommel, about 50 percent of the plastic was removed. With new equipment that is on order, Islip officials expect that the system will remove 70 to

90 percent of the plastic.

The other approach to mechanical debagging is the use of the turning equipment to debag as it moves through a windrow. In Muskegon, Michigan, the composting staff uses its Wildcat compost turner to remove bags. In the process, during the initial turnings, bags wrap around the tines of the Wildcat as it goes through the windrows. Every five minutes or so, the operator stops the machine and removes the plastic bags either by hand or by cutting them off using a hack saw. While this process slows the initial turning of material, Robert Fountain, who heads the project believes that it's far superior to manual debagging. Fountain claims that between 50 and 70 percent of the bags are removed using this method.

Other compost turners can be used in a similar fashion. In Hennepin County, Minnesota, a Scarab has been used to debag leaves in this manner. Another compost turner used to debag is manufactured by Scat Engineering. The Scat Composter's designed differently from most composting machines, in that it uses an elevating face which contains hundreds of sharp teeth that shred and aerate material in the windrows. Those teeth also rip open bags as the machine moves through the wind-row. Tests done on windrows show that 90 percent and more of the bags are emptied using this approach. The bags are then easily pulled off the teeth when the Composter reaches the end of the windrow, while the other emptied bags can be manually removed from the pile.

As can be seen by the amount of plastic left in the windrows when using mechanical debagging, to develop a fine compost product other steps must be taken to remove the remaining plastic. A final step that is used in many yard waste composting projects is to screen the finished compost prior to marketing it. This final process is used to clean up the compost by not only removing plastic but other foreign material including stones, glass and uncomposted material.

When yard waste composting was a relatively insignificant component of solid waste management, in most cases dealing only with leaves, program managers often had to handle debagging in an inefficient manner. However, now that yard waste composting has moved beyond leaves and is becoming more and more commonplace and increasingly large and sophisticated, debagging techniques must be refined.

Section
V

CASE STUDIES

EFFICIENCY IN THE WINDROW

M.R. Berdan

PART OF THE municipal leaf composting program in Wellesley, Massachusetts (pop. 27,000) is done in the Department of Public Works' 80-acre yard. We have four large windrows, 10 to 12 feet high and over 100 feet long. We allow these leaves to compost in the windrows for about a year—from the time the leaves come in one fall season until we consolidate them into a curing pile the following October.

Year-old compost in the curing pile is screened. Snow fence has been installed around the pile to keep the compost from "walking away." Leaves are trucked in each fall by commercial landscapers to whom we sell permits at $150 per vehicle for the leaf season, or until the yard gets filled, whichever is first.

After the leaves are pushed into the curing pile, and after screening, this material is used for maintaining municipal lands, such as parks, recreational facilities, etc.

We use woodchips as mulch around trees to retain moisture and to keep the mowers away from the trees and their inherent damage, as well as walks around wet areas.

We also compost leaves and yard wastes at our Recycling and Disposal Facility. There are probably 1500 tons at the RDF, which we allow residents to take unscreened, or we sell or barter it to nurseries and other users of soil amendments. At times, we have also given it away for various community gardening projects.

The encouragement of backyard composting, the drop-off area for residents' yard waste, the voluntary source separation recycling program—all are part of the waste minimization/reuse community effort.

Recycling has grown to the point where we now have a 75 percent participation rate, and last year, we recycled about 3,050 tons, which amounts to a 19 percent capture rate of the waste stream from households and businesses. The 19 percent does not include composting of leaves, grass nor several reuse strategies. If these are added, we recycle about 35 percent of the total trash by weight.

SECOND GENERATION RECYCLING PROGRAM

Because our contract with a state-approved commercial landfill expires in November, 1990, we anticipate disposal costs to burn or bury are about to double. To help control cost increases, we are developing an improved and expanded second generation recycling program.

The best strategy is to reduce wastes. Some examples of this strategy: An important factor of the reduction strategy is to send the right pricing signal, which I call "true cost pricing." In many cases, the public is not aware of the true costs of waste management because they are buried in tax rates. In order to make the public more aware of waste management costs, we should develop a *pay-as-you-throw* system so the more you throw, the more you pay. I think it is common knowledge that when municipalities start charging for water on a usage basis, rather than a flat rate basis, per capita consumption goes down. I believe the result will be the same if waste disposal were on a "pay as you throw" basis.

Our second best strategy is to *reuse*. Reuse, includes redistribution of unwanted, serviceable items and using them again in their existing form without reprocessing or remanufacturing, rather than discarding them.

The third best strategy is *recycling,* which is the separation and collection of discarded items in order to recover their constituent materials that can be processed to make new or useful products. I include within the recycling strategy the composting of leaves and grass to obtain soil amendments. Another portion of our recycling strategy is the removal of wood wastes from the waste stream and grinding them to be used as mulch around plantings, a biomass fuel or sludge bulking agent.

M.R. Berdan is Public Works Director for Wellesley, Massachusetts.

COUNTY APPROACH TO 12-TOWN PROGRAM

THE COST for disposing of bagged leaves is estimated at a rousing $109 per ton when hauled to the transfer station in Newark that serves communities in Essex County, New Jersey. Until two years ago, only a few towns such as Caldwell operated municipal leaf composting programs. But faced with those quadrupled disposal fees and the state Recycling Act that mandates leaf recycling, 12 county municipalities began trucking leaves in November, 1987 to a 23-acre county site in West Caldwell.

"The leaves are dropped by public works personnel at a staging area, then distributed into windrows following the guidelines of the Rutgers University municipal leaf composting manual," explains Jonathan Forsell, the county's cooperative extension agricultural agent who has been offering technical advice on proper turning and pile moisture. "The individual communities have agreed to remove the reduced leaf volume (50 percent reduction) before the next leaf season, a period of 10 months or less from initial deposition."

As part of his county extension role, Forsell has been gathering data on material breakdown. "Temperatures generally are 130 to 145° F in the first two weeks or so, then drop down below 100°F, at which time (generally after three to four weeks), the adjacent piles can be combined into one. The oxygen levels have ranged from 8–12 percent, an ideal value for aerobic biological decay," Forsell observes. "Occasionally anaerobic conditions have been observed, but this is common during the early phase of decay. Several turnings of the piles will be accomplished to hasten the decomposition process.

"Our goal is to utilize large volumes of finished compost by commercial landscapers, arborists, growers and land use management developers. Smaller volumes can be made available to homeowners for improvement of garden soils and as a surface mulch."

TOWNS TO SAVE $1.3 MILLION IN FIRST YEAR

Paul Petto, Essex County Recycling Coordinator, calculates that the compost center will save participating towns around $1.3 million in the first year of operation, not counting use of the mulch. The site is located on land once farmed by inmates of the county penitentiary. The operation is open five days per week and during Phase I (Oct. 20–Dec. 23, 1987) was expected to receive 165 truckloads of leaves per day, adding up to 1,600 cubic yards daily. After trucks are recorded by load size or estimated tonnage, they are directed by utility men, provided by each participating municipality based on the number of tons of leaves expected to be delivered to the site, to one of seven fields.

As reported in the *Caldwell Progress*, the trucks dump the leaves, where they are picked up by front-end loaders after they have been crushed and watered by the large-tired vehicles. Then the leaves are windrowed.

Each day there are three or four utility men at the compost center in addition to five or six county public works men. In addition, round-the-clock surveillance of the site is maintained by county police who are charged with the job of preventing midnight dumping and making sure leaves in windrows are not disturbed.

Phase II will go into effect in late January.

Then late delivery of leaves will be accepted and windrows will be turned over and watered. By February, the leaves should be reduced by 33 percent in volume.

Phase III goes into effect from March 21 to April 23, when piles will again be turned over and possibly watered. Leaves from spring cleanup will also be accepted from the participating towns and county. The projection is that leaves will then be reduced by half and well on their way to becoming useable mulch.

They will be checked over the summer and watered and turned as deemed necessary until Phase IV goes into effect Aug. 1. By then, Petto said the leaves should be reduced to 50,000 cubic yards of mulch and the results will begin to be picked up by the towns that brought them in the first place.

All participating municipalities will be allowed mulch dependent upon the number of truckloads and cubic yards/tons they delivered in the fall or winter to the center.

"It is noteworthy how clean the leaves are that have come in. Usually there are stones, hubcaps, even sneakers in leaves collected but we have found nothing," Petto reported in the newspaper account.

The county has also set aside a test field for using 30-gallon, three-foot tall paper biodegradable bags for leaves to see how well they compost—bags, leaves and all.

"So if you drive through Verona and see giant bags that say 'Recycle for Leaves Only,' you know they are part of an important experiment to see if it is feasible to use bags rather than rake leaves into the streets for pick-up," Petto stated.

Petto said it costs the county around $40 per ton to run the Hilltop operation, but since participating municipalities contribute some manpower necessary to regulate and prepare the leaves to compost, the cost quoted to the towns to compost is $25 per ton.

27

FROM ROADSIDE
TO WINDROWS

Alison Rothschild

LEAVES are routinely picked up from Ottawa's parks and roads during a three to four week period from the end of October to mid-November. A vacuum truck or street sweeper is used to collect leaves from the streets, while leaves coming from city parks are picked up by a front-end loader and loaded into garbage packer trucks.

To avoid contaminants, plastic bags and items such as pop cans were removed as windrows were first formed and each time they were turned. Leaves picked up by the street sweepers were kept separate since they contained larger amounts of sand, gravel and other contaminants. The only leaves that were relatively free of debris were those collected by vacuum trucks (items as large as sewer covers and old sinks were, on occasion, found in leaves collected by front-end loader and packer trucks). Vacuum trucks also broke up and compacted the leaves prior to delivery and were, therefore, the preferred collection method.

Leaves were delivered to the City's tree nursery four kilometers south of the City. The 46.2 ha. site is flatland underlain by a mantle of sandy gravel over shale. The surface material and gently sloping ground means that drainage is good, and given the virtually unlimited space, the site is ideal for composting.

Leaves were piled in nine triangular-shaped windrows approximately 3 m x 3 m x 70 meters. To allow easy access and maneuvering by a front-end loader a space of about 5 m was left between windrows. Since leaves from previous years had already reached varying degrees of decay they were piled separately from leaves collected in 1988.

To speed up decomposition, attempts were made to shred the leaves using snow blowers. Unfortunately, the machines were unable to work through large piles of heavy leaves and problems were encountered with broken sheer pins. As a result, the leaves were piled in the condition they were collected.

At the time of piling, leaves requiring additional moisture were watered using a watering truck and all the piles were fertilized (20 kg. of NPK 25-15-10 per 150 cu. yards). In some cases the fertilizer was not properly mixed into the piles until several weeks after application and much of it may have been washed away by rain. It is important therefore, to ensure the fertilizer is worked into the piles as near as possible to the time it is applied.

Piles were turned using a front end loader (bucket size 2 cu. yards) by rolling them over into the adjoining space between the windrows. Initially, two people required one full day to turn a single windrow (one person to operate the loader, a second to pick out debris). As decomposition proceeded and the piles grew smaller, turning became easier and up to two windrows could be done in one day. A front-end loader with a larger bucket size could be helpful in reducing turning time, but care must be taken to break up clumps of leaves for proper aeration.

The intention was that leaves would be turned every 3-4 weeks. However, this was not possible during the winter since staff and equipment were required for snow removal. The piles remained unturned for up to ten weeks at a time. Pile temperatures were not measured, but the fact that whole chunks of leaves remained frozen together upon turning indicated that the composting process was not taking place. A front end loader was leased during the late winter and early spring in order to ensure that the piles were turned more regularly. Since it was suspected that the leaves lacked nitrogen an additional application of fertilizer NPK-34-15-10 was made.

When leaves are first placed in windrows, watered and fertilized, the temperature in the piles should ideally rise to approximately 130-140°F (54-60°C) within the first few weeks. After this, the temperature should gradually decrease to about 100°F (38°C).

A thermometer was not available in the first few months of the project, so it is not clear whether ideal temperatures were reached in the early phases of composting. Temperatures recorded between May 23 and July 1, 1989 reached as high as 126°F (52°C) in the windrows composted of leaves collected in 1988 but varied considerably within each windrow. By July, these leaves were looking partially decomposed and were completely composted by the fall.

By May, 1989 the windrows composed of old leaves appeared to have completed the composting process; that is to say, turning, watering, etc. no longer resulted in a rise in temperature and the material was made up of small brownish particles that both looked and smelled earthy.

The compost was screened in mid-summer using a topsoil screening machine with a one-inch screen and then mixed with various ratios of sand and low grade topsoil to achieve the desired quality. The compost is being tested for nutrient levels and heavy metal concentration, and preliminary indications are that heavy metal concentrations are well below the acceptable levels suggested by the Ministry of Environment.

With this experience behind it, Ottawa expanded its 1989 autumn composting program with an organized collection of leaves from residences.

Pat McFarlane is managing editor of Ontario Recycling Update, *the newsletter of the Recycling Council of Ontario. Alison Rothschild is a waste reduction assistant with the city of Ottawa.*

RECYCLING PLANT MATERIALS AT AN OLD LANDFILL

Albert T. Bergeron

THE SITE of the former city landfill is where San Mateo, California operated a compost project since April, 1982. Compostable plant waste—primarily garden and tree trimmings—are brought by commercial gardeners, tree surgeons, local agencies and the general public. Front-end capital costs for equipment were partially funded with a $75,000 grant from the California Solid Waste Management Board, which entered into a five-year operating agreement with the City of San Mateo.

A $4.50 fee is charged for each incoming cubic yard of material. Quality control of incoming material is essential to the success of the compost operation, so loads are checked for conformance with a published list of acceptable materials. The plant materials are ground for size reduction, stockpiled in windrows, aerated and irrigated to maintain air and moisture levels conducive to the aerobic bacterial process. With proper care, temperatures of 130° to 150°F are achieved and maintained in the piles for several weeks while the bacteria do their work. These sustained temperatures are sufficient to control insects, odors and pathogens within practical limits.

Production data for the 1986-87 fiscal year show that 41,000 cubic yards of raw materials were converted into 27,000 cubic yards of valuable compost. An estimated 135,000 cubic yards of compost have been produced in five years of operation. Approximately 150 cubic yards per year are used by the Parks Department to condition planting soils in parks and gardens, with excellent results. The department has not had to purchase soil conditioners for the past four years. The bulk of material produced to date has been stockpiled and reserved for future use in the development of the 35 acre landfill site, into a Shoreline Park overlooking San Francisco Bay. It is anticipated that 200,000 cubic yards of this material, with an estimated value of $2,000,000 will be available when park development takes place. Although the product is not commercially sold, it has an estimated market value of $10 per cubic yard in an area (San Francisco Peninsula) where constituted topsoils sells for $16 per cubic yard.

Annual operating costs for fiscal year 1987-88, adjusted to reflect the capital expenses of the start-up years, are estimated at $152,000. (Unit cost of processing a cubic yard of incoming material is $3.73. Allowing 33 percent for shrinkage, the end product cost is approximately $5.65/c.y.) The capital expenses of the start-up years, are estimated at $152,000. Revenue from gate receipts in calendar year 1986 was $154,000 and rising. The current charge for incoming material ($4.50 per cubic yard) compares favorably to other disposal options in the area. Essentially the project is expected to be self-supporting over a period of seven to eight years, while producing 200,000 cubic yards of compost.

This is "recycling" in real terms. Approximately 6,000 tons per year of garden waste are diverted from landfilling and returned to the earth as soil replenishment in an urbanized area where "topsoil" is a manufactured product in short supply. In the process, commercial gardeners, local agencies and the community at large are benefiting from a successful local government enterprise.

A.T. Bergeron is the Maintenance Manager in the San Mateo, California Department of Public Works.

GRASS COMPOSTING
METHODS

Doreen Cantor

YARD waste makes up approximately 18 percent of the waste flow in Montgomery County. Of that 18 percent, approximately 40 percent is leaves, 35 percent is grass, and the remaining 25 percent is brush.

A grass composting pilot program was established in summer, 1989 at the Dickerson leaf composting site (described in the EPA report in the preceding chapter.) In preparation for the program, the County in 1988 tested several leaf/grass/brush combinations in windrows at the site, to determine the most efficient mix for composting. The County determined that the best combination (considering speed and completeness of composting) was a 1:1 or 2:1 mixture of leaves to grass, and that brush neither composted well nor aided the composting process. However, the windrows formed for purposes of the test were much smaller than the windrows which would be used in a full-scale program, allowing aeration to occur easily. Concerns that the relatively high leaf to grass ratio of 1:1 would inhibit aeration in a larger windrow were taken into consideration during design of the pilot program.

In April of 1989, the County began a pilot program to collect and compost grass clippings on a larger scale. The program is in cooperation with the city of Rockville, and is being partially funded through a $70,000 grant received from the Urban Consortium Energy Task Force. Grass is being collected from approximately 2,400 homes, chosen to include a variety of economic groups and yard sizes. An initial survey of current grass disposal practices showed that 30 percent of the homeowners were already composting some or all of their grass in their backyards. Those already composting all of their grass clippings were not provided with containers (see below), but grass is collected from these homes if it was put at curbside.

The homes were divided up into four collection routes. Several different types of containers are being tested, including large wheeled plastic carts, bio-degradable plastic bags, large paper bags, and regular plastic lawn and leaf bags. Each collection route was assigned a different collection method, and all containers were furnished to residents free for the length of the pilot.

Grass is collected once per week using a packer truck. Each route is assigned a collection day. Consideration was given to the collection method when establishing the collection schedule - biodegradable plastic bags and paper bags are collected on Wednesdays and Thursdays, respectively. This provides the longest possible time from the weekend (when most people mow their lawns) to collection day, so that these bags will be tested under the worst case for curbside durability.

The packer trucks unload grass at the County's centrally-located transfer station. The grass is loaded into a 45-yard trailer and taken to the compost facility daily. It is then combined with the leaves collected the previous fall.

Public reaction to the grass composting pilot program has been positive. All routes have shown very high (above 90 percent) participation rates, with the exception of the route using regular plastic bags. For this route, low participation may be due either to the lower visibility of that collection method (all other routes involve containers not otherwise seen at curbside on collection day), or to collection crews mistakenly collecting grass as part of the household trash. Participants will be asked to respond to a survey asking them about the acceptability of the various collection methods, and this will be tabulated and reviewed before implementing a larger-scale program.

The pilot program will be evaluated on the basis of public participation; cost and efficiency; odor problems at curbside, at the transfer station, and at the compost site; ease of handling; and effects on the compost. Because the County has not found any conclusive data on the degradation rate of either bio-degradable plastics or paper in a compost pile, they are monitoring both of these bags, which are being placed in separate windrows, for the speed and completeness of degradation. Both the compost and the leachate will also be monitored for pesticide residuals and for residuals from the biodegradable plastic as well. However, pesticide testing of the incoming grass showed no detectable residuals for a wide range of pesticides.

Through the end of June, the pilot program has resulted in approximately 430 tons of grass being diverted from the landfill. Climate in Montgomery County is such that the prime grass-growing season is in May and June, with a rapid drop-off in grass clippings by mid-summer. The compost site can easily accommodate the volume of grass expected even if the program is significantly expanded. Although the site is about at maximum capacity solely with the volume of leaves collected, the addition of grass is expected to speed up the composting process and allow for more rapid turnover. Preliminary observations of leaves collected last fall have shown that, without the addition of grass, small particles of leaves are discernable in the piles, but that no leaf pieces are noticeable in the piles which received the addition of grass.

In July of this year, the County also began accepting grass clippings from lawn companies and other sources that can provide large loads of unbagged grass. Those companies delivering clean loads of grass to the transfer station are charged half of the normal tip fee, both as an incentive to participate and to reflect the lower cost of composting.

Ms. Cantor is a planner with the Montgomery County, MD Division of Environmental Planning.

EPA ANALYSIS OF YARD WASTE COMPOSTING PROGRAMS

Alison C. Taylor and Richard M. Kashmanian

THE U.S. EPA Office of Solid Waste and Emergency Response has targeted a national goal of 25 percent source reduction and recycling by 1992. Yard waste composting has great potential as an MSW management option to help achieve that goal. In 1988, the authors studied methods and products of yard waste composting in the context of eight programs currently in operation in the United States. The following information briefly reviews six of those programs:

The communities compost their yard wastes at a combination of 10 centralized facilities of which 3 practice minimal-level technology, 4 practice low-level technology, 3 practice intermediate-level technology, and none practice high-level technology. Four of the communities also actively promote backyard composting. Six of the 8 programs include some form of curbside collection and 4 communities allow private landscaping companies to drop off their collected yard wastes at their composting facilities (typically for a fee). Of course, private composting facilities are available to public and private clients alike. In addition to bulk collection, containers used for curbside pickup include: degradable paper bags, degradable and non-degradable plastic bags, and wheeled plastic bins. All of the programs accept yard wastes at least during the fall and spring (by curbside pickup or centralized drop-off). Four of the 8 programs accept significant portions of grass for composting at their centralized facilities.

The study looked at composting from the perspective of the community (town, city or county) rather than the facility. Where a community has more than one way of diverting its yard wastes

from disposal in a landfill (e.g., a program promoting backyard composting, as well as, centralized composting at publicly and/or privately operated facilities), every effort was made to collect information on all facets of the program. Information about the number of households served and level of household participation is summed by program, where more than one method of yard waste collection (curbside or drop-off) or more than one method of centralized composting is performed as part of the program (see Table 1). Information about the collection method and frequency, and about the composting process is presented separately for individual facets of each program in Tables 2 and 3, for example Westfield is served by two private composting facilities, each of which has its own distinct operations and techniques.

YARD WASTE COLLECTION AND PROGRAM PUBLICITY

Many of the communities actively promote multiple methods of yard waste composting. These may include backyard composting, source separation followed by centralized collection and composting, or self-haul and drop-off by residents at a composting facility or transfer facility.

There are several methods by which yard wastes may be collected for centralized composting (see Table 2). Six programs include some form of curbside collection, i.e., by bulk pickup, collection of containerized wastes in degradable paper bags, degradable and non-degradable plastic bags, or from wheeled plastic bins. Four communities allow private landscaping companies to dispose of yard wastes at the public composting facility (for a fee). Four of the communities encourage backyard composting as part of their overall program.

At a minimum these programs accept yard wastes during the fall and spring (by curbside pickup or centralized drop-off) and collection service frequency varies from weekly to seasonally. Choice of seasons for collection service is in part determined by the type of yard wastes composted. In the communities studied, yard wastes are collected independently of the regular municipal trash collection. Separation and collection methods chosen by the communities for centralized composting depend on convenience, costs, and the volume and weight of yard wastes which can be diverted from landfills.

DAVIS, CALIFORNIA

Davis (pop. 44,000) contracts out its municipal garbage collection (including yard waste pickup) and yard waste composting to a private hauler, Davis Waste Removal Company (DWR). DWR runs a separate route for yard waste collection where, for example, homeowners rake leaves out to the curb weekly and a device called the "Claw" lifts the piles (which are not to exceed 5 feet × 5 feet × 5 feet) into a 32-cubic yard rear-loading packer truck for transport to the composting facil-

ity. The Claw is a device with "jaws" that swing open to scoop up the leaves from the roadside. Although participation is voluntary, yard waste pickup service has been available for over 15 years and is accepted and utilized by residents. The city distributes pamphlets to residents describing the benefits of composting and techniques for curbside pickup and backyard composting. Since yard wastes are generated year round in California, this service is available in all 4 seasons; however, there is some variation through the year in the composition of the yard wastes generated. For example, the yard waste stream contains a high concentration of leaves in the fall season, whereas grass and brush are disposed of all year.

The method used in David involves curbside collection of yard wastes throughout the year and transport to their buffered 2.5-acre composting site, followed by grinding of the leaves with a tub grinder to accelerate the composting process. Currently, only leaves are composted, representing approximately 10 percent of the yard wastes picked up; bagged grass is pulled out prior to grinding. Windrows, 6-8 feet high by 10 feet wide, are then formed and turned every 2 weeks with a front-end loader. The warm climate of California accelerates the composting and the product is ready in 3-4 months, although the composting process may not be completed.

TABLE 1:
Background Information on Cities/County Selected

City or County	State	Density (a)	Total City/ County Popn.	Total Yard Waste Stream	Yard Wastes as % of MSW Stream	Total Households	% of Households Served	Participation of Served Households (as %) (b)	% of Total Yard Wastes Composted Centrally
Davis (c)	CA	U/S	44,000	5,475	25	10,000	100	70-80	9
East Tawas	MI	R	2,600	350	10 (d)	1,350	100	70	39 (e)
Mont. Co. (f)	MD	U/S/R	633,000	110,000	19	244,000	48	90-95	14
Omaha	NE	U/S	350,000	48,000	33 (d)	100,000	1	66	1
Seattle (c)	WA	U/S	500,000	92,000	12	229,000	100	n/a	4
Wellesley	MA	S/R	27,000	8,000	28	8,500	100	90-95	81
Westfield	NJ	U/S	30,000	n/a	n/a	10,400	100	100; 25 (g)	n/a
Woodbury	MN	U/S	13,520	1,092 (h)	18 (h)	4,790	17	80	11 (e)

Notes:
(a) U - urban, S - suburban, R - rural
(b) estimated by local officials
(c) estimate of total yard waste stream does not include amount generated and collected by lawn service companies and public work crews
(d) yard wastes are estimated as percent of residential solid waste stream
(e) does not include amount of brush chipped or shredded
(f) Montgomery Co. estimates based on 1986, other program estimates based on 1987 figures
(g) participation rate was 100% for curbside collection of leaves and 25% for drop-off of grass and brush; the remaining households compost in the backyard or use a landscaping service
(h) yard waste estimate does not include brush
n/a: not available

Source: Taylor and Kashmanian, 1988

MONTGOMERY COUNTY, MARYLAND

Montgomery County (pop. 633,000) is the most heavily populated community included in this study; however, the program currently serves nearly one-half of the county's households. The entire program is administered by the county's Department of Environmental Protection. Responsibility for curbside leaf collection (and drop-off at the transfer stations) belongs to the county's Department of Transportation. Leaf-loader vacuums have been used to pick up (and partially shred) leaves for composting since 1984. The same trucks that push the snowplows in winter are used to pull the curbside vacuums on their route twice in the fall and once in the spring. The curbside collection program has received an excellent response from residents who participate voluntarily by raking leaves to their curbsides. Residents are informed of the scheduled collection route by notices which are posted on trees and telephone poles in each neighborhood. The county discourages residents from bagging leaves prior to pickup, but some plastic bags are put out at curbside and these are broken open prior to vacuuming.

The composting facility is located in the town of Dickerson which is in the western part of the county. The facility lies within 270 acres of county-owned land and consists of a 47-acre asphalt pad and 3 sedimentation ponds to collect runoff. It was originally built for composting municipal sewage sludge and was switched to leaf composting in 1984. Responsibility for hauling the leaves from the transfer stations to the compost facility, operating the compost facility, and selling the finished compost rests with a private contractor.

The only reported problem with this facility is the tendency of soil to erode from around the sedimentation ponds, as a result of runoff from the asphalt pad during heavy rains. The contents of the ponds are monitored regularly for compliance with the facility's surface water discharge permit, and are consistently found to comply. A double fence surrounds the facility to prevent the wind from carrying plastic debris off-site.

Windrows, 6 feet high by 12-15 feet wide, are formed, and then shredded, aerated, and turned monthly with a rotoshredder. Water is not added during the composting process since rainfall provides sufficient moisture. The compost is shredded

TABLE 2:
Yard Waste Collection and Program Publicity

City or County	State	Collection Method(s) (a)	Frequency of Collection (b)	Collection Seasons (b)	Means of Raising Awareness and Support for the Program in the Community
Davis	CA	backyard	n/a	Sp,Su,F,W	public ed
		curbside - claw	1/week	Sp,Su,F,W	public ed
East Tawas	MI	curbside - plastic bag	1/week	Sp,F	newspaper ad
		resident drop-off			
Mont. Co.	MD	curbside - vacuum	1/Sp, 2/F	Sp,F	pickup schedule signs
Omaha	NE	curbside - wheeled bin and degradable bag	1/week	Sp,Su,F	neighborhood assoc
		landscaper drop-off	n/a	Sp,Su,F	
Seattle	WA	backyard	n/a	Sp,Su,F,W	hotline, public ed
		resident drop-off	n/a	Sp,Su,F,W	
		landscaper drop-off	n/a	Sp,Su,F,W	
Wellesley	MA	backyard	n/a	Sp,Su,F,W	public ed, newspaper, bill stuffers
		resident drop-off	n/a	Sp,Su,F,W	public ed, newspaper, bill stuffers
		landscaper drop-off	n/a	Sp,Su,F	word-of-mouth
Westfield	NJ	curbside-front loader	2/F	F	hotline, newspaper ad
		resident drop-off	n/a	Sp,Su,F	newspaper ad, mailings
		landscaper drop-off	n/a	Sp,Su,F	newspaper ad
Woodbury	MN	backyard		Sp,Su,F	public ed
		curbside - degrad. bag	1/week	Sp,Su,F	free bags yr 1, mailings

Notes: (a) "backyard" refers to backyard composting
(b) Sp - spring, Su - summer, F - fall, W - winter; (2/F - 2 collections per fall, etc.)
n/a: not available
Source: Taylor and Kashmanian, 1988

and screened to remove contaminants which include shredded plastic bags, tennis balls, and brush. Composting of leaves presently takes between 6 and 12 months, depending on whether the leaves are collected in the fall or spring. Since finished compost is more likely to be sold during spring than fall, it may need to be stored on-site for 6 months. The finished compost is sold in loads of 10 cubic yards or more, primarily to landscapers and nurseries as a soil amendment.

At present, Montgomery County is pilot-testing combining grass and partially composted leaves in various proportions. This addition of grass will increase the required frequency of turning, but it is hoped that it will also speed up the composting process. The finished compost will be tested for heavy metals, weed seeds, residual herbicides, and pesticide levels before a final decision is made on composting grass with leaves.

OMAHA, NEBRASKA

Omaha (pop. 350,000) operates a yard waste composting program in which grass clippings are composted along with leaves. Dan Slattery of the Department of Public Works estimates that 60 percent of the yard wastes composted in Omaha consist of grass. Yard wastes are also accepted from lawn service companies but are turned away if found to be contaminated with, e.g., tree stumps, rocks, PVC pipe, lawn mower handles, or tires. Partially composted and fresh grass are mixed by tub grinder with newly received leaves and tree trimmings and then wetted. Grinding this material decreases particle size to a maximum diameter of one-tenth inch, reduces yard waste volume, aerates the composting material, and accelerates composting. A front-end loader (shared with the county) piles the material into windrows, 6 feet high by 12-15 feet wide, which are left until the following year when they are turned.

The biggest concern of most facilities that refuse to compost grass is the odor generated as it decomposes; however, Omaha has not experienced a problem with odor complaints from the public (except infrequently from lawn service companies at drop-off) due to their facility's remote location, wide buffer zone (the two-acre facility is at the 80-

TABLE 3:
Yard Waste Composting Facility Operations and Results

City or County	State	Public/ Private Facility	Type of Compost Tech Used	Turning Frequency	Grind/ Shred/ Screen Material	Composting Time (months)	Total Yard Wastes Composted (tons/yr)	Tons of Finished Product (tons/yr)	Yard Waste Volume Reduction (%)
Davis	CA	private	Low	1/week	G	3 - 4 (a)	500	250	50 - 60
East Tawas	MI	public	Low	6/year	n/a	24 - 36	138	70 - 80	65
Mont. Co.	MD	public/ private	Intermed	1/month	SH,SC	6 - 12	15,600	3,500	85
Omaha	NE	public	Minimal	2/year	G	18 - 24	500	350	50 - 60
Seattle	WA	private	Minimal	1/year	G,SH,SC	6 - 8	3,600	(b)	80
Wellesley (c)	MA-RDF	public	Minimal	1/year	SC	24	n/a	1,800	60 - 65
	MA-DPW	public	Low	1/month	SC	12	n/a	800	60 - 65
Westfield (d)	NJ-MCI	private	Intermed	>1/week	SH,SC	3 - 4	1,730	(e)	80
	NJ-WL	private	Intermed	as needed	SH,SC	5	1,400	(e)	50 - 70
Woodbury	MN	private	Low	1/month	n/a	12	~116	(f)	70

Notes:
(a) the composting process may not be complete in 3-4 months
(b) Pacific Topsoils Inc., composts wastes for Seattle and other cities; hence, it is not possible to separate out data for Seattle alone
(c) MA-RDF - Wellesley's yard waste composting facility located at its Recycling and Disposal Facility for resident drop-off of yard wastes
MA-DPW - Wellesley's yard waste composting facility located at its DPW yard for landscaper drop-off of leaves
(d) NJ-MCI - Middlebush Compost, Inc., a private facility used by Westfield to compost leaves
NJ-WL - Woodhue Ltd., a private facility used by Westfield to compost grass clippings
(e) Middlebush Compost, Inc. and Woodhue Ltd. compost leaves and grass, respectively, from Westfield, and primarily leaves from other communities and private clients. It is not possible to separate out data for Westfield alone.
(f) Composting Concepts composts yard wastes from Woodbury and other communities; hence, it is not possible to separate out data for Woodbury alone.
n/a: not applicable
G: grind, SH: shred; SC: screen
Source: Taylor and Kashmanian, 1988

acre county landfill), and relatively small operation. It is reported that odors are not a problem for workers at the facility either. Odors are strong when material is ground in November which is the only time during the composting process that these windrows are turned, but the buffer zone protects residents from being affected.

Currently, just three subdivisions of the city (or approximately one percent of its population) are involved in the program; however, Omaha looks forward to expanding this program. The finished compost is used by the county (whose land is used for the operation) as a substitute for landfill topsoil and a soil amendment at county parks.

An interesting aspect of Omaha's program is the container in which homeowners leave yard wastes for pickup. Residents rent 90-gallon plastic yard waste bins or carts (from the city for $12 per year) which can be wheeled to the curb. A special hoist lifts and dumps the yard waste bins into the packer trucks used for collection and returns them to the sidewalk for reuse. No shredding takes place in this step. Initially, the bins were susceptible to being crushed by the hoist because it was lifting at an excessive speed. To solve the problem, a control was installed on the trucks to limit the speed of lifting, and also the structure of the carts was reinforced by their manufacturer (without charge). This year, Omaha has distributed 5,000 free degradable cornstarch plastic bags with instructions to households that they should only be used when the carts are full.

WESTFIELD, NEW JERSEY

From the early 1970's until 1987, Westfield (pop. 30,000) composted its leaves at the town conservation center. Due to large increases in volume, Westfield now uses a combination of private operations to compost yard wastes in compliance with New Jersey's mandatory composting requirement (i.e., the ban on landfilling leaves). Although the town does not provide pickup services for general MSW, three rounds of leaf pickup from town curbside are performed each year by front-end loaders and dump trucks. Residents, alerted by mailings and advertisements, rake their leaves to the curb on the appropriate days. Leaves mixed together with household trash will not be picked up by the privately contracted garbage haulers. Residents may also separate and drop off their grass and brush for a fee at the town's conservation center where it is collected for transport.

During 1988, the town transported all collected yard wastes to one of three private composting (or, in the case of brush, shredding) facilities: 1,730 tons of leaves to Middlebush Compost, Inc. for composting; 1,400 tons of grass clippings to Woodhue, Ltd. for composting; and 1,423 tons of

tree trimmings and brush to Alternate Disposal Systems, Inc. for shredding. These facilities also accept yard wastes from other communities in New Jersey.

Middlebush Compost is located on a 25-acre site (including a 150-foot buffer surrounding residential areas), of which 15 acres are used for composting leaves from approximately 10-12 New Jersey communities (including a few served by contract haulers). A large windrow turning machine is used to form windrows, 7 feet high by 16-18 feet wide, after shredding, aerating, and fluffing the material. Middlebush Compost is currently investigating a modification in its state solid waste facility permit to allow it to also compost grass clippings. The finished compost is sold as a soil amendment, mulch, or potting soil for $25 per ton.

Woodhue, Ltd. is the site of a privately run 126-acre farm, which also operates a 4.5-acre yard waste composting facility under a solid waste permit issued by the state of New Jersey. In 1988, Woodhue accepted grass clippings from Westfield and two other communities and mixed them at a one to two ratio with partially composted leaves received from approximately 10 other communities. A windrow turning machine is used to shred, aerate, and fluff the composting yard wastes and to re-form windrows, 6 feet high by 12 feet wide.

WOODBURY, MINNESOTA

Woodbury's (pop. 13,520) yard wastes are collected and composted by Composting Concepts. When the program began in April 1987, bags were provided free of charge as an incentive to residents to participate in the yard waste composting program. Degradable paper bags are preferred by waste haulers since they eliminate the need for manual debagging or purchasing special debagging or shredding equipment. Workers load the bags into packer trucks which are also used for regular garbage pickup. Use of the degradable paper bags was discontinued by Composting Concepts because most residents opted to buy regular plastic bags rather than uses the free paper bags and debagging costs were therefore still incurred. Composting Concepts also sells cornstarch plastic bags.

Alison Taylor was a National Network for Environmental Policy Studies Fellow at Harvard University when this study was done. Richard Kashmanian is Project Officer, Office of Policy, Planning and Evaluation, EPA. Copies of the complete report, Study and Assessment of Eight Yard Waste Composting Programs, *may be obtained from him at EPA, 401 M St., SW, Washington, DC 20460.*

Section VI

PRINCIPLES OF COMPOSTING

31

COMBINING RAW MATERIALS FOR COMPOSTING

George B. Willson

COMPOSTING is a biological process in which biological wastes are stabilized and converted into a product to be used as a soil conditioner and organic fertilizer. This process depends upon the activity of microorganisms. To carry out these activities, the microorganisms must be provided with a suitable environment and a source of nutrients that should be present in proper proportions. The extent to which we supply those two needs and the way in which we do so, determine to a large degree our influence on the compost process and its optimization.

The major sources of nutrients for composting are organic waste materials. However, it is rare that a waste material in the condition in which it is available consistently possesses all of the characteristics essential for efficient composting. To compensate for this deficiency, it is usually necessary to blend in suitable proportions of another waste or low cost material. For example, in the U.S., the excessively high moisture content of sewage sludge usually is lowered by blending a "bulking" agent such as wood chips or sawdust. In Europe, municipal solid wastes often serve as the bulking agent. For farms, an excessively moist manure can be blended with crop residues, or perhaps with waste from a nearby lumber operation.

REQUIRED FEEDSTOCK CHARACTERISTICS

Carbon (C), nitrogen (N), phosphorus (P), and potassium (K) are the primary nutrients for the microorganisms involved in composting. Because they also are the primary nutrients for plants, their concentrations in the compost product also influence the value of the compost. Generally, supplying C and N in the appropriate ratio (C/N) ensures the presence of required concentrations of other nutrient elements. Initial C/N's between 15 and 30 will consistently bring about good composting results. At ratios lower than about 15/1, nitrogen is lost—usually as ammonia, which can constitute an odor problem. Although ratios between 30 and 50 may be permissible, the required composting time is longer because of the additional time microorganisms need to oxidize the excess carbon and thereby lower the C/N to the desired level. Provided that the initial C/N was high, C/N can serve as an indicator of product stability.

C/N has an important bearing on the utility of the compost product. Incorporation of a product having an excessively high C/N into the soil leads to nitrogen deprivation for plants grown on that soil. To oxidize the excess carbon, the microorganisms need more nitrogen. To meet this need, they must compete with the crop plants for the insufficient supply of soluble nitrogen in the soil. Being more competitive than plants, the microorganisms flourish at the expense of the plants. The result is that plant growth is inhibited until the excess C has been oxidized. The nitrogen shortage is avoided by using a compost product that has C/N ratio of 15/1 or lower. In the case of sewage sludge bulked with wood chips, the sludge usually starts at a lower C/N than desired for composting. Adding the chips increases the ratio to the optimum range for composting. Finally, screening the large chips out for reuse usually lowers the C/N of the product to the desired range for nitrogen availability to plants.

The availability of the nutrients also influences the process. If the C is in a form that is difficult to decompose, such as lignin or other woody forms, the rate of stabilization will be slow. It is important to note that fungi are the only type of organisms that can efficiently utilize woody materials and that they do not tolerate temperatures as high as some forms of bacteria or actinomycetes. Virtually no fungi survive above 60°C. Thus the rate of decomposition of materials, like municipal solid waste with its high content of paper (made from wood), slows rapidly above 55°C.

For practical purposes, because the mobility of the microorganisms is negligible, it is necessary to provide intimate contact between the microorganisms and the nutrient elements in the waste. This can be done by grinding the wastes and thoroughly mixing them.

A certain amount of moisture is necessary to support the metabolic processes of the microbes and to permit transport of the nutrients. Experience has shown that the process will not be inhibited if the moisture content is at least 40 percent.

The composting process is relatively insensitive to pH, probably due to the broad spectrum of organisms that is usually involved. The optimum is probably in the range of 6.5 to 8.5, however, the natural buffering capacity of the process permits a much wider range of initial values (5-12). Most well stabilized composts will have a pH between 6.5 and 7.5. Controlling the pH of the initial composting mix can become important with certain wastes that have large amounts of protein (N), as was found in a research project on composting crab wastes at the University of Maryland. Adjusting the pH downward to near neutral reduced volatilization of ammonia and other odorous compounds.

The porosity, texture, and structure also affect the process by their influence on the effectiveness of aeration and its functions. These factors can be adjusted by selection of the materials used and by grinding or shredding and mixing. (Materials added to adjust these properties are usually called bulking agents). Porosity determines the resistance to air flow and is a function of the particle size and size gradation of the materials. The voids must also be interconnected to permit air movement. Large particle size, and the more uniform size distribution, result in increased porosity. Structure is derived from the rigidity of the particles, and is measured by their ability to resist settling and by loss of porosity in the moist environment of the compost.

Texture controls the available area for aerobic activity. Most of the aerobic decomposition of composting occurs on the surface of particles, whereby aerobic microorganisms on the surface of particles utilize the available oxygen in a thin film at the surface, leaving the interior in an anaerobic state. Since the surface to volume ratio increases with decreasing particle size, the rate of aerobic decomposition will increase with decreasing particle size

within limits. When the particles become too small, however, there is a loss of porosity, so a compromise is needed. Good results are usually obtained when the particle sizes range from 1/8 inch to 2 inch mean diameter.

Porosity, texture and structure are all influenced by moisture content. Loss of porosity can be caused by excessive moisture filling most of the voids. The excess moisture also eliminates any tendency for crumbling that would increase the effective surface area. Many wastes used for composting such as leaves and paper lose their structural rigidity when wet. The detrimental effects of moisture are not significant for most materials below 60 percent moisture content (wet basis) and a few materials may have higher or lower critical moisture contents.

Porosity cannot be predicted with accuracy from ingredient characteristics. Bulk density can be related to porosity and is easily measured so it is sometimes used to estimate the probable porosity. Bulk densities of the mixture with less than 35 to 40 pounds per cubic foot are usually adequate. Sometimes porosity is expressed as free air space, which should exceed 30 percent. Porosity, texture and structure are a function of moisture content, characteristics of the mixture of materials, and compaction.

As described above, a good feedstock for composting will have a C/N ratio of 15 to 30 and a moisture content of 40 percent to 60 percent on a wet basis. Although a few materials will fall in

TABLE 1:

Approximate Nitrogen Content and C/N Ratios of Some Compostable Materials, Dry Basis*

Material	N	C/N
Poultry manure	6.3	—
Mixed slaughterhouse wastes	7–10	2
Night soil	5.5–6.5	6–10
Sheep manure	3.75	—
Pig manure	3.75	—
Horse manure	2.3	—
Sea weed	1.9	19
Cow manure	1.7	—
Potato tops	1.5	25
Combined refuse, Berkeley, CA	1.05	34
Oat straw	1.05	48
Wheat straw	0.3	128
Sawdust	0.11	511
Paper	nil	—

*From Gotaas, H.B., Composting, Sanitary Disposal and Reclamation of Organic Wastes. World Health Organization, Geneva. 1956

these ranges, it is usually necessary to blend materials. Tables 1 and 2 give typical values for the N content, and the C/N ratio. From them, appropriate mix ratios can be calculated for the C/N ratio. Moisture contents of waste materials are usually variable with time from most sources, so the ratio may need continuous adjustment to stay within the optimum moisture range. It generally will be possible to calculate an acceptable mix ratio from the typical analysis given in Tables 1 and 2. However, it is advisable to conduct pilot tests to verify the suitability of the computed mix ratios.

TYPICAL INGREDIENTS AND CONDITIONING APPROACHES

Sludge: Sewage sludge has a C/N ratio on the low end of the acceptable range, is too wet and lacks porosity. It is usually conditioned by mixing with wood chips, sawdust, bark, or dry compost. Occasionally, fly-ash has been added to the mix to reduce the moisture content and the amount of other bulking material needed. Sometimes, the sludge has been mixed with municipal solid wastes or a fraction thereof, which have a low C/N ratio and moisture content.

MSW: Most plans for composting municipal solid wastes (MSW) are part of an overall resource recovery system which removes a variety of recyclable materials from the MSW. Thus it is difficult to generalize about its need for conditioning. However, fine grinding prior to composting should be avoided, if possible, to maintain porosity. The MSW and most of its fractions will need added water and will benefit from additional nitrogen.

Yard Waste: Leaves have a very high C/N ratio and tend to be dry. They benefit from added water and nitrogen. Shredding improves their porosity and exposes the interior of the leaf, which is more susceptible to decomposition than the outer surfaces. Lawn clippings lack the structure to maintain their porosity for aeration, but have a favorable C/N ratio and moisture content for decomposition. Thus the lawn clippings are likely to deplete the oxygen in a windrow and become anaerobic and generate odors. Brush and tree trimmings need shredding for size reduction. A combination of these yard wastes can make a good composting mix, if the leaves can be stored until the other materials are available. Research would be helpful to determine optimum preparation and proportions of these materials.

Food Wastes: Wastes from food and feed processing plants can vary widely in their characteristics. Many will be too wet to have the necessary porosity and will need a bulking material. Dewatering could help reduce the amount of bulking material required. Others may need grinding to reduce particle size. The C/N ratio may need adjustment; fruits and vegetables are mostly deficient in N. By judiciously blending them with other wastes, most could be effectively composted.

Some waste materials, especially industrial and municipal wastes, will contain toxic substances that would make the compost unsuitable for the intended uses. Thus, it is important that the compost operator obtain copies of any analysis that may be required for disposal of the waste by pollution control authorities having jurisdiction over those wastes, and that metals concentrations be kept to levels acceptable to regulators for land application. If questionable materials are used, the compost must be analyzed.

Analysis of the nutrients contained in the compost will be useful for determining application rates and for marketing. Typical availability of nutrients for the first cropping season is 15 percent for N and 40 percent for P with lesser amounts in succeeding seasons.

Almost any organic waste material can be made into compost, if a market can be found that warrants the expense. It will usually be possible to operate an effective composting process if the ini-

TABLE 2:
Nitrogen Content and C/N Ratio of Various Materials Used In Municipal or Industrial Compost*

Material	%N	C/N ratio
	(Dry Wt)	(Wt/Wt)
Garbage:		
Raleigh, NC	1.92	15.4
Louisville, KY	2.90	14.9
Total raw refuse		
(residential including garbage):		
Savannah, GA	1.30	38.5
Johnson City, TN	0.6	80
Chandler, AZ	0.57	65.8
Sewage Sludge:		
Activated	5.60	6.3
Digested	1.88	15.7
Fruit Wastes	1.52	34.8
Wood (pine)	0.07	723
Fish scraps	6.50	—
Paper	0.25	173
Grass clippings	2.15	20.1
Grass clippings/garden weeds	2.03	19.3
Leaves (freshly fallen)	0.5–1.0	40–80
Lumber mill wastes	0.13	170
Pharmaceutical wastes	2.55	19

* From Poincelot, R.P., The Biochemistry and Methodology of Composting. Bulletin 754. The Connecticut Agricultural Experiment Station, New Haven. 1975.

tial mixture of materials has a C/N ratio of 15 to 40, a moisture content of 40 percent to 60 percent, a pH of 5 to 12, and porosity (free air space) of greater than 30 percent.

SAMPLE CALCULATIONS

Blending Materials to Correct a Moisture Problem:

Assume that a farm has chicken manure that usually has a moisture content of 70 percent when removed from the buildings. Both the moisture and the N contents are too high for optimum composting and the manure needs greater porosity. Sawdust is available with a moisture content of 30 percent. Using values from the tables and assuming that the C/N ratio of the manure is no more than 10, the calculation is done as follows:

1# of wet manure will contain:

Water 1# $\times$ 0.7	=	0.7#
Dry matter 1# – 0.7	=	0.3#
N 0.3 $\times$ 0.06	=	0.018#
C 0.018 $\times$ 10	=	0.18

1# of damp sawdust will contain:

Water 1# $\times$ 0.3	=	0.3#
Dry matter 1# – 0.3	=	0.7#
N 0.7 $\times$ 0.0011	=	0.00077#
C 0.00077 $\times$ 500	=	0.39#

The moisture content should not exceed 60 percent and stated in terms of 1# of wet mix:

$$MC = 60\% = 0.6 = \frac{\text{wt } H_2O \text{ in manure} + \text{wt } H_2O \text{ in sawdust}}{\text{total weight}}$$

$$MC = 0.6 = \frac{0.7 + 0.3x}{1 + x}$$

where x is the amount of sawdust needed

$$0.6 (1 + x) = 0.7 + 0.3x$$

$$x = 0.33\# \text{ sawdust/\#manure}$$

To check the C/N ratio:

$$C/N = \frac{C \text{ manure} + C \text{ sawdust}}{N \text{ manure} + N \text{ sawdust}}$$

$$C/N = \frac{0.18 + 0.33 \times 0.39}{0.018 + 0.33 \times 0.00077}$$

$$C/N = 16.9 \text{ OK}$$

Since this is near the low end of the acceptable range, the amount of sawdust added should not be reduced even if drier materials are available.

Blending Materials to Correct a C/N Ratio:

Assume that wheat straw is available which has a moisture content of 15%:

1# of wheat straw will contain:

Water 1# $\times$ 0.15	=	0.15#
Dry matter 1# – 0.15	=	0.85#
N 0.3 $\times$ 0.003	=	0.0026#
C 0.0026 $\times$ 128	=	0.33#

The amount of straw should be estimated on the basis of a C/N ratio of 20 instead of the minimum of 15, to reduce the possibility of loss of nitrogen and odor production.

$$C/N = 20 = \frac{C \text{ in } 1\# \text{ manure} + x(C \text{ in } 1\# \text{ straw})}{N \text{ in } 1\# \text{ manure} + x(N \text{ in } 1\# \text{ straw})}$$

where x is the amount of straw needed.

$$20 = \frac{0.18 + x(0.33)}{0.018 + x(0.0026)}$$

$$x = 0.65\# \text{ straw/\# manure}$$

To check the mix moisture content:

$$MC = \frac{\text{wt } H_2O \text{ in } 1\# \text{ manure} + \text{wt } H_2O \text{ in } 0.65\# \text{ straw}}{\text{total weight}}$$

$$MC = \frac{0.7 + 0.65 \times 0.15}{1.65} = 48\% \text{ OK}$$

George Willson of George B. Willson Associates in Laurel, Maryland, is a consultant on composting/organic waste recycling.

32

PUTTING PRINCIPLES INTO SUCCESSFUL PRACTICE

Clarence G. Golueke

COMPOST SYSTEMS can be classified on three general bases, namely, oxygen usage, temperature, and technological approach. If oxygen usage is the basis, the division is into aerobic and anaerobic. When temperature serves as the basis; the division becomes mesophilic and thermophilic. Finally, using technology as the key, classification is into open or windrow and mechanical or "enclosed" composting.

Aerobic composting involves the activity of aerobic microbes, and hence the provision of oxygen during the composting process. The opposite prevails in anaerobic composting—i.e., anaerobic bacteria accomplish the decomposition and oxygen (air) is excluded from the composting mass. Aerobic composting generally is characterized by high temperatures, the absence of foul odors, and is more rapid than anaerobic composting. Anaerobic decomposition is characterized by low temperatures (unless heat is applied from an external source), the production of odorous intermediate (reduced) products, and generally proceeds at a slower rate than does aerobic composting. The advantages of aerobic composting over anaerobic composting arise from the differences in their characteristics—in other words, aerobic composting is more rapid, permits high temperatures, and is not odorous.

As the term implies, in mesophilic composting, the temperatures are kept at intermediate levels (15° to 40°C), which in most cases is the ambient temperature. Thermophilic composting is conducted at temperatures from 45°C to 65°C. In practice, most processes include the two ranges.

Compost systems falling under the category of "open" or "windrow" are those in which the entire process is carried out in the open. The manner of arranging the material for handling or processing usually is to stack the materials in elongated windrows. In mechanical systems, on the other hand, the greater part of the initial composting activity takes place in an enclosed unit, the digester.

GENERAL CONSTRAINTS

A point of major importance in designing, planning and evaluating a compost process as a waste management device is that since it is a biological operation, factors and requirements peculiar to the maintenance of biological activities in general also affect the compost process. Therefore, composting is subject to well defined biological limitations which are: 1) A suitable microbial population must be present; 2) The rate and efficiency of the process are functions of the rate and efficiency of microbial activity; 3) The capacity of a given operation is limited by the size and nature of the microbial population; 4) The substrate subject to composting generally must be organic; 5) Environmental factors are of key importance.

The origin of the first constraint is quite obvious and is implied in the definition of composting itself. Since the process is a biological one, living organisms are the agents for accomplishing it. The limitation to microbial organisms is indirectly implied by the term "decomposition," in that in nature, decomposition in the commonly accepted sense of the term is done by microscopic organisms. Not only must a microbial population be present, but it must also be one that is suited to the task.

The limitation on rate is one of practical importance, because it means that no matter how well a piece of compost equipment is designed mechanically, composting with it will proceed at a pace commensurate with that of the bacterial activity permitted by the particular set of conditions provided by the machine. The microbial limitation on capacity also has practical ramifications. It means that once the maximum-sized microbial population has been reached under the conditions provided by a given piece of compost equipment, the loading cannot be increased without giving rise to nuisances. Loading in excess of the maximum permissible will inhibit the process either partly or entirely, and at the least will result in only partial treatment of the waste material.

The constraint arising from the influence of environmental factors usually manifests itself through the mechanism of the limiting factor. If any factor is present in less than optimum concentration or level, the functioning of the entire process is inhibited in proportion to the extent of the deficiency of the factor. For example, for a given set-up in which the temperature is optimum, aeration is complete, and a suitable microbial population is present, but nitrogen is deficient, the only way to increase the efficiency of that set-up would be to add nitrogen in an amount sufficient to make up for the nitrogen deficiency. Adding more bacteria would only aggravate the problem, since the nitrogen is not sufficient even for the existing population. Building a more elaborate digester would not suffice, since the effective component of the process, namely the bacteria, do not have the nitrogen to meet their metabolic requirements.

MICROBIOLOGY

Occasionally, a proposal for commercial composting includes the use of some special inoculum, the composition of which is known only to the discoverer who claims it to be fundamental to the successful operation of his process. Some inoculums are described as mixtures of several pure strains of laboratory cultured organisms especially prominent in the decomposition of organic matter and in nitrogen fixation. Others are purported to contain as well such things as "enzyme systems," "hormones," "preserved living organisms," "activated factors," "biocatalysts," etc.

The idea of inoculation has even been carried to the extent of inoculation of the finished compost. The addition of organisms is supposed to be of inestimable value to the soil. While it is true that certain bacteria promote soil fertility, the mere addition of such organisms is of no use if environmental conditions are not appropriate in the soil. On the other hand, if environmental conditions are suitable, the addition of the organisms would be superfluous because the native population would already be present in more than ample numbers.

The number of bacteria is rarely a limiting factor in composting, since bacteria are always present in great abundance on all exposed objects, especially on municipal refuse. They can be eliminated only by a drastic measure such as sterilization at high temperature and pressure. When environmental factors are appropriate, native bacteria, because they are better adapted than forms attenuated under laboratory conditions, multiply rapidly and composting proceeds at a rate governed by the environmental conditions. The vast number of enzymes involved in decomposition, as well as the difficulty and expense involved in isolating and synthesizing them, would make composting with enzymes alone highly impractical even were such a preparation available. The addition of enzymes to raw refuse is unnecessary however, because bacteria synthesize efficiently and rapidly all of the enzymes required. For a time, "hormones" served as the "catch" word and was popularly used to designate growth factors and vitamins needed by bacteria. However, the organic constituents of refuse contain all the growth factors and vitamins needed for normal growth.

Inoculation would be of value to the composting process only if the bacterial population in any emerging environment were unable to develop rapidly enough to take full advantage of the capacity of the environment to support it. In such a case, a time lag would result, which could be overcome by supplementing the initial population indigenous to the refuse. No such time lag was observed in composting studies conducted at the University of California. Composting is a dynamic process, representing the combined activity of a wide succession of mixed bacterial and fungal populations associated with a wide succession of environments, one overlapping the other and each emerging gradually as a result of continual change in temperature and substrate. The substrate changes are due to a progressive breakdown by bacteria of complex foodstuffs to increasingly simple compounds. As will be seen later, temperature increases steadily in proportion to biological activity, so that initial mesophilic conditions are soon superseded by thermophilic ones. Because the process is dynamic and any individual group of organisms can survive in a rather wide environmental range, one population begins to emerge while another is flourishing, and yet another is disappearing. Inasmuch as any group of bacteria is capable of multiplying at a pace equal to that of its developing environment, the addition of similar organisms as an inoculum would be superfluous.

In the University of California studies, the composting process was neither accelerated nor the final product improved in those runs in which inoculums were tested, even though the inoculums were rich in bacteria. Inoculums that were tried were horse manure, "rich" soils, composting material, and two commercial preparations. The University findings have been duplicated at several other laboratories.

In closing this discussion on inoculums, a distinction should be made between inoculation in terms of microbiological research and that in sanitary engineering practice. The difference between the two interpretations is one of magnitude. The microbiologist usually thinks of inoculation as minute additions; whereas the sanitary engineer thinks of what may be described as "mass inoculation." Although the preceding discussion was concerned primarily with inoculation in terms of microbiological usage, it also is applicable to mass inoculation provided the magnitude of the mass inoculum is not such as to *significantly affect the physical and chemical characteristics of the mass of material* receiving the inoculum. Any apparent improvement following a large mass inoculation cannot be attributed solely to the addition of organisms inasmuch as such an inoculation may also significantly alter the physical and chemical nature of the material to be composted.

NUTRIENT BALANCE

To keep on reproducing and thus bring about decomposition, all microorganisms, indeed all organisms, must have a minimum supply of all of the elements of which their cellular matter is composed. In addition, they need a minimum amount of certain elements that enter into the metabolic activities of the organisms as an energy source or enzyme constituent and do not necessarily contribute to an increase in the mass of the organisms. As one knows almost intuitively, the amounts required vary from element to element, and at a somewhat constant ratio of one to another. In other words, a balance is struck. The balance arises from the fact that, as stated earlier, growth is limited by that factor (or factors) which is (or are) present in less than the required concentration. The balance is especially important as far as the macronutrients are concerned. (Macronutrients are those required in relatively large amounts—e.g., carbon and nitrogen.)

One of the more important balances with respect to composting is the carbon-nitrogen balance or ratio (C/N ratio). Because part of the carbon is lost as CO_2; and depending upon the type of organism, carbon is present in the cellular material in greater concentration than is nitrogen, the amount of carbon required considerably surpasses that of nitrogen.

The optimum range with most wastes falls within 20 or 25 to 1. The more carbon-nitrogen balance deviates from the optimum, especially in the upper range, the slower the process proceeds. However, the actual upper limit for an individual

application depends upon the degree of availability of the carbon. If the carbon is present in a form highly resistant to bacterial attack, it is of little use to microbes. Hence, if a waste has a large percentage of carbon in a resistant form, the permissible carbon-nitrogen ratio can be higher than 25/1. Examples are wastes having a heavy concentration of paper, fiber, wood, or straw.

The principal deleterious effect of too low a C/N ratio is the loss of nitrogen through the production of ammonia and its subsequent volatilization. Apparently, the excess nitrogen ends up as ammonia. As far as the composting process is concerned *per se*, such an event is not detrimental. But since nitrogen conservation should be one of the objectives of composting, the loss becomes significant on that score. The loss is greatest when high-rate composting is being employed. The increased loss is due to the fact that high-rate composting involves a great deal of aeration, is generally occurring under thermophilic conditions, and is characterized by a pH level of 8.0 or above. The high pH fosters ammonia formation; the high temperature accelerates the volatilization of ammonia, and the aeration drives off the volatilized ammonia. While the factors involved in the volatilization may suggest the remedy, applying the remedy may not be practical. For example, the pH could be lowered by adding some type of acid. Of course such a procedure would be impractical from the standpoint of processing and expense. Without aeration, the process no longer is high-rate composting. The temperature could be lowered, but this would only reduce the rate of loss, and not necessarily the total amount of loss. Consequently, the most appropriate approach is to avoid the low carbon-nitrogen ratios if possible.

RATE CONTROLLING FACTORS

Since the compost process is essentially a biological one, rate controlling factors are those influencing biological activity in general, namely, environmental factors. In fact, organism-related factors are perhaps the ultimate rate limiting factors, because they determine the rate of growth and degree of activity of the microbial population, and hence the rapidity and nature of the compost process. The principal environmental factors in composting are moisture, temperature, pH level (hydrogen ion concentration), nutrient concentration and availability, and oxygen concentration.

Nutrient concentration is not discussed in this section because it was given sufficient consideration in the previous section.

● **Moisture Content**—With composting in general, the structural strength of the material to be composted determines the upper permissible moisture content. The relation between structure and moisture content stems from the fact that modern composting is an aerobic process. Oxygen is made available to the bacteria by way of the air contained in the interstices at the time the windrow was formed. In a mechanical composter, the supply is by way of the air introduced between the particles as they are tumbled or stirred in the digester. In either case, if the interstices are filled with water, obviously the air has been displaced and no oxygen is available to the organisms. As a result, the mass of waste becomes anaerobic, the composting process is slowed and foul odors are generated. The size of the interstices is determined by the particle size of the material, and their stability is determined by the structural strength of the composting material—i.e., the capacity to resist compaction and consequent obliteration of the interstices.

As Table 1 indicates, the maximum permissible moisture content for composting wastes that are largely "fibrous" (straw, hay, dry leaves, etc.) or woody (sawdust, small wood chips, bark, etc.) is within the range of 75 to 85 percent. On the other hand, wastes consisting mostly of paper or of green vegetation (lawn clippings, vegetable trimmings, wet garbage, etc.) have a maximum permissible moisture content within the range of 50 percent to 60 percent. If the maximum permissible moisture content for a given waste is excessively low, the problem can be lessened by adding an absorbent waste to the material. Thus, if straw is added to vegetable trimmings, the maximum permissible moisture rises in proportion to the amount of straw added. The addition of an absorbent also is required if the moisture content of the waste in its "raw" state is excessively high, as for example cannery wastes.

The minimum moisture content at which bacterial activity takes place is from 12 to 15 percent.

TABLE 1:
Maximum Permissible Moisture Contents

Type of Waste[a]	Moisture Content %
Straw	75-85
Wood (sawdust, small chips)	75-90
Paper	55-65
"Wet" Wastes (vegetable trimmings, lawn clippings, garbage, etc.)	50-55
Municipal Refuse	55-65
Manures (without bedding)	55-65

[a]The major component of the waste.

Obviously, the closer the moisture content of a composting mass approaches these low levels, the slower will be the compost process. As a rule-of-thumb, the moisture content becomes a limiting factor when it drops below 45 or 50 percent.

● **Temperature**—Temperature has long been recognized as one of the key environmental factors affecting biological activity. In general, each group of organisms has an optimum temperature, and any deviation from the optimum is manifested by a decline in growth and activity of the organism. For convenience of reference, the total range of temperatures at which life is possible generally is divided into three "sub-ranges" into which are grouped those organisms whose optimum temperature falls within one of the sub-ranges. The three sub-ranges are cryophilic, mesophilic, and thermophilic. The boundary temperatures of each of the ranges have been somewhat arbitrarily assigned as being from about 5°C to about 10°C for the cryophilic range; from 10°C (or as high as 15°) to 40° or 45°C for the mesophilic range; and from 40° or 45°C to 70°C for the thermophilic range. (As is well known, certain blue-green algae and bacteria can survive and even grow at temperatures as high as 80° to 90°C.) Modern composting processes are designed to operate within the mesophilic and thermophilic ranges.

Much can be said in favor of composting at either of the two temperature ranges—mesophilic and thermophilic. The proponents of mesophilic composting (i.e., in the upper range—about 35°C) claim that mesophilic bacteria are more efficient than thermophilic bacteria, and that composting therefore proceeds more rapidly. An important advantage claimed by the proponents of thermophilic composting, in addition to improvement in the process, is that pathogens and weed seeds are killed at the high temperatures. This latter feature probably is one of the main reasons why most modern composting processes involve thermophilic composting at some state in the overall process. Some evidence indicates that the process may proceed more efficiently in the lower thermophilic range, viz, 50° to 55°C. All groups agree that the operating temperature should be at least 35°C.

The question of temperature probably is academic, since, as is explained in a later section of this chapter, the temperature of a reasonably large or insulated mass will gradually rise to well within the thermophilic range due to excess energy of microbial origin. This increase will inevitably take place unless positive measures are taken to dissipate the heat. Inasmuch as the heating involves no expenditure of external energy and positive measures would be needed to dissipate it, it would be more reasonable to design the operation to include thermophilic temperatures during the most active stages of the compost process.

There is no doubt that the process becomes less efficient when the temperature exceeds 60°C if for no other reason than that spore forming organisms begin to enter the spore or resistant stage at temperatures of 60°C and higher. When in the resistant or spore stage, activity diminishes to practically zero, and hence the composting process is correspondingly retarded.

The range of optimum temperatures for the composting process as a whole is quite broad, i.e., from about 35°C to about 55°C, because of the many groups of organisms taking part in the process. Each group has its particular optimum temperature which may or may not coincide with that of another group. Consequently, the optimum temperature for the process as a whole is an integration of, or perhaps better expressed, a compromise between the optimum temperatures of the various forms of microbes involved in the process. Of course, it should be remembered that unless a closely controlled digester is used, a uniform temperature does not prevail throughout the mass of composting material at any one time—except at the start of the process when all material is at ambient temperature. The existence of a plateau from the mesophilic into the thermophilic range is due not only to the involvement of many types of organisms, but also to adaptation of organisms to the temperature range.

As stated earlier, in a practical operation, the desired temperature range includes thermophilic temperatures. The reasons are: 1) Some of the organisms involved in the process have their optimum temperature in the thermophilic range. 2) Weed seeds and most microbes of pathogenic significance cannot survive exposure to thermophilic temperatures. 3) Unless definite counter measures are taken, a composting mass of any appreciable volume will assume high temperatures.

● **Hydrogen Ion (pH Level)**—Many of the reasons offered for the broad permissible temperature range apply to the factor pH level. As a generality one can state that the fungi tolerate a wider range of pH than do the bacteria. The optimum pH range for most bacteria is between 6 and 7.5, whereas for fungi it can be between 5.5 and 8.0. In fact, the upper pH limit for many fungi has been found to be a function of precipitation of essential nutrients from the growth medium, rather than of any inhibition due to pH *per se*.

33

BIOLOGICAL TREATMENT FOR HAZARDOUS WASTES

Clarence G. Golueke and Luis F. Diaz

CROP RESIDUES contaminated with pesticides or other toxic organics can be satisfactorily and safely treated by windrow composting. The reason is that concentrations of contaminants on crop residues usually are relatively low, and the contaminants generally have a short "half-life" because of the destructive effect of many of the physical conditions that develop during composting. Chief among the latter are temperature and pII variation. Nevertheless, safety demands that all incoming material as well as the working environment be carefully monitored and controlled. Of course, the situation would change if highly toxic or resistant contaminants are present. Well designed, constructed, and operated in-vessel systems would be indicated for certain wastes, because they (i.e., in-vessel systems) permit good control of input and of solid, liquid, gaseous emissions.

In addition to the many advantages it has in common with biodegradation systems in general, composting has some peculiar to it. In comparison with incineration, composting has lower capital and operational costs. Moreover, its impacts are less adverse. Regarding landfarming, it is safer in terms of impact upon the water, land, and air resources. Additionally, retention times are shorter and the land requirements are correspondingly less. An additional advantage is the destructive effect exerted on less persistent pesticides (e.g., Malathion, carbaryls[12]) by the combination of physical and chemical factors generated in the compost process. Examples of the factors are temperature and pH.

Composting has some definite disadvantages that sharply constrain its utilization in hazardous waste treatment and disposal. For example, costs and the work involved in properly preparing a particular hazardous waste material for composting may be so great as to render the undertaking economically unfeasible. Another consideration is the cost of necessary precautionary measures (enclosure, etc.). It may be sufficiently great as to make composting economically noncompetitive with other means of hazardous waste disposal. Despite the constraints that may be imposed upon the disposal of crop residues, contaminated municipal solid waste, and oily waste, composting may be competitive with thermal and non-thermal non-biological methods.

A consideration of the future prospects of composting hazardous wastes must take into account the advantages and disadvantages inherently characteristic of composting as compared with those inherent in physical, chemical, and thermal methods of waste treatment. An important consideration is the fact that the composting of hazardous agricultural wastes and petroleum sludges also has the economic advantage that accounted for the increase in land spreading of sewage sludge at the expense of incineration. Thus, the sizable volumes of the agricultural residues involved account for the economic advantage of composting over incineration. The difficulties and expenses of incinerating petroleum sludges as compared to composting them account for the greater popularity of the compost option. The acceptance of composting petroleum sludges as a practical disposal measure has greatly benefited from the extensive record of successful landfarming.

USE OF MICROBES

Biological treatment of hazardous wastes is the use of microbes (microorganisms) to break down the harmful compounds in the wastes to innocuous intermediate or end products. The present, albeit belated recognition of the biological approach as an attractive means for treating hazardous waste, undoubtedly is due in great part to the sense of desperation generated by the shortcomings of conventional systems, hitherto considered adequate. The reaction parallels that which led to the recent surge of interest in composting municipal solid wastes (MSW).

The neglect of biological treatment of hazardous wastes in the past undoubtedly was largely due to certain limitations ascribed to biological systems in general. Some of the limitations are genuine, whereas others are based upon mistaken impressions and convictions. Among the unfounded limitations are inadequate predictability and lengthy detention periods involved, i.e. relative to thermal and chemical approaches. Among the genuine limitations are: 1) a relatively narrow permissible pH range; 2) inhibitory or lethal effect of certain toxic substances at all but very low concentrations; 3) nutrient deficiencies of most hazardous wastes with respect to microbial growth and reproduction; 4) the worrisome possibility of producing an intermediate product that is equally or even more hazardous and 5) microbes cannot transmute heavy metals into non-toxic elements, although some can incorporate them into organic molecules (compounds). Unfortunately, the resulting compounds almost invariably are soluble—a condition even less desirable than the elemental condition. Fortunately, with the exception of the one pertaining to heavy metals, these limitations can be overcome or compensated for by the institution of appropriate measures.

REQUIREMENTS

The term "microbes" includes all microorganisms, e.g., bacteria, fungi, single-celled algae, microscopic protozoa; "active" refers to microbes capable of attacking the particular hazardous waste; "nutrient" refers to those required by the active microbes; "environmental conditions" refers to those which are favorable to the active microbes; and "wastes" refers to hazardous wastes.

With few exceptions (e.g., enzymatic hydrolysis), all biological treatment systems have these key requirements: 1) Population of microbes capable of attacking the hazardous compound or compounds; 2) Organisms more toxic than the untreated waste; must retain their specialized metabolic capability; 3) Access to an adequate concentration of micro- and macro-nutrient elements (N, P, K, Ca, Mo, etc.) essential to the growth and reproduction of the active microbes; 3) Environmental conditions (temperature, pH, aerobiosis or anaerobiosis) favorable to the active microbial pop-

ulations, and ideally less than favorable to their competitors; and 4), Intimate contact between hazardous waste molecules and the active microbes.

Among the several advantages of biological systems over most thermal and chemical systems are: 1) Ability to break down toxic substances *in situ* at lower cost and in less time. According to Nicolas and Giamporcaro, costs of *in situ* bioremediation can be as little as 1 percent of off-site incineration. 2) Off-site biological treatment also is less expensive and can be done under conditions far less extreme than those required by competitive non-biological systems. 3) Because operating conditions are less extreme, elaborate equipment and controls are not needed. Hence capital, maintenance, and operational expenses are lower. 4) Finally, potential and actual environmental impacts are with minor exceptions, fewer and less undesirable than those with thermal and chemical systems.

MICROBES

If active microbes are not indigenous in the waste, they must be introduced by way of inoculation, mass inoculation, recirculation, or other means. The introduced microbes either may be naturally occurring types or genetically engineered to attack the hazardous waste. Thomas and Ward[2] found that the treatment of chlorinated aliphatic compounds (e.g, carbon tetrachloride, chloroform, tetrachloroethylene) generally requires mixed cultures. Murthy *et al*[3] have shown that the correct consortium or organisms is central for optimizing the glyphosate degrading activity.

Genetically engineered microorganisms are those which have been manipulated such that they become endowed with a capability they hitherto lacked. Although the concept of "genetically engineering" microbes for special purposes, e.g., breaking down toxic molecules, is intriguing and seems to be "the way to go," its realization is beset with two or three obstacles which are almost insurmountable at present. One of the obstacles is imposed by nature. As of the present, microbes "engineered" apparently do not fare well when placed in competition with other microbes in a practical setting. Consequently, they eventually disappear or function very slowly and inefficiently. Another exceedingly difficult obstacle is regulatory, i.e., severe restrictions imposed at Federal and state levels. These two obstacles have resulted in a general abandonment of the use of genetically engineered microbes by most bioremediation companies.[1] Unfortunately, there is the danger that the regulatory obstacle may not be confined to "engineered" microbes. Reports are being heard of a developing interest on the part of the EPA in regulating the use of microbes that have been isolated from natural settings.[1]

Naturally occurring active microbes can be isolated and their nutritional and environmental requirements determined by way of conventional microbiological techniques. Knowledge thus acquired is used to develop a treatment system in which proliferation of the active microbes is encouraged. This knowledge can also be used in design of an enrichment technique. "Enrichment" simply means maintenance of nutritional and environmental conditions that favor the active microbes, and ideally—but not necessarily—do not favor their competitors. The key point is that the active organisms thrive and constitute the largest population in the culture. Hence, enrichment cultures are not to be confused with pure cultures. If the indigenous population is extremely small or insufficiently large, it may be brought to proper size by the introduction of a treatment regimen based largely on the enrichment approach.[3a]

Referring to another publication,[4] Nicolas and Giamporcaro state that an estimated 42 different pollutants can be biodegraded. In the list that follows (developed from various sources) are given a few of the organisms that have been isolated, identified, and studied. The name of the organism is followed by the identity (in parentheses) of the organic compound susceptible to attack by the particular organism: 1) *Pseudomonas putida*, LB40 1. (PCB soil remediation);[5] 2) *Ps. putida*, PpF1 (Chlorinated aliphatic solvents);[2] 3) *Corynebacterium sp.* (mineralizes p-nitrophenyl in lake water);[6] 4) *Arthrobacter spp.* (chlorinated aromatics).[7]

NUTRIENTS

Microbial cultures can be designed to be operated as continuous cultures, batch cultures, or semi-batch cultures. Accordingly, treatment systems based on those cultures can be operated on a continuous basis, a batch basis, or a semi-batch basis. With continuous systems, activity and reproduction must be at a rate sufficient to compensate for the continuous discharge of microbes. A continuous culture has the advantage of being maintained such that its active microbial population consists principally of microbes at the most effective stage of their growth. Requirements of batch cultures are not as critical as those of continuous cultures. An advantage is that they can be operated either in a growth or in a non-growth mode. The non-growth mode is used in the production of enzymes or certain products, such that the products are less contaminated with other materials. The non-growth mode requires full-size populations. They are kept in a non-growing, but active condition by eliminating all nitrogen sources.

Nitrogen (N) usually is the limiting nutrient in hazardous wastes. The nitrogen must be added in a form available to active microbes and in concentrations needed for a growth rate equal to or in excess of that of competitive microbes. Inasmuch as carbon (C) is one of the key elements of most hazardous waste molecules, theoretically, it need not be supplied. The reality is that most microbes can not use the hazardous waste carbon. The microbes lack the enzymes needed to break up the toxic molecules and thereby make their carbon available. The exceptional microbes, namely those which either possess the needed enzyme or which have the ability to synthesize it, can attack the toxic molecule and assimilate and use its carbon. They make up the active populations. Hence, normally, no carbon source is added to the culture. This constitutes an enrichment factor. However, some toxic molecules may be so resistant that their carbon is only difficultly available to the active organisms. Under such a circumstance, it may be necessary to add carbon to the extent that the active population can remain sufficiently large.

If a hazardous waste is involved, normally all other nutrients (e.g., phosphorus [P], trace elements, calcium [Ca]) are present in sufficient concentration.

ENVIRONMENTAL CONDITIONS

The optimum temperature is that of the active microbes. If they are thermophiles, then the system should be maintained and operated under thermophilic conditions. However, in common with most microbes, the optimum temperature usually is mesophilic. If the active population is facultatively thermophilic, a thermophilic level can serve as an enrichment factor, inasmuch as the majority of the competitors are mesophiles.

Oxygen [O_2] availability is an important environmental factor, because most microbes capable of attacking toxic molecules are either obligate or facultative aerobes. Usually, facultative aerobes function more efficiently under aerobic conditions. Consequently most biological systems for treating toxic wastes are designed to be operated under aerobic conditions. However, within the past decade, it has been demonstrated that the breakdown of certain wastes (e.g., halogenated hydrocarbons, some pesticides) can only be broken down under a combination of the two conditions, namely, an aerobic phase and an anaerobic phase in series 8, 9, 10.

The end products of aerobic processes usually are increased microbial mass, carbon dioxide, and various intermediates. The identity of the latter varies with that of the predominant microbial population and the degree of aerobiosis. Although there is some debate on the subject, aerobic processes generally are assumed to be more efficient than anaerobic processes. At any rate, they are not characterized by the foul odors that accompany anaerobic processes. Much higher temperatures also are attainable with aerobic processes. Certain anaerobic processes have the advantage of producing useful end-products, e.g., methane, ethanol, lactic acid; whereas, the utility of aerobic processes usually is limited to effectiveness in treatment.

As a rule, a pH level within the range, 6.0 - 7.5 is desired. Highly acidic or alkaline wastes may have to be buffered such that their pH levels be within the appropriate range. As with temperature and aeration, the pH level can serve as an enrichment factor for active microbes that function efficiently at a pH level below or above the neutral range.

TECHNOLOGY AND PROCESSES

Basically, the function of technology and processing (i.e., of treatment), is to bring the active microbes, their nutrients, and the materials to be detoxified (broken down) into close contact. This should be done in a manner such that environmental, nutritional, and operational conditions are maintained at an optimum level with respect to the needs of the active organisms. Therefore, as pointed out in the preceding section, environmental and nutritional conditions and their application and control generally are conducive to biological activity, and specifically are those that promote the activity of microbes responsible for the break down of the toxic component of the waste.

TYPES OF TREATMENT

Type of treatment is in part, a function of the physical state of the waste, i.e., whether it is in a liquid, solid, or intermediate form ("sludge"). Most hazardous wastes are in the liquid state either because of the nature of the waste or because the waste solids have been dissolved or suspended in a liquid medium. Being in the liquid state is not of itself disadvantageous. Many contend that liquid and liquefied wastes are easier to process and treat than are solid wastes and sludges.

Normally, hazardous wastes are processed before they are discharged into the external environment. In other words, they no longer are a threat to the quality of the environment. Unfortunately, until relatively recently, the norm has been to discard untreated wastes. The outcome is the present sorry state of the environment and contaminated land, air, and water resources.

IN SITU REMEDIATION

Among the approaches to restoring the quality of the environment and resources, *in situ* remediation has gained favorable attention to the extent that it is now accepted as a category of treatment. *In situ* remediation simply means treating the wastes without removing them from the particular resource into which they had been discarded. Thus, *in situ* can refer to land treatment, groundwater treatment, aquifer treatment, etc. Biodegradation is especially suitable for *in situ* applications.

In situ biodegradation (bioremediation) is accomplished by promoting and accelerating natural biodegradation by introducing oxygen and nutrients into contaminated soils or sludges. Therefore, the implementation of the *in situ* biorestoration process requires a subsurface matrix permeable enough to allow perfusion with a solution of oxygen and nutrients. Secondly, contaminant-degrading microbes must be present. With regard to microorganisms, naturally occurring or genetically engineered microorganisms capable of degrading the waste to be treated may be introduced. The alternative is to optimize conditions for indigenous microbes.

As stated earlier, genetically engineered microbes are not being used for *in situ* applications, primarily because of regulatory obstacles. Instead, the trend is to concentrate on the identification and isolation of indigenous microbes present at the sites.[1]

TREATMENT OF SOLID HAZARDOUS WASTES

Composting and land treatment ("landfarming") are the two most commonly used methods for treatment of solid hazardous wastes. Anaerobic digestion ranks a distant second (or third).

Land Treatment (Landfarming): Tun Phung aptly defines land treatment as a "waste treatment and disposal process whereby a waste is mixed with or incorporated into the surface soil and is degraded, transformed, or immobilized through proper management."[11] He describes it as a dynamic, management intensive system in which waste, soil, climate, and biological activities are the main components. Because landfarming is so closely akin to *in situ* treatment, the information presented in section "In Situ Remediation" also applies to landfarming, whether it be of liquid, solid, or sludge wastes. Hence, the remainder of this section is devoted to a few highlights of land application.

Principal factors are 1) the characteristics of the waste; 2) presence of microbial population or populations capable of attacking the hazardous wastes; and 3) the pH, moisture content, temperature, and nutrient content of the soil.

Among the advantages of landfarming are these four: 1) Because the waste decomposes, or is transformed, or is immobilized, the degradation of does not endure as long as it does when other land disposal systems are employed. 2) Because the site is continually monitored, the potential of wastes to migrate is sharply reduced or even eliminated. 3) Costs involved are lower than those for landfills and incineration. 4) A closed landfarm site can be put to recreational use. (It must not be used for food production, inasmuch as toxic ions may be taken up by the crop plants.)

Disadvantages include the following six: 1) Waste storage may be required on occasion. 2) Land farming is land intensive as well as management intensive. 3) Air and odor emissions may become nuisances and hazardous to the health. 4) An improperly designed and operated facility can lead to the development of adverse environmental impacts. 5) Site selection and permitting may become time consuming. 6) As is true with most treatment systems, landfarming is suitable only for selected wastes.

Composting: The principles and technology characteristic of composting in general are applicable to the composting of hazardous wastes. The only differences are the modifications needed to adapt the process to certain characteristics of the waste to be composted. Thus, hazardous wastes and sludges characterized by a high moisture content or an amorphous consistency would of necessity be mixed with a bulking agent. Similarly, a bulking agent would be added to dilute a bactericidal waste to a level tolerated by needed microbes. If the C/N is too high, nitrogen is added. The same applies to all other nutrients.

REFERENCES

1. Nicolas, R.B. and D.E. Giamporcaro, "Nature's Prescription," *Hazmat World, 2* (6): 30-36 (June 1989).
2. Thomas, J.M. and C.H. Ward, "In Situ Biorestoration of Organic Contaminants in the Subsurface." *Environ. & Sci. Technol., 23* (7): 76-766 (July 1989).
3a. McClellen, K.L., N. Burns, R.C. Bales. "Biodegradation of Trichloroethlene by Bacteria Indigenous to a Contaminated Site," *Journ. Environ. Sci. Health, A24* (6): 561-570 (1989).
3. Murthy, D.S.V., R.L. Levine, L.E. Hallas, "Principles of Organism Selection for the Degradation of Glyphosate in a Sequencing Batch Reactor", in *Proceedings of the 43rd Industrial Waste Conference,* May 10-12, 1988 (Lewis Publishers) pp. 267-274.
4. *New Developments in Biotechnology: U.S. Investment in Biotechnology,* OTA Report, pp. 226-227. (from ref. 1).
5. McDermott, J.B. and six co-authors, "Two Strategies for PCB Soil Remediation: Biodegradation and Surfactant Extraction," *Environmental Progress, 8* (1): 46-51 (Feb. 1989).
6. Zaldi, B.R., Y. Mubakami, M. Alexander, "Predation and Inhibitors in Lake Water Affect Success of Inoculation to Enhance Biodegradation of Organic Chemicals," *Environ. Sci. Technology, 23* (7): 859-863 (1989).
7. Haider, K.G. Jagnow, R. Kohnen, S.V. Lim, "Degradation of Chlorinated Benzenes, Phenols, and Cyclohexane Derivatives by Benzene and Phenol-Utilizing Soil Bacteria under Aerobic Conditions," in *Decomposition of Toxic and Nontoxic Organic Compounds in Soils,* ed. M.R. Overcash, Ann Arbor Science Publishers, Inc., Ann Arbor, MI 48406 (1981), pp. 207-223.
8. Ghosal, D., L.S. You, D.K. Chatterjee, A.M. Chatterjee, "Microbial Degradation of Halogenated Compounds," *Science, 228* (4,4698): 135-142 (1985).
9. Rose, W.W. and W.A. Mercer, *Fate of Insecticides in Composted Agricultural Wastes,* Progress Report, Part I; National Canners Assoc. (presently, National Food Processors Assoc.), 1968.
10. Epstein, E. and J.E. Alpert, "Composting of Industrial Wastes," in *Toxic and Hazardous Waste Disposal,* ed. R.B. Pojasek, Ann Arbor Science, The Butterworth Groups, Ann Arbor, MI. 1980, pp. 243-252.
11. Phung, Tun, "Land treatment of Hazardous Wastes" in *Standard Handbook of Hazardous Waste Treatment and Disposal,* ed. H.M. Freeman, McGraw-Hill Book Co., N.Y. (1988) pp. 9.41-9.51.
12. Mount, M.E. and F.W. Oehme, "Carbaryl: A Literature Review," *Residue Reviews, 80:* 1-64 (Springer-Verlad, New York, 1981).

34

STRATEGIES FOR PROBLEM PREVENTION

FOR LEAF composting, prevention of odor problems means avoiding prolonged anaerobic conditions. As explained in the Rutgers University manual, under anaerobic conditions, volatile organic acids (which have vinegar, cheesy, goaty, and sour odors), alcohols (fruity, floral, alcohol-like), and amines and sulfur compounds (barnyard, rotten) can be produced. In contrast, with aerobic conditions only a mild earthy odor is expected. If excessive ammonia or urea-based fertilizer is added, an ammonia odor may also be produced.

ODOR

The major cause of odor production at leaf composting sites is making the windrow too large, especially when first assembled. At an initial high concentration of readily degradable material, there is a high demand for oxygen. If the piles are too large, sufficient oxygen cannot penetrate from the outside, and a large anaerobic core develops. Decomposition slows down, switching over to the odor-producing acid fermentation described above.

A second important source of odor production is failure to form windrows quickly enough once the leaves are collected. Unless they are very dry, leaves cannot be simply dropped at the site for later composting or collected and stored elsewhere. Although the intention might be to store them, vigorous decomposition will nonetheless begin within one to two days, anaerobic conditions will develop, and odors will be produced.

If odors should be produced at a site, or if odorous materials are dropped off at the site, the second line of defense is to prevent their release. Theoretically, this can best be accomplished by leaving the odorous mass undisturbed until oxygen has penetrated sufficiently to destroy the odors, though this may take several months or even years. Shaving off thin (perhaps 1-2 foot) layers from the edges as they become aerobic may help speed this process.

If a long wait is not practical, another approach may be possible. Since many of the odorous compounds are acidic in nature, raising the pH (neutralizing the acids) will convert them to an ionized (negatively charged, dissociated) form. In this form they cannot be released to the air and will remain in the pile.

Application of pulverized limestone is probably the best way to raise the pH. Sprinkling the limestone in powdered form directly onto surfaces from which odors are escaping may be the simplest approach, although a liquid slurry of limestone in water could also be used.

If odors are still produced and released despite these precautions, it may still be possible to minimize their offsite impact. This approach relies on timing odor-releasing operations to coincide with favorable wind conditions. A wind sock should be installed at the site to determine wind direction, and odor releasing operations performed only when the site is downwind of residences and other sensitive neighboring land uses. Also, higher winds are preferable to calm and light conditions because the higher the wind speed and turbulence, the greater the dilution of any released odors.

LEACHATE

One way in which leachate may pose a problem is by forming small pools or "ponds." Ponding is a concern because it can create an odor problem (since anaerobic conditions are likely to develop), serve as a place for mosquito breeding, and interfere with operations on the site (soft, muddy areas). Prevention, by properly grading the site, is the best remedy. Also, windrows should run down slopes rather than across, making it easier for the water to run off rather than accumulate between windrows. If ponding occurs and odors are released from the pools, adding pulverized limestone may be helpful.

Pollution of surface waters (lakes, streams) is the other major concern with leachate. While leachate from leaf composting is generally not toxic, it may deplete the dissolved oxygen in the water, possibly even to the point where fish kills could occur. Because of its dark color, it might also lead to a discoloration of the water.

In order to prevent this potential pollution, leachate should not be allowed to enter surface waters without prior treatment. This treatment might consist of simple percolation down into or through the soil, or passage through a sand barrier constructed to intercept the horizontal flow. In passing through the soil or sand, the leachate is both physically filtered and biologically degraded to remove a substantial portion of the pollutants. Contamination of ground water does not appear to be a problem associated with leaf composting.

TROUBLESHOOTING GUIDE FROM MICHIGAN

The Michigan Guidebook on Yard Waste Composting includes a section on troubleshooting that covers odor prevention, ponding and "leafate" control similar to New Jersey's explanation. Following are its suggestions for troubleshooting that cover slow composting rates, dust and vector control, and excessive noise:

SLOW COMPOSTING RATE

"Slow is a relative term. It usually means not quick enough to get the material off site. Slow composting implies that the material has failed to decompose and still looks a lot as it did when it arrived. If the compost site is thought of as a "bacteria farm," the "farmer" might ask whether the "livestock" are getting sufficient food, air, warmth, and water. Food shortage implies a carbon to nitrogen ratio that is too high, thus requiring more nitrogen. Air deficiency means inadequate oxygen from too much water, insufficient free air space, or infrequent turning. Inadequate warmth can be caused by piles that are too small. Warmth can be lost by piles that fail to hold heat from too much of free air space, or a turning frequency that allows heat to dissipate too quickly.

Water deficiency implies too little moisture or moisture unevenly distributed through the pile.

Turning or shredding is often used as a cure-all for a slow composting rate. Other than inadequate moisture problems, turning or shredding solves most food, warmth, and air problems by homogenizing the material. Shredded and blended compost exposes more undigested matter to bacteria and increases the total exposed surface area. It mixes moisture with the food and exposes nitrogen to carbon sources.

DUST

Dust is the least anticipated problem, yet is one of the most frequently experienced nuisances at compost sites. During the dry summer months, dust is created in the access areas, roadways, aisles, and from the compost itself. While the dust is not an environmental hazard in its content, it is a hazard like all other dusts and should not be inhaled on a regular basis. "Black lung" or "farmer's lung" type problems can be caused by compost and soil dusts.

Dust is as hard on equipment as it is on the operators. It clogs radiators, causing equipment to overheat. It fouls filters, contaminating oil and fuel. Dust can also accumulate inside engine compartments and ignite when exposed to high exhaust temperatures. In addition, bearings must be lubricated in dusty conditions more often. An infrequent occurence, dry, dusty piles can be susceptible to fire and spontaneous combustion. Firebreaks separating ground cover from compost areas can help control fires if they occur.

Wearing respirators or dust masks is one way to manage dust for the safety of the operators. Enclosed air conditioned or heated cabs in tractors or front-end loaders is another dust control measure. Water trucks may be necessary to control dust on the access roads. Dust is generated more by turning windrows with compost turners than with loaders. Dust is especially a problem when screening or shredding, particularly on windy days. The screening plant might need to be enclosed.

NOISE

Composting equipment that creates excessive noise should be avoided. Screening plants, shredders, and other equipment can be purchased and maintained that do not mandate ear protection. Ear plugs are a good safety practice around all heavy machinery, but noisy equipment should be either repaired or replaced. Neighbors often complain about the incessant "back up warning beeps" of loaders and other equipment. This problem could be an additional reason to locate the site away from residences.

VECTORS

Vectors include rodents, flies, gnats, and other living nuisances. These problems come with neglected or mismanaged sites. Rodents can invade piles that are turned infrequently. While rates and mice will not usually eat compost, they like the warmth and insulation of piles, especially in winter. Rodents vacate when piles are turned and will not burrow into cured piles. While many homeowners believe they should enclose compost piles to keep out dogs, dogs are not usually a nuisance at compost sites. Flies breed in odorous and semi-anaerobic conditions. They can be found in animal manures, fresh grass clippings, or organic matter in standing water. Flies are managed by regular turning and by preventing pond water. Gnats appear in standing water but will disappear at a well managed site.

UNDERSTANDING THE BASICS

Understanding the process as well as the limits of composting will help project managers avoid many problems. *The Connecticut Leaf Composting Guide* includes this brief overview of the basics of composting:

● **Microorganisms:** Decomposition is conducted primarily by microscopic organisms naturally present in leaf waste, including bacteria, actinomycetes, and fungi. These microorganisms grow rapidly on the organic material, using it as a source of food. Heat, carbon dioxide, water vapor, and compost are produced in the process.

● **Nutrients:** The availability of carbon and nitrogen is a limiting factor in the composting process. The microorganisms need nitrogen for protein, body building and population growth, and carbon is their energy source. In addition, efficient composting requires carbon and nitrogen to be present in the proper balance.

The optimum range of the carbon to nitrogen (C:N) ratio is from 20:1 to 30:1. The more the C:N ratio deviates from this range, the slower the decomposition process becomes. With a ratio of greater than 40 to 1, nitrogen represents a limiting factor and the reaction rate slows. With a C:N ratio lower than 15 to 1, excess nitrogen is driven off as ammonia. While this loss of nitrogen is not detrimental to the process of decomposition, it lowers the nutrient value of the compost product.

The C:N ratio in leaves tends to range between 60:1 to 80:1, thus, leaf composting is generally slower than most composting applications. By adding nitrogen-rich materials, such as seaweed or grass clippings, the C:N ratio will be reduced and improved.

● **Oxygen:** An adequate supply of air is essential to efficient composting. Aerobes, the organisms primarily responsible for the rapid decomposition of organic material, require oxygen to convert organic waste to compost. Normal air is about 21 percent oxygen. If the oxygen content falls below the optimum level of 5 percent, these organisms begin to die off and the composting process is taken over by anaerobes, organisms which do not require oxygen. They operate much less efficiently and can cause severe odor problems.

● **Temperature:** Temperature is a key environmental factor affecting biological activity and should be monitored frequently. The metabolism of the microorganisms present in the leaves results in a natural temperature increase. Due to the insulating effect of the leaf compost pile, the temperature achieved in the pile affects the makeup of the microbial population. The optimum temperature range is between 100 and 140 degrees F.

Two categories of microorganisms are active in aerobic composting. At temperatures above freezing, mesophilic organisms become active. As a result of their activity, the temperature within the compost pile increases. At temperatures in excess of 110 degrees F, thermophilic organisms become active, increasing the rate of decomposition. As the temperature approaches 140 degrees F, the rate of decomposition begins to decline rapidly as organisms begin to die off or become dormant.

● **Moisture:** In leaf composting, the optimal moisture content is 40 percent to 60 percent, by weight, or about the consistency of a wrung-out sponge. Moisture is required to dissolve the nutrients utilized by microorganisms as well as to provide a suitable environment for bacterial population growth. A moisture content below 40 percent limits the availability of nutrients and limits bacterial population expansion. When the moisture content exceeds 60 percent, the flow of oxygen is inhibited and anaerobic conditions begin to develop. Leaves usually require additional water at the start of the process.

● **pH:** During the composting process, the material will become slightly acidic and then return to near neutral conditions as stability is approached. Decomposition is most efficient with a pH of between 6.0 and 8.0. If the pH is too high, nitrogen is driven off as ammonia.

As the pH drops below 6.0, the microorganisms begin to die off and the decomposition slows. The pH level of the compost pile partially determines the type of organisms available to the decomposition process.

Bacteria are most successful as decomposers when the pH is between 6.0 and 7.5. Fungi have an optimum range between 5.5 and 8.0. Normally, operating leaf compost systems should not present a pH (acidic) problem. Should such an occurrence develop, the addition of lime may be necessary. To minimize this possibility, keep the pile in an aerobic state. The normal pH range for finished leaf compost is neutral to slightly alkaline (7-7-5).

● **Particle Size:** The microorganisms act on the surface of the composting materials. Smaller particles (the size of a quarter or smaller) have greater surface area and break down more quickly. How-ever, extremely small particles limit air flow so some compromise is required.

● **Time:** The time required to transform leaves into finished compost varies considerably, depending on the process utilized, from 10 days to 3 years. Frequent aeration, fine particle size and the proper ratio of carbon to nitrogen speed the process. The process is slowed by low temperatures and materials with a high proportion of cellulose and lignin.

TABLE 1
Troubleshooting Guide

Symptom	Problem	Recommendation
Odor. Piles are wet and smell sour.	Piles too large; not enough air	Form piles no wider than 14 feet, no higher than 6 feet.
	Windrows not formed immediately.	Allow no more than 1-2 days between collection and windrow formation.
	Piles too wet	Spread to dry. Add dry matter. Improve drainage.
Standing water	Inadequate slope	Establish 1-2 percent slope with proper grading.
	Improper windrow alignment	Run windrow down slope, not across.
	Ruts and mudholes	Avoid equipment operation when site is too wet.
Pollution of surface waters	Leachate discharge	Treat leachate before it leaves site by constructing settling or catch basin.
Center is dry and contains tough materials.	Not enough water	Chip woody materials. Moisten and turn.
Inadequate composting rate	Material too dry	Add water initially, or as corrective measure when turning.
	Pile too large, leading to anaerobic conditions.	Makes piles smaller. Add limestone if necessary to raise pH and control odors.
	Piles too small, leading to heat loss.	Make piles 6 feet high. Colder regions may require greater height. Balance against need for control of anaerobic conditions.
	Uneven distribution of air, moisture, or nutrients.	Turn or shred pile, wetting if necessary.
Piles are damp and sweet smelling but will not heat up.	Lack of nitrogen	Mix in a nitrogen source such as grass clippings or urea.

Adapted from Peter F. Strom and Melvin S. Finstein, Leaf Composting Manual for New Jersey Municipalities.

35

PUBLIC HEALTH ISSUES AND COMPOSTING

Eliot Epstein and Jonathan I. Epstein

WHEN DISCUSSING public health issues related to the design and operations of composting facilities, we place particular emphasis on methods that reduce the impact of potential health problems. The following are representative incidences which have occurred in the past two years regarding the above issues.

1. At a public hearing in conjunction with a leaf and yard waste composting site, a question was asked as to the potential threat of Aspergillus fumigatus to the health of residents near the site.

2. Similarly, the issue of Aspergillus fumigatus was brought up at a meeting regarding a solid waste facility and worker health.

3. Endotoxins were a concern at a wastewater treatment plant having a composting operation. Workers were concerned about dust and endotoxins.

4. A soil blender was concerned about the health of employees in relation to use of sludge compost products.

ASPERGILLUS FUMIGATUS

Aspergillus fumigatus is a fungus which is ubiquitous. It is found throughout the world and is common in a variety of materials, such as hay, grain, decaying vegetation, compost, and soil. Aspergillus fumigatus is found in commercial soil potting products (Millner et al., 1977) and wood-chip piles in the forest product industry (Passman

1980). Hirsch and Sosman (1976) studied the occurrence of Aspergillus fumigatus in homes. They found the fungus in 42 percent of bedrooms, 56 percent of bathrooms, and 85 percent of basements. It was the fourth most common mold in households and present in all seasons. Aspergillus fumigatus was more frequent in homes with pets. Similar data were found by Solomon (1974), who investigated the indoor atmosphere of 150 homes. Salvin and Winzenburgen (1977) found the fungus in basements, bedding, and house dust.

Aspergillus fumigatus is common in composting operations. Table 1 shows concentrations of Aspergillus fumigatus found at a compost site. Millner et al. 1977 reported similar data. It is heat tolerant and grows well at thermophilic temperatures (above 45°C) and therefore survives the composting process. Passman (1980) and Millner et al., (1977) showed that viable conidia can be recovered in the immediate vicinity of agitation of aerosolization of fungal-containing material but the counts drop rapidly only a short distance from the source or a short time after cessation of the activity.

Studies by Clark et al. (1984) showed no trend to infection or allergic responses to workers at compost sites in the United States. The authors found no consistent difference between compost workers and workers not involved in compost activities as determined by antibody methods. The lack of increased antibodies to Aspergillus supports the conclusion that, though Aspergillus colonization is more common in compost workers, infection with the organisms is not. One would expect a rise in antibodies to the fungus if there were infections due to the fungus.

Severe Aspergillus infections from any of the species occur almost exclusively in people who are severely debilitated or immuno-compromised (Rippon, 1974) e.g. persons with kidney transplants, leukemia, or lymphoma.

ENDOTOXINS

Endotoxins are noxious substances produced by gram negative bacteria. The term endotoxin refers to the gram negative cell wall lipopolysaccharide. It is produced by many bacteria including many which are non-pathogenic. This suggests that it plays no part in virulence, i.e. in the degree of disease producing properties of a species of bacteria. One of the more important properties of these lipopolysaccharide substances is their heat stability. The metabolic products of gram negative bacteria may remain in the dead bacteria or their fragments after they break up. Endotoxins can be present in airborne dust particles. If inhaled in large quantities they can cause tissue damage. Airborne endotoxins have been directly or indirectly implicated in occupational worker health problems in many different situations. Some examples are: agricultural animal housing and animal processing plants (Jones et al., 1984, Olenchock, et al., 1982), textile mills and cotton dust (Olenchock et al., 1983, Castellan et al., 1984), poultry handling plants (Thelin et al., 1984), cotton carding (Rylander et al., 1985) humidifiers (Rylander and Haglund, 1984) wastewater treatment plants and composting operations (Rylander et al., 1982; Rylander and Lundholm, 1979; Rylander et al., 1977).

Levels in composting plants showed airborne endotoxin ranging from 0.001 to 0.014 mg/m^3. In an office environment, levels as high as 0.39 mg/m^3 were found (Rylander and Hagland, 1984).

Human exposure to large quantities of airborne endotoxin produce symptoms which include fever, diarrhea, fatigue, headaches, nausea, irritation, nasal irritation, chest tightness, cough, and expectoration of phlegm (Olenchock et al., 1982).

Many of the normal bacterial flora of humans are gram negative. The mucous membranes of the nose, throat, and gut contain large numbers of gram negative bacteria, both living and dead and large amounts of endotoxins (Sheagren 1986). There is no evidence that the physical presence of large numbers of gram negative bacteria, living or dead, or extremely large quantities of endotoxins within the gut (intestines of man) cause any symptoms of any kind.

Table 2 shows endotoxin levels in compost from several sources. The endotoxin levels in sludge compost, 3.9 to 6.3 ng/gm were similar to levels found in compost from leaves, cattle, and sheep.

The data today show that many other work environments have higher levels of endotoxins and workers are at a greater risk than at composting facilities.

Dr. John Rippon, Director of The Mycology Services Laboratory, The University of Chicago, Division of the Biological Sciences and The Pritzker School of Medicine (personal communication) states that:

> "It is concluded therefore that the examination and monitoring of compost operations in several sites in several counties has not indicated a significant level of bio-hazard risk associated with viable bacteria or fungi, dust or endotoxin. Studies directed at detecting work-associated health problems have also been unable to find significant abnormalities. It would appear that at the present time, significant bio-hazards from composting operations have not been established. It should be noted that this environment of composting operations does contain potential bio-hazards (fungal conidia, endotoxins, allergins, etc.) and particular individuals hypersensitive to allergens or predisposed to opportunistic infections may be at risk."

TABLE 1:
Levels of Aspergillus fumigatus at a Compost Site and Surrounding Areas

Location	Concentration CFU/M^2
Mix area	110-120
Near tear down pile	8-24
Compost pile	12-15
Front end loader operations	11-79
Perifery of compost site	2
Centrifuge operating room	38-75
Grit building	2
Pump house	10
Background level	2

Data from compost site at Windsor, Ontario, Canada. Clayton Environmental Consultants Ltd. Windsor, Ontario. 1983.

TABLE 2:
Comparison of Endotoxin Levels in Composts from Various Sources

Source	Levels
Sludge compost	3.9-6.3
Cattle manure	2.3
Sheep manure	4.9
Leaf compost	4.5

PATHOGENS

The main pathogen groups found in sludge are:

- **Bacteria**
  salmonella, tuberculli bacteria, yersinia
- **Virus**
  entroviruses (poliovirus), hepatitis, adenoviruses
- **Helminths**
  nematodes (roundworms), cestodes (tapeworms)
- **Protozoa**
  giardia lamblia, entomoeba histolytica

These pathogens are sensitive to heat and are eliminated at temperatures exceeding 55°C (131°F). This is the basis for the Federal Regulations 40 CFR Part 257 "Criteria for the Classification of Solid Waste." Proper composting should result in the elimination of these organisms. Recently, a document by William Yanko of the County Sanitation Districts of Los Angeles County was produced for the U.S. EPA providing results on pathogen analysis of sludge products from various facilities (Goldstein et al., 1988).

An intensive sampling was conducted at one static pile facility in Pennsylvania and a windrow facility in California. Subsequent bi-monthly samples were carried out at 24 sites which included static pile, in-vessel, aerated windrow, heat drying, and other sludge facilities.

The bi-monthly samples at 24 sites generally showed low bacterial contamination in compost products. Some salmonella were found in air-dried sludge, thermal filter press sludge, and one static pile, and one in-vessel facility. The study found that sludge products were free of pathogenic viruses and viable parasite ova. Salmonella was detected in a significant number of samples, and a non-pathogenic variety of Yersinia was also found at very high concentrations. The authors indicated that there were no known cases of salmonellosis traceable to the use of sludge-based soil amendments. Unfortunately, the study did not describe the facility design and operations. A re-examination of data clearly shows that at facilities where temperatures exceeding 55°C were maintained throughout the pile and cross contamination between sludge and compost did not occur, the compost was pathogen free. We located most of these facilities and upon review determined that the design and operations contributed significantly to the potential for pathogen survival in compost products. The main contribution of this study is to point out that pathogen survival can exist in compost products, as well as in sludge which may be land applied.

Data from Windsor, Ontario, where the Provincial Government's public health authorities have conducted monthly analysis of compost from 1980 to 1985, showed no salmonella or other pathogens. Similarly, at Nashville, Tennessee, for the past year no salmonella were detected. In both of these facilities the compost product has also been free of pathogens.

The public today is very much concerned with health issues and, although it is favorably disposed to composting as a method of recycling of wastes, it is concerned about the public health issues discussed. Not only are citizens concerned about the siting of the facilities, but they are also concerned about the design and operation as related to health and environmental issues.

KEY FACTORS IN DESIGN AND OPERATION

The key factors in the design and operation of composting facilities as related to health of workers and the surrounding population are:

- Uniform mixing
- Moisture control
- Temperature control
- Dust control
- Hygiene conditions
  —building ventilation
  —vehicle/equipment ventilation
- Odor control
- Paved surfaces for leachate and runoff control

Uniform mixing is essential for good composting and adequate disinfection since clumps of materials may not be exposed to high temperatures for pathogen destruction. Furthermore these clumps could remain anaerobic and produce odors.

Moisture, temperature, and aeration affect the composting process; their control is essential for disinfection and pathogen destruction. These factors also impact odor generation. Low moisture (less than 25 percent) reduces biological activity and slows the composting process. At low moisture contents more dust is generated which can impair worker health. At high moisture contents (greater than 60 percent) porosity of the mix is reduced, and the potential for anaerobic conditions exists which results in excessive odors and reduces the pile temperature. Temperature control is essential for pathogen destruction and effective composting. For pathogen destruction, temperatures exceeding 55°C need to be maintained for several days. Temperatures in the 45°C to 55°C range enhance biodegradation and reduce the potential of odors. Proper aeration is necessary to maintain aerobic conditions and control temperature and moisture.

Dust is principally generated by vehicular traffic and during screening operations. Good housekeeping such as sweeping and watering roads can control much of the dust generated by vehicles. Proper moisture maintenance during composting and selection and design of screening equipment and housing will result in low dust emissions. In municipal solid waste composting operations which involve shredding, grinding and separation, adequate ventilation in the facility is necessary.

Hygienic conditions in buildings and vehicles are important to worker health. These principally relate to dust control. The principal mitigation measures involve ventilation and air filtration. Air conditioning and/or dust filters in front-end loaders and other vehicles should be installed and properly maintained.

The single most vexing problem to composting operations has been odors. Odors have plagued composting facilities regardless of type, i.e. static pile, windrow or proprietary in-vessel. Odor control can be achieved through proper aeration and other operations, odor scrubbing and good housekeeping. Haug (1980) points out that odor emissions can increase significantly if the thermodynamic and operational constraints are exceeded. In most cases the surface odor emission rate is greatest at the beginning of the compost cycle and decreases with time.

Leachate and runoff contamination of ground and surface waters have not been a problem at composting sites since most activities are on a sealed paved surface or under a roof. Provision needs to be made for collection and disposal of any excess water which is a by-product of the composting operation.

One of the most significant aspects in the maintenance of good environmental and health conditions at a composting site is the provision of sound operator training. Coupled with the training is the need for good operation and maintenance manuals. These manuals need to be clear, concise and specific to the facility. All too often one finds generic manuals loaded with vendor equipment specifications which neither instruct the operator as to the importance of various operations, nor instruct the operator on the mitigating measures that must be taken to correct or avoid problems.

LITERATURE CITED

1. Epstein, E., Willson, G.B., Burge, W.D., Mullen, D.C. and N.K. Enkiri. A forced aeration system for composting wastewater sludge. *J. Water Pollut. Control Fed.*, 48:688-694, 1976.
2. Lundholm, M. and R. Rylander. Occupational symptoms among compost workers. *J. Occu. Med.* 22:256-257, 1980.
3. Epstein, E. and J.E. Alpert. Pathogenic health aspects of composting sewage sludge. A report submitted to the State of Utah Department of Public Health and Central Valley Sewage authority, Salt Lake City. 1980.
4. Burge, W.D., and P.D. Millner. Health aspects of composting: primary and secondary pathogens. In "Sludge - Health Risks of Land Application." C. Bitton, et al. (Eds.) Ann Arbor Sci. Pub. Inc. Ann Arbor, MI. 1980.
5. Clark, C.S. Bjornson, H.S., Schwartz-Fulton, J., Holland, J.W., and P.S. Gartside. Biological health risks associated with the composting of wastewater treatment plant sludge. *J. Water Pollut. Control Fed.* 56:1269-1276, 1984.
6. Millner, P.D., Marsh, P.B., Snowden, R.B., and J.F. Parr. Occurrence of *Aspergillus fumigatus* during composting of sewage sludge. *Appl. and Environmental Microbiol.* 34:765-772, 1977.
7. Passman, F.J. Monitoring of *Aspergillus fumigatus* associated with municipal sewage sludge composting operations in the state of Maine. Final Rept. to Portland Water District. 1980.
8. Hirsch, S.R. and J.A. Sosman. A one-year survey of mold growth inside twelve homes. *Annals of Allergy.* 36:30, 1976.
9. Solomon., W.R. Assessing fungus prevalence in domestic interiors. *J. of Allergy and Clinical Immunology.* 53:71, 1974.
10. Slavin, R.G. and P. Winzenburger. Epidemiological aspects of allergic aspergillosis. *Annals. of Allergy.* 38:215-218, 1977.
11. Rippon, J.W., Medical Mycology. The pathogenic fungi and the pathogenic Actinomycetes. 2nd ed. W.B. Saunders, Chpts. 23 and 28. 1982.
12. Jones, W., Morring, K., Olenchock, S.A., Williams, T., and J. Hickey. Environmental study of poultry confinement buildings. *Amer. Ind. Hyg. Assoc. J.* 45:760-766, 1984.
13. Olenchock, S.A., Lenhart, S.W., and J.C. Mull. Occupational exposure to airborne endotoxins during poultry processing. *J. Toxicol. Environ. Health* 9:339-349, 1982.
14. Olenchock, S.A., Castellan, P.M., Cocke, J.B., Bodak, D.J., Hankinson, J.L., and J.C. Mull. Endotoxins and acute pulmonary function changes during cotton dust exposures. Proceedings Cotton Dust Research Conference. 1983.
15. Castellan, R.M., Olenchock, S.A., Hankinson, J.L., Millner, P.D., Cocke, J.B., Bragg, C.K., Perkins, H.H., and R.R. Jacobs. Acute bronchoconstriction induced by cotton dust: Dose-related responses to endotoxin and other dust factors. *Ann. Int. Med.* 101:157-163, 1984.
16. Thelin, A., O. Tegler and R. Rylander. Lung reactions during poultry handling related to dust and bacterial endotoxins. *Eur. J. Resp. Dis.* 65:266-271, 1984.
17. Rylander, R., P. Hagland and M. Lundholm.

Endotoxin in cotton dust and respiratory function decrement among cotton workers in an experimental card room. Am. Rev. Resp. Dis. 131:209-213, 1985.

18. Rylander, R. and P. Haglund. Airborne endotoxins and humidifier diseases. *Clinical Allergy* 14:109-112, 1984.

19. Rylander, R., and M. Lundholm. Responses to wastewater exposure with reference to endotoxins. In: Pahren, H, and Jakubowski, W. eds. Wastewater aerosols and disease. Proc. of a Symp. held Sept. 19-21, 1979. Cinn, OH. EPA Doc. EPA-600/9/80 - 028 pp. 90-98, 1980.

20. Rylander, R., Anderson, K., Berlin, L., Bergland, G., Bergstrom, R., Hanson, L., Lundholm, M., and I. Mattsby. Studies on humans exposed to airborne sewage sludge. Schweiz. Med. Wschr. 107:182-184, 1977.

21. Sheagren, J.N. Role of inhaled endotoxin symptoms suffered by workers in the West Windsor pollution control plant. Paper submitted to the City of Windsor. 1986.

22. Goldstein, N., W.A. Yanko, J.M. Walker, and W. Jakubowski. Determining pathogen levels in sludge products. *BioCycle* 29:44-67, 1988.

23. Haug, R.T. Compost engineering principles and practice. Ann Arbor Science. Ann Arbor, MI. 1980.

Eliot Epstein is Chief Environmental Scientist with E&A Environmental Consultants in Stoughton, MA. Jonathan Epstein, M.D., is Assistant Professor of Pathology at the Johns Hopkins Medical Center in Baltimore.

Section
VII

PRIVATE
MANAGEMENT

36

ENTREPRENEURS FILL AN IMPORTANT NICHE

THE VAST majority of yard waste composting projects are currently managed by municipal staff. However, increasingly the private sector is seeing an opportunity in providing municipalities with yard waste processing services, while municipalities are beginning to look to the private sector to manage these systems. Even when a municipality intends to operate a yard waste facility, it will often seek help from the private sector to develop the procedures.

From a municipal perspective, utilizing private companies in managing yard waste may offer a number of advantages over taking the project on as a municipal function. While many do not view composting yard waste, particularly leaves, as a complex task, most municipalities have no expertise. As one borough manager put it, "We've never composted before and we're not real interested in learning." In addition to the fact that the composting process is foreign to most public works managers, marketing the final product does not often fit well within the municipal framework either. The identification of markets and negotiation with users is a task that many private firms do continuously, while in the public sector it is a rarity.

Another important reason for a municipality to turn to a private firm to manage yard waste is cost. As the sophistication of the composting process increases, so also does the cost. According to one source, municipal programs typically have operating costs in the $5 to $10 per cubic yard range. Those costs don't include capital and land costs. With some firms charging in the $3 to $10 per cubic yard range to accept yard waste, they are competitively priced. Especially when by using a private site, you don't have to become involved in permitting or operating the facility.

LOCAL COMPANIES TACKLING LOCAL PROBLEMS

Firms that are offering yard waste processing services come from a variety of backgrounds including landscaping, solid waste collection and sewage sludge. Generally, the people in landscaping and sludge fields have experience in marketing similar products such as topsoil and mulches or in composting and marketing compost made from sludge. Solid waste collectors view yard waste processing as a means of reducing their tipping fees or as a way of expanding their services.

To a large degree, the firms entering the business are local companies that concentrate on processing yard waste and marketing the products in a relatively small geographic area. Perhaps the best known example of local firms processing and marketing products made from yard waste are in the Portland, Oregon area where two well-established business, Grimm's Fuel and McFarlene's Bark, process yard waste. Both of the firms began accepting yard waste years ago (McFarlene's first accepted yard waste in 1956 and Grimm's in 1981) and have added various yard waste based products to their respective organic product lines over the years. Also in the northwest, the City of Seattle has contracted with Pacific Topsoil to accept yard waste.

Two other firms that have entered the yard waste processing business are Imperial Mulch in the Syracuse, New York area and Woodhue, Ltd. of Wrightstown, NJ. Ted Stetler, owner of Imperial, got involved in yard waste because he saw an expanding market for a firm that could process the material that was becoming available from municipalities. After viewing other processing facilities around the country, Stetler felt that mulches made from yard waste could compete readily with mulches made from other materials. On the other hand, Woodhue was already involved in composting other types of materials and decided that providing municipalities with a place to compost yard waste would be a logical extension of its processing capabilities.

To firms in the landscaping field, yard waste is a feedstock in the manufacture of products. To solid waste collection companies, yard waste is a material to be kept out of the local disposal system. If they can process that material at less than disposal cost, they've improved their bottom line and become more competitive.

BEYOND LOCAL BOUNDARIES

If a problem has a local solution, it is never long before companies with enough experience begin to provide that expertise to more and more of the country. This trend is evident in the yard waste processing field. In 1985, Beng Ooi began to market the knowledge of composting he learned from his family's composting business in Malaysia. Beng formed Organic Recycling, Inc., which provides management services for municipalities with yard waste composting facilities. Organic Recycling's approach is to oversee the utilization of a municipality's labor force and facilities, providing the expertise to develop a system to improve the facility's efficiency. Currently, Organic Recycling is servicing at least 11 facilities in New Jersey, New York and Connecticut.

Another company that has begun to offer similar services is Middlebush Compost, Inc. Middlebush started its own composting facility in New Jersey in 1987 that, according to Pat Kennedy, is capable of processing 120,000 cubic yards annually. In addition to processing leaves from municipalities in the area of its facility, Middlebush began to offer management services to municipalities outside of the facility's service area in 1988. Beyond these services, Middlebush is also interested in providing operating services at municipal sites.

At least one company is offering a range of service options to municipalities. Compost Management, Inc., of Doylestown, Pennsylvania has been in the business of marketing compost, particularly compost made from sludge, for more than 10 years. Recently, the company, headed by Roger Tuttle, has also turned its resources to yard waste composting—offering four different programs including design and consulting, marketing finished compost, as well as operating municipally-owned yard waste composting sites. Beyond these services, Compost Management is also interested in owning and operating facilities that accept yard waste on a contract basis.

APPROACHES TO PRIVATE MANAGEMENT

There are three basic approaches to private management of yard waste processing facilities: Private Oversight; Private Operation/Public Ownership; and Private Operation/Private Ownership

Private Oversight—This type of service is really a management consulting service, where firms with expertise in composting assist a municipality in operating its facility. At existing facilities, the management firm oversees the use of the municipal staff and equipment in the composting operation, monitors progress and corrects problems if they arise. In some cases, the firm would also assist in marketing the program's finished compost.

In cases, where a municipality does not have a facility, the firm will also help to select sites and prepare permit applications, as well as manage the site preparation work. This type of management service is usually done under a contract that has a duration of at least 12 months, with the municipality being billed at a flat rate or on a per hour basis.

Private Operation/Public Ownership—Under this approach, a company provides for the complete operation of the composting facility with the municipality providing the site and equipment. In cases where the finished compost is to be marketed, the operator is responsible for its sale. The operator is also responsible for ensuring that the facility meets operating standards set by the local and state regulating agencies.

Private Operation/Private Ownership—There are a number of options that fit under the private owner/operator approach to yard waste management. The most structured option is where a municipality contracts directly with a private firm to own and operate a facility that will be used to process that municipality's yard waste exclusively. In this instance, the municipality would be obligated to deliver yard waste to the facility, which the private firm would own and operate for a fee based on the amount of yard waste delivered. Presently, at least one firm, Compost Management, is providing this option to municipalities. Contracts for this type of service are typically for an extended period of time.

The second option is where a company develops a facility and then contracts with a number of municipalities and private sources to provide the yard waste. In these cases, the contracts are typically for 12 months and are based on the amount of waste sent to the facility.

The final option in the private owner/operator approach is where a firm develops a facility and does not contract with generators to provide the yard waste but, relies instead on providing the least cost alternative to bring in sufficient material.

37

FROM HAULERS
TO RESEARCHERS

IN THE FALL of 1987, Able Sanitation of Grandville, Michigan began a leaf composting project on a 3½ acre site. Over the last two years, the pilot project diverted 18,000 cubic yards from the landfill. Explaining his rationale as a hauler for getting into composting, John Pluger of Able said at the time: "At the price of tipping we pay today, we know this operation doesn't make sense, but two years from now, when it will cost $40 per ton to dump at the new waste-to-energy facility, it will be the best investment we could have made."

Bouyed by the success of the pilot program, Able in 1989 embarked on changes that will result in an expanded yard waste collection and composting program. In early 1989, the company developed a 100 acre composting facility on a site north of Grand Rapids, Michigan. According to Brian Vander Ark, Able's Recycling Coordinator, the facility with the aid of a front-end loader and a Wildcat Turner is capable of handling 75,000 cubic yards of yard waste per year.

COMPETITIVE EDGE WITH RECYCLING

In order to supply the compost site with material, Able initiated a yard waste bag program. It no longer accepts any yard waste as part of its regular residential service. They have begun to sell biodegradable yard waste bags, charging one dollar per bag for bag, collection and composting. In the first month, the firm sold 22,000 bags through local retailers. Initially, Able picked up yard waste with the garbage, and removed it at its transfer station. Now, as volume is increasing, a separate truck is used for collection from 18,000 residents.

John Rumsey, ex-owner of Christman Sanitation, Inc. in Fogelsville, Pennsylvania was forced into 90-mile round trips to the landfill to serve his 15,000 individual households. Tipping costs are between $45 and $60 per ton.

"With disposal rates climbing, customers are getting discouraged. But it's hard to cut rates, as all the haulers are fairly competitive," said Rumsey. To gain a competitive edge, Christman Sanitation offered rate discounts to customers for recycling. Rumsey designed a new program to collect grass clippings, leaves, as well as glass, metal and newspaper.

The company charged all of its 15,000 customers a flat rate for garbage collection—about $16 to $17 per month. The fee is the same, whether a homeowner puts out two or ten bags of trash. To encourage recycling, Rumsey has created a fee system whereby customers will buy garbage bags from Christman Sanitation for two dollars per bag. Recyclable materials will be placed on the curb separately. "This system gives customers a way to control costs," explains Rumsey. "The more they recycle, the lower their annual bill will be. We don't have a limit on how many two dollar bags they can put out; it's just that if they put fewer out, they will pay less." Bags are sold quarterly.

"We started the grass clippings collection and had 98 percent participation," he says. "(When the program began), customers had two options—to pay an annual lawn maintenance fee to have clippings and yard waste picked up with our regular collection or to separate them out and put them on the curb on a designated day, where they would be picked up at no charge. From the 2,700 customers who were offered this choice, we were hauling 32 tons per week less to the landfill."

Christman Sanitation worked out an arrangement with a local farmer who used grass clippings on his land. The company paid $15/truckload versus the usual $400 fee at the landfill.

YARD WASTE DEMONSTRATION PROJECT

The Wood Recovery Company in Gainesville, Florida had its beginnings in the days when Fred Shore was primarily a home builder and developer. "There was no way to dispose of the trees from our land clearing operations," recalls Shore, "after Florida passed tough environmental rules on land clearing, so we launched a new company called Wood Resource Recovery." Originally, his intent was to chip the wood and have it used as fuel, but he gradually shifted an increasing amount of wood into a shredding and mulching operation. Then, following passage of Florida's recycling legislation, Shore's facility was selected to be the site of a research program that jointly involved his firm, Gainesville, Alachua County, and two state agencies—the Florida Departments of Environmental Regulation and Agriculture.

The objective of the demonstration project was "to demonstrate composting and evaluate compost products from yard trash in a typical municipal waste stream for providing technical assistance on composting and compost utilization, to aid community adoption, and to assist in formulating product standards to facilitate market development."

Gainesville and Alachua County have rebid their waste collection contracts so that yard trash is collected separately. Wood Resources obtained the contract to receive the yard trash at a convenient permitted site. The cooperators have negotiated with equipment manufacturers to fabricate and install, at cost, a prototype screening unit and in-bin composter to complement the on-site equipment of Wood Resources Recovery Inc. (scales, chipper, knuckle-boom loader; front-end loader, field lab/office and permitted site for composting). At present the site is receiving over 100 tons of yard trash per week from the hauler (BFI). The compost unit will comprise a covered concrete slab, equipped with side walls that support a compost turner that moves along tracks on the walls aerating the composting waste. In addition, windrows turned with a front-end loader and static piles will be composted for comparative purposes. This study proposes to evaluate bin, windrow, and static pile composting with respect to time requirements, space requirements, and characteristics of the final products. The bin process requires the least space, however, it has a higher capital cost. On the other hand, static pile composting is relatively inexpensive but requires more land area because the process takes much longer to complete. There are also differences in the final product. "The compost from a bin system is more likely to be uniform and to completely destroy plant pathogens and seeds," notes the research description, which further states:

"Maturity of the compost will be evaluated by several techniques, including temperature rise, changes in pH, nitrate and ammonium nitrogen content, changes in carbohydrate content, and changes in alkaline extractable humic substances and cation exchange capacity (CEC).

"Each batch of compost formed from the different mixes will possess different physical and chemical characteristics which will determine suitability of the material in utilization options. The following characteristics will be investigated for both finished compost and for potting media containing compost: particle size distribution, bulk density, cation exchange capacity (CEC), soluble salts, volatile solids, pH, and major and minor nutrients. Finished compost will be screened for rejects and to classify for different end uses. Other analyses on finished compost and potting media will be conducted in the Ornamental Horticulture Department, including water holding capacity, total pore space (percent capillary and non-capillary). Quantities of mature compost and potting media mixes will be placed in storage and evaluated for changes in quality over time.

"The composted materials will be made available for evaluation in horticultural and agricultural uses as constituents of potting media and as soil amendments. Growth trials with a variety of plants will give information which will allow further refinement of the composting raw materials mix, nutrient additions, and processing to produce composts with compositions required for specific horticultural needs. Selected tests will be performed to monitor for weed seed viability, root pathogens, nematodes and pesticide residues with cooperators.

"The overall goal is to relate yard trash characteristics and treatments such as size reduction and supplements to processing variables and product properties. In comparison tests conducted by others, end use evaluations will relate utilization success with the properties of the compost produced in the three systems—bin, windrow, and static pile."

FROM LAND CLEARING
TO STUMP MULCHING

When Larry Smith started to search for alternatives to burying and burning stumps accumulated from land clearing operations, he decided to develop a grinding and shredding system capable of making mulch. But cost was the problem with the system he wanted to use. Even though Smith's company was the largest developer in Pennsylvania's Monroe County, his operation did not produce a sufficient volume of stumps to justify the million dollar equipment investment.

Rather than abandon a good idea, Smith opted to accept stumps from other developers and land clearers. A little over a year after start-up in October, 1988, Smith's Silver Valley Recycling Corporation in Brodheadsville, Pennsylvania accepts stumps from as far away as Connecticut. In 1989, Silver Valley processed about 75,000 cubic yards of stumps.

Explains Bob McCabe, Silver Valley business manager: "The equipment you need to process material the size of stumps is so big and so expensive, you must have a substantial volume of material coming in the gate to justify the expense."

Silver Valley sits on 15 acres in the middle of a sand and gravel quarry also owned by Smith. When stumps are delivered to the site, they are put through a shearer that helps to size the material and remove soil and stones. The sheared stumps are put through a Universal Refiner that shreds them into mulch, which is then mechanically separated into various grades. Finally a tub grinder is used to generate a "landscape grade" mulch.

According to McCabe, the operation produces three general mulch grades: a coarse material, "Rip Chip," ideal as a temporary roadway on construction sites; a two-inch commercial grade; and a $1\frac{1}{4}$-inch grade for residential use. "About 10 percent of the mulch is sold as 'Rip Chip,' 30 percent as commercial grade, and 60 percent as residential," notes McCabe. Silver Valley also processes and sells the stone and soil generated from the shearing operation.

When the project was launched, McCabe used a direct mail campaign to make contractors aware of the services offered. "We knew that contractors in New Jersey, New York and Connecticut were having a difficult time getting rid of stumps," says McCabe, "and that other facilities were charging four and five times what we charge (currently $55 per tractor trailer load). Another bonus was that we could offer them backhaul possibilities of not only mulch, but soil, sand and gravel."

38

TOPSOIL MANUFACTURING IN THE NORTHWEST

IN BUSINESS since 1978 selling manufactured topsoil and other materials, Pacific Topsoils began accepting yard and garden waste in fall, 1986. Landscapers, private citizens, builders and commercial haulers drop off yard waste. Pacific Topsoils also has contracts with the Seattle Solid Waste Utility and Sno King, a private hauler that serves Kirkland, to process yard and garden wastes from those cities.

As part of her Masters thesis at Washington State University on "Centralized Yard and Garden Waste Composting," Cheryl Clemens (now with the Washington Department of Ecology) surveyed both public and private facilities and summarized operations, costs and markets of companies in Washington and Oregon.

Incoming materials (90 tons) are initially shredded with a hammer hog shredder to pieces 12 inches and smaller and are then stockpiled for composting. The materials go through up to three passes through the hogs with screening between shredding. Finally, they are shredded to pieces one inch and smaller. Manure and chemical fertilizers are added during composting to enhance nitrogen content. Piles are turned every 45 days to six months (depending on the type of material composted and the seasons of the year) using front end loaders.

After composting, another screening of 5/8 to 1 inch minus takes place with rejects being reprocessed through the system. Composting takes up to 10 months depending on the type of material and the time of year.

Users are charged $5.50 per cubic yard for incoming yard and garden debris. (The nearest landfill charges a $35 per ton tipping fee. Compost is sold as a mulch and also within soil mixes. Compost sells for $9 to $10.50 per cubic yard picked up and for $11.50 to $15.50 delivered.

GroCo, Inc. in Kent, Washington began composting yard waste in 1987 and then contracted with Seattle. Woody wastes are shredded to two inches and smaller using a hammermill shredder. After composting, compost is shredded to pieces 3/4 inch and smaller. About ten percent of the composted material is screened out and recomposted. Shredded YGW has been used successfully as a bulking agent for sewage sludge in some soil mixes. GroCo currently has a contract with METRO of Seattle to accept 12,000 wet tons of sewage sludge per year. GroCo estimates that it costs about $30 per ton to compost YGW. The nearest landfill, King County's Cedar Hills Landfill, charges a tipping fee of $47 per ton.

The principal market for compost is commercial landscaping although compost is sold to a variety of users including private citizens and nurseries. The compost is sold in bulk for $6 to $10 per cubic yard after testing for nutrient and heavy metal content. Also being studied are the reduction ratio from bulk YGW to shredded material, the possibility of using YGW as a bulking agent in sludge composting, and the marketability of YGW compost products.

Grimm's Fuel Company of Tualitin, Oregon has been composting yard waste since 1982, receiving material from three sources: Dropoff by homeowners and landscapers (75 percent); Local hauler (10 percent); and Hauling by Grimm employees (15 percent). Composting operation is on 11 acre site, with incoming material shredded. Grimm estimates $20 to $25 per ton to compost yard waste. Tipping fee is $2.50 per cubic yard.

Yard waste compost is used in seven different

products that Grimm's sells. These products are sold in bulk to the general public and to commercial landscapers and nurseries for $6.50 to $10 per cubic yard depending on volume. The products are used as ground covers or soil amendments.

Another company composting and marketing yard waste in the Portland area is McFarlane's Bark, Inc. Fine compost sells for eight dollars per cubic yard, and medium compost for four dollars.

Grimm's Fuel is a good example of how entrepreneurial effort can be shaped to fulfill a need and fill a niche. As noted in a "Recycler's Profile" of the company, wood and sawdust were the heating materials when Fred Grimm began the family business in 1929. Looking for alternative uses for wood, recalls, Rod Grimm, Fred's son and current president, led to the world of horticulture. "We were one of the first companies to use fresh sawdust for landscaping in the 1940s and 1950s. People thought we were crazy, but the idea caught on." Yard debris was a natural followup. "We intend to stay in the yard debris recovery business," says Grimm, who is constantly expanding his capability to process woody debris. "We provide a needed service."

39

ON-FARM COMPOSTING OF LAKE WEEDS

THOUGH NOT YARD WASTE, lake weeds that are so commonly clogging northeastern waterways offer another example of the potential for on-farm composting. As part of control measures, harvesters are used, and huge quantities of aquatic weeds such as Eurasian milfoil must be disposed of as a solid waste. In 1987, a farmer in Pittsfield, Massachusetts demonstrated that harvested lake weeds can be rapidly composted and incorporated into corn fields as a fertilizer.

Approximately 900 tons of weeds were harvested from Pontoosuc Lake by the Berkshire County Commissioners over an eight-week season. Finding a disposal site for the harvested weeds was critical. The problems with using an existing facility were capacity and cost. Moisture content would have generated little combustion in the incinerator, with the weeds coming out like a steaming batch of leaves. The closest landfill was about 40 miles and $70 per ton away. For a harvesting project with a seasonal budget of $30,000, disposal of over 900 tons of weeds would cost $63,000 in tipping fees, plus transportation.

A better option was to compost the weeds. A closed town landfill was evaluated as a potential site, but rejected due to regulatory requirements. Complicating the search for a disposal site was the uncertain status of the harvested weeds as solid waste under Massachusetts law. According to one statute, the definition of a solid waste facility includes the words, "a refuse composting plant." If harvested weeds were to be composted, one interpretation of the law could trigger public hearings and siting process for a solid waste facility, a time-consuming and potentially controversial process which might have resulted in denial of any site except an already approved facility.

A decision was made by Pittsfield farmer Silvio Rotti and the County Commissioners to consider the weed composting project as a storage operation of an agricultural product which would be incorporated into the soil. Although this created some bureaucratic controversy within the Massachusetts Dept. of Environmental Quality Engineering (DEQE) whether a solid waste facility was being operated without necessary approvals, the state regulators did not halt the project. In fact, a policy is now being prepared by the DEQE which would allow the operation of yard waste, and lake weed, composting operations without going through the formal siting process for a solid waste facility. That policy would include a review of the proposed composting site by DEQE for some basic criteria.

SITE OPERATION

The Rotti farm composting site is an open air bunker silo, which is basically a concrete slab with walls on two sides. The bunker allowed water to drain from the weeds into the surrounding farm property, where it was absorbed by the soil. The farm bucket loader was used to push the weeds into piles approximately six to eight feet in height.

The goal of the compost project was to sufficiently degrade the weeds so that they could be applied to the soil with a manure spreader without snarling the spreader. Within three months of static pile composting, the weeds had disintegrated sufficiently, and approximately one-half of the 900 tons was applied to the field that fall. Biological decomposition slowed way down in the portion of the weeds which were stored through the winter and then plowed into the soil in the spring.

It is significant to note that there was minimal odor produced by the weed composting operation. Temperatures within the pile reached 130°F. Apparently, the rapid desiccation of the weeds and associated settling of the piles provided suitable conditions for biological decomposition of virtually all of the weeds without anaerobic symptoms.

Since this is the first year that the Rotti farm has used the weeds, fertilizer will still be applied at the normal rate on the 3.5 acres of corn field which received compost. However, an adjacent field which did not receive weeds will also be planted with sweet corn, and the yields of the two fields will be compared by Rotti.

Fertilizer value of the 900 tons of weeds was estimated at 139 pounds of nitrogen per acre, 44 pounds of phosphorus, and 27 pounds of potassium. Typical annual commercial fertilizer on the Rossi sweet corn acreage is 120 pounds of N, 120 pounds of P, and 40 pounds of K. (Nutrient analyses were based on a sample of weeds at compost site for one week). Based on these estimates, compost will provide a significant percentage of N,P,K requirements of sweet corn.

Section
VIII

MARKETING AND UTILIZATION

40

PRODUCT QUALITY FROM COMMERCIAL OPERATIONS

A STUDY, *A Users Guide to Yard Debris Compost,* conducted by Portland (Oregon) Metro analyzed the quality and horticultural applications of the end product. The analysis was done on compost from two private businesses — Grimm's Fuel Company of Tualatin, Oregon and McFarlane's Bark, Inc. of Clackamas, Oregon. Both Grimm's "Garden Fine Mulch" and McFarlane's "Fine Compost Stuff" have been approved for use as a soil conditioner in landscape projects by the Oregon Department of Transportation. Grimm's blends and sells a product composed of 100 percent yard debris compost.

McFarlane's sells pure yard debris compost in fine, medium and coarse grinds.

As related in the Metro report, Grimm's and McFarlane's use different methods to process the yard debris delivered by landscapers, haulers and local residents. Material received at Grimm's is ground by a hammerhog within two weeks and allowed to decompose up to about five months. It is then reground, sized, composted for about two months and sold. Grimm's has developed a new aeration process to speed up composting. McFarlane's grinds both mature yard debris and newly received material into 12-inch minus pieces.

TABLE 1:
Nutrient availability of yard debris compost and competitive products (major plant nutrients)

Material	Percent dry weight		Phosporus P	Potassium K	Calcium Ca	Magnesium Mg
	Nitrogen NO 3	NH 4				
Yard debris[1] compost	0.002–0.008	0.003–0.052	0.085–0.171	2.0–3.8	2.5–4.7	0.6–0.9
Bark[2] (Douglas fir)	0.004	—	0.011	0.11	0.52	0.01
Saw dust[2] (Douglas fir)	—	—	0.006	0.09	0.12	0.01
Peat[3]	—	0.01	0.11	0.04	0.006(4)	0.18(4)
Vermiculite[3]	0.02	0.00	0.06	0.23	—	—

[1]Source: Agricare, Inc.
[2]Source: Bollen, W.B. p. 4
[3]Source: Naylor, L.M. et al. p. 48

136

Material is then allowed to compost for at least three months before it is re-ground, sized and marketed.

In 1987, approximately 25 percent of the yard debris generated in the region was diverted from landfills. A recent ruling by the Oregon Environmental Quality Commission has classified yard debris as a "principle recyclable material" and is aimed at increasing this amount to 80 percent by 1992. In an introduction to its report, Portland Metro notes that "Oregonians have a unique opportunity to help solve one of the region's solid waste problems by recycling a large component of the waste stream. By purchasing locally produced yard debris compost, individuals, nurseries and landscapers help support local business and regional recycling efforts."

METRO TESTING PROGRAMS

Portland Metro has been conducting quarterly tests to determine yard debris compost nutrient content which include examination of major and minor elements for plant growth. Following are some of the tables from *A Users Guide to Yard Debris Compost* which summarize these results:

OREGON STATE EVALUATION

R. L. Ticknor at Oregon State University's North Willamette Experiment Station analyzed yard debris compost from McFarlane's and Grimm's for porosity, water retention, pH and soluble salts to test the materials for use as a part of growing media. Air space and water retention, he found, were in the normal ranges for soil mixes, while pH and specific conductance were slightly higher than desirable for acid soil plants.

Concluded Ticknor based on his studies with five mixes with varying percentages of compost, bark, pumice and peat:

"The mix in which most plants, both herbaceous and woody, were the largest was 50 percent yard debris compost, 25 percent peat moss and 25 percent pumice. In most cases the difference when bark was substituted for the peat was not statistically significant. All plants, herbaceous and woody, were able to grow in pure yard debris compost for both sources. Media shrinkage was greatest in straight compost and least in ⅓ each of compost, bark and pumice. No weed seedlings developed in the piles of compost until late in the season when seeds were ripe and blowing.

"Yard debris compost is a good material to use as part of a potting mix. It supplies more nutrients than bark dust while still giving good aeration to the media. Some additional fertilizer will be required for optimum growth."

TABLE 2:
Water holding capacity

Material	
Quartz sand	28
Clay loam soil	44
Half quartz sand/half peat moss	89
Half clay soil/half peat moss	114
Yard debris compost[2]	110
Reed peat	289
Moss peat	1,057

Pesticide residues

Metro has tested yard debris compost for the presence of the following pesticides:

2,4D	DDT	Diazanon
2,4DT	Chlordane	Dursban
2,45-T	Aldrin	Parathion
2,4,D-B	Toxaphene	Dicamba
MCPA	Lindane	Silvex
MCPP	Malathion	
Dichloprop	1,4,D-P	

Although Metro has tested yard debris compost during a two-year period, the number of samples tested is quite small. Of the 190 compounds tested, only four were found to be present at extremely low levels. The presence of these compounds is not toxic to seed germination or plant growth as evidenced by seed germination tests and demonstration plots utilizing locally produced yard debris compost products. Metro will continue to test for pesticide residues.

TABLE 4:
Heavy metal concentration in yard debris compost (parts per million)

Metal	Yard debris compost	Minnesota regulations
Mercury	0.06	5.00
Arsenic	5.00	no limit
Cadmium	0.80	10.00
Chromium	23.00	1,000.00
Nickel	22.00	100.00
Lead	72.00	500.00
Zinc	160.00	1,000.00

Single samples of Grimm's and McFarlane's yard debris compost were tested for the presence of mercury, arsenic, cadmium, chromium, nickel, lead and zinc. No federal or Oregon state limits have been established for heavy metal content of yard debris compost; however, the state of Minnesota has established regulations for compost products. The following table presents Metro's single test data and the Minnesota established limits.

41

MARKETING COMPOST FROM MUNICIPALLY OWNED FACILITIES

IN 1988 an amendment to the Illinois Solid Waste Management Act called for the Illinois Department of Energy and Natural Resources (ENR) to "prepare a report on strategies for distributing and marketing landscape waste compost from centralized composting sites operated by units of local government." The report, *Landscape Waste Compost*, issued in 1989, among other areas evaluates the effects of product quality, assured supply, cost and public education on the availability of compost, free delivery, and public sales.

The emphasis on markets was accompanied by three other bills on yard waste that "placed the communities of Illinois on a path of short duration toward the complete removal of yard waste from landfills. (These bills banned yard waste from landfills effective September 1, 1989; made it simpler to permit composting facilities; and required residents to separate yard waste from trash going to landfills). The Illinois EPA estimates that 5 million cubic yards of yard waste will potentially be diverted to composting facilities annually as a result of the new legislation. Based on experiences in other states, actual recovery rates will be around 70 percent, or a total of 3.5 million cubic yards. That material when composted will produce one million cubic yards of compost in Illinois each year to be utilized.

To obtain data on potential demand, the Illinois ENR conducted a statewide phone survey of professionals with high knowledge of the use and quality of compost and other soil amendments. Several highly-respected landscape and nursery professionals believed that the greatest demand for yard waste compost would be in urban and growing suburban areas, especially near Chicago and St. Louis, as a medium to high quality soil amendment. Lower quality compost (ie. with uncomposted material, varying sized particles, etc.) would have application as landfill cover or in reclaiming strip mined lands, etc.

"During the survey," reported the Department of Energy and Natural Resources, "the greatest enthusiasm for using yard waste compost was voiced by landscape contractors and nurserymen in the greater Chicago metropolitan area. That enthusiasm, though not quantifiable, should be viewed as a significant positive factor that could facilitate the demand for the product. Other users would likely follow suit when the benefits of yard waste compost are widely known."

Much stress in market development is placed on two areas: 1. Educating the public (the ultimate consumer) and 2. Legislative initiatives to insure demand from public agencies. There should be a strong effort to educate the public to understand the need and value of adding organic materials to soils. Regarding legislative initiatives, a new bill effectively assures a significant demand for compost in many state construction and reclamation projects by mandating: "All state agencies responsible for the maintenance of public lands in the state shall, to the maximum extent feasible, give due consideration and preference to use of compost materials in all land maintenance activities which are to be paid with public funds."

The Illinois ENR points out that municipalities and regions can also take steps to promote the use of compost products. For example, local ordinances should be enacted requiring public bodies to use compost in land maintenance activities."

OBSTACLES TO MARKETS

Along with any "new" product, yard waste compost faces obstacles to reach its potential markets successfully. The Illinois report cites several:

● **Costs** — Achieving proper quality (i.e., porosity, texture, nutrient balance) requires capital investment ranging from minimal expense for low-tech operations to expensive bagging and other equipment costs for other operations.

● **Competitive Products** — Compost will have to compete in the soil amendment market with several high quality materials. "However, existing high quality products are not always considered obstacles to the marketing of new products," says ENR optimistically. "Good examples include the propensity of national fast food restaurants to congregate on opposite corners of the same intersection. . . . A municipality would have only to fill a niche and compete profitably in the existing market to succeed."

● **Contaminants** — Concern over contamination by such pollutants as lawn chemicals, tree spray pesticides, car exhaust residues, plastics, etc. needs to be addressed. Points out the ENR: "Utilization of proper monitoring procedures can eliminate or substantially reduce the potential for contamination. Further, a composting period of 12 to 18 months is believed to be sufficient for the degradation of most commonly used pesticides. Dilution of toxics also occurs from many sources are processed into a finished product."

● **Consumer Reluctance to Change** — Overcoming conservative inertia is another challenge common to new product entries. The suggested strategy: Reluctance to change can be overcome by a variety of marketing strategies. Among the keys to acceptance is the provision of accurate information about the product to consumers. A municipality would do well to employ targeted public education in concern with other strategies.

MARKET STRATEGIES

(These comments on marketing strategies are from the Illinois ENR report *on Landscape Waste Compost*.)

In general, it would seem prudent for a community to enter into this "business" by first investing in low cost processes for producing a simple compost distributed for free, or at a minimal price. Second, communities should educate the public on the merits of compost, thereby increasing demand for the product. Over time, communities can assess the need and potential for implementing a more sophisticated process aimed at manufacturing higher valued (higher quality) compost products; compost that may even be saleable.

Each of the alternatives outlined below has the potential for generating revenue for composting programs, revenue that may be sufficient to cover all or many of the processing costs. However, it also appears unlikely at this writing that the revenues would be sufficient to cover facility development, collection, processing, and marketing costs. On the other hand, if tipping fees were charged by the municipalities to individuals and companies bringing in yard waste materials to a central processing site and those fees were incorporated into the program, *total* program revenues may be able to equal or even exceed program costs.

Components of a public program for either free distribution or sale would include:

● Requiring compost use by government entities and specifying its use by private contractors performing land maintenance activities;

● Direct-retail free distribution or sale of *bulk* compost by truck-load, or in small quantities on site;

● Direct free distribution or sale of *bagged* compost on site and at special distribution centers; and

● Direct free distribution or sale to wholesalers for processing and resale in bulk or bags to retailers.

42

COMPOST STANDARDS FOR HORTICULTURAL INDUSTRIES

Francis R. Gouin

COMPOSTING is looked upon by many as an effective means of stabilizing sludge and garbage. But it is also a manufacturing process—an efficient means for converting organic waste materials into a marketable product called compost. To the horticultural industries, compost is as old as the "Garden of Eden" and as new as "tomorrow." However, technological advances in the science of composting have accelerated the process and increased the availability of the material. But if compost is to be used by the horticultural industries, it must be of uniform quality, have minimal odor, maintain consistency from day to day and be readily available.

Producing quality compost for most of the horticultural industries requires establishing standards, close supervision and quality control from beginning to end. It requires maximizing biological systems to degrade cellulose, fats, oils and proteins to minerals, carbon dioxide and water within a mass of lignins that resist decomposition. Every effort should be made to avoid using liming or acidifying agents on organic materials prior to composting to insure process efficiency and a product that will have wide horticultural applications.

Non-spec or unacceptable compost is almost as costly to produce as quality compost, but there is little market for it, while the horticultural market for quality compost has yet to be saturated. The use of non-spec compost is generally limited to reclaiming disturbed soils, capping landfills, improving crop land for non-food crops, and dumping in landfills. These are disposal outlets and not income-producing markets.

Horticultural outlets that can provide a ready market for quality compost include: nurseries, landscape contractors, greenhouse growers, and urban gardeners. At the present time these markets utilize mostly peat moss, pine bark, composted hardwood bark and spent mushroom soil. These materials are used to improve soils and in blending potting media. In most instances, all or nearly all of these organic materials are imported from surrounding states and/or from other countries. The shipping costs for some of these products often exceed the cost of the material. Some of these materials are frequently in short supply due to weather conditions or building trends, and most cost in excess of $12 per cubic yard F.O.B.

Because the plants produced by the nursery and greenhouse industries and utilized by landscape contractors and home gardeners are high-value crops, it is important that the organic amendments be of the highest quality possible. If the intent of composting is to manufacture compost for horticultural use, it is necessary to design, construct and manage composting facilities to insure quality. This means providing adequate space, time and technology to assure proper composting and storage—and to make each load of compost of the highest quality.

Marketing an odorous, improperly-composted product can result in complaints, total rejection and bad publicity. It only takes one bad experience by a well-respected grower, landscape contractor or popular home gardener to ruin the reputation of an otherwise good product. Bad news spreads like wildfire and composting facilities can ill afford to acquire a bad reputation with a product that already generates a high level of public skepticism.

Every facility should be over-designed to assure optimum composting conditions, and storage space should be sufficiently large to allow room for stockpiling compost during periods of slack sales.

It is a well-recognized fact that sales are highly seasonal; therefore, adequate storage space and proper storage is of utmost importance. The compost should either be stored under cover or outdoors in low windrows not to exceed 6 feet in height. The compost should never be allowed to go anaerobic during curing and storage. Experience has clearly demonstrated that many sludge-composting facilities are too small, which results in overloaded systems, improper storage and an end product that cannot be marketed.

To compensate for insufficient capacity, the ratio of sludge and/or soggy organic matter to bulking agent is increased, and fine-textured bulking agents are used in place of coarse-textured materials. This results in inadequate air flow through the bio-mass when air is either drawn or blown through the system. To hasten the composting process, some systems use continuous aeration and frequent stirring. The problems with these systems are excessive drying and rapid cooling of the bio-mass, resulting in a product that is not thoroughly composted.

To compensate for insufficient curing and storage space, compost is "PHD" (piled higher and deeper). Since composting continues during curing and storage, but at a reduced rate, the results from piling compost too deep are strong odors and sometimes the production of alcohol. Neither is acceptable and both contribute to a bad reputation for compost.

ESTABLISHING STANDARDS

It is impossible to establish uniform horticultural standards for all composted products, because composts are made from numerous raw materials and come from different sources. However, since compost is made from organic products and byproducts, e.g., discarded plants, plant parts, and animal and human wastes, it should be comparatively uniform, providing that additives such as metals and salts are within approved limits. The factors which influence the quality of compost most are: improper use of hydrated lime or alum, materials high in cellulose and low in lignins, improper composting and/or storage, and compost particle size. If the compost is going to be used to grow a wide variety of plants, it must be ready to use and its pH must be adjustable. The following is a sampling of specifications. These are based on composted sludge and wood chips.

Container Nurseries, Landscape Contractors and Greenhouses: These end users require a premium compost with minimal odor, pH between 6.0 and 7.0, particle sizes no greater than 1/2" diameter and no liming materials. Because these users grow plants with different pH requirements, they must have the flexibility of raising or lowering the pH

with limestone or sulfur as desired. Even the natural acidity in peat moss should be sufficient to lower the pH of recommended amounts of compost to a desired level, in a potting medium. The amount of compost used will vary with the quality and quantity of compost used and other amendments in the blend, and the crop to be grown. To insure accuracy, laboratory testing should not be conducted until approximately two to three weeks after blending. Preliminary media testing is highly recommended to avoid delays in potting.

The compost should have a moisture concentration less than 50 percent, blend easily and be free of hard chunks. When quality compost is blended 20 percent to 33 percent by volume in container media, it should be able to supply the nitrogen needs of plants for the first one to two weeks of growth. The compost should also provide all of the minor nutrient needs of the plants through the first growing season. Like good wines and cheeses, compost improves with age. Compost that has been aged for three to four months after the initial composting period has a higher concentration of nitrate nitrogen and a lower concentration of ammonium nitrogen, a ratio which is preferred by most plants. In most instances, this additional curing period can be provided by the user with some advance planning.

Home Gardeners: This group also requires a premium compost similar to that of nurseries, landscape contractors and greenhouses; however, many states require composted sewage sludges that are retailed to be limed to a pH near 7.0 and clearly labeled. In this instance, the lime should be added after composting and not before. This allows for two types of compost to be manufactured from the same facility. The compost should have minimal odor, particle sizes no larger than 1/2" diameter and should have a moisture concentration less than 40 percent, especially if it is going to be bagged. Alcohol has been known to accumulate in excessively wet bagged compost stored at the bottom of pallet stacks.

Field Grown Nursery Plants and Sod: A lower grade of compost can be used for these applications. In the harvesting of trees and shrubs, approximately 250 tons of topsoil are removed per acre with each crop. A lesser amount of topsoil is removed with each crop of sod. A lower grade of compost can be utilized because these crops are grown in more isolated areas, outdoors, and workers have limited contact with the compost. In addition, these crops are grown in soil, which has the ability to buffer variations commonly found in non-spec compost. Even compost that is not cured can be used for field-grown nursery plants and sod. However, because of the diversity of crops grown, the preferred compost should have a pH between 6.0 and 7.0 and the particles should be less than one-inch diameter. Although unscreened compost can be used for this purpose, it will compete with plant roots for soil nitrogen. To avoid any potential problem with contamination of ground water, compost levels should not exceed 50 dry tons per acre and soil testing is highly recommended.

Land Reclamation and Landfill Caps: Non-spec compost can generally be utilized for these applications. However, these are disposal outlets and not market outlets, and are generally one-time application uses and not repeat customers.

There is a market for quality compost, but few outlets for non-spec compost. Substituting non-spec compost for quality compost can only aggravate marketing problems by creating unwanted bad publicity from bad experiences. If composting of organic waste and sludge is going to have an environmental impact it must be done properly. Good composting can make a major contribution to recycling. The horticultural industries stand ready to utilize compost—but only if the quality is "up to snuff."

Francis Gouin is a professor of horticulture at the University of Maryland.

REFERENCES

Falahi-Ardakani, A., J.C. Bouwkamp, F.R. Gouin and R.L. Chaney. 1987. Growth response and mineral uptake of vegetable transplants grown in a composted sewage sludge amended medium. Part I. Nutrient supplying power of the medium as measured by tissue analysis. *J. Environ. Hort.* 5:107-112.

Falahi-Ardakani, A., F.R. Gouin, J.C. Bouwkamp and R.L. Chaney. 1987. Growth response and mineral uptake of vegetable transplants grown in a composted sewage sludge amended medium. Part II. As influenced by time of application of N and K. *J. Environ.* 5:112-116.

Falahi-Ardakani, A., K. Corey and F.R. Gouin. 1987. Influence of pH on Cd and Zn concentrations of greenhouse grown Cucumis sativus L. 'LaReine' using media amended with composted sewage sludge and sulfur. *HortScience* (in press).

Frankos, N.H., F.R. Gouin, and L.J. Sikora. 1982. Using wood chips of specific species in sludge composting. *BioCycle J. of Waste Recycling* 23(3):38-40.

Gouin, F.R. 1977. Conifer tree seedling response to nursery soil amended with composted sewage sludge. *HortScience* 12(4):341-342.

Gouin, F.R. 1983. Growing azaleas in composted sewage sludge. *The Azalean* 5(4):70-71.

Gouin, F.R. 1985. Greenhouses and Nursery Crops In chapter 4. Benefits of Land Spreading of Sludges in the Northeast. pp. 23-25. Criteria and Recommendations for Land Application of Sludges in the Northeast. Bull. 851: The Penn. State Univ. Penn Agr. Exp. Sta., Univ. Park, PA.

Gouin, F.R. 1985. Growth of chrysanthemums in containers of media amended with composted municipal sewage sludge. *Jour. Environ. Hort.* 3:53-55.

Gouin, F.R. and Conrad B. Link. 1982. Sulfur may be an important supplement when using composted sewage sludge in blending potting media. *Amer. Nurserymen* 156(2):71-80.

Gouin, F.R. and J.M. Walker. 1977. Deciduous tree seedling response to nursery soil amended with composted sewage sludge. *HortScience* 12(1).

Graunke, L., and F.R. Gouin. 1983. Pre and post plant herbicide applications as they affect the germination and growth of 4 hardwood and 1 coniferous species growing in sewage sludge compost amended soil. Proc. International Plant Prop. Soc. 33:445-450.

Korcak, R., F.R. Gouin, and D.S. Fanning. 1979. Metal content of plants and soils in a tree nursery treated with composted sludge. *J. Environ. Qual.* 8:63-68.

Lewandowski, R.J. and F.R. Gouin. 1982. Vegetative propagation of euonymus cuttings under thermo-blankets and greenhouse intermittent mist in propagating media with and without composted sewage sludge. Proc. International Plant Prop. Soc. Vol. 32, 525-534.

Shanks, J.B. and F.R. Gouin, 1984. Compost suitability for greenhouse ornamental plants. *Biocycle J. of Waste Recycling* 25(1):42-45.

Vega-Sanchez, Fernando, F.R. Gouin and G.B. Willson. 1987. The effects of curing time on physical and chemical properties of composted sewage sludge and on the growth of selected bedding plants. *J. Environ. Hort.* 5:66-70.

Wootton, R.D., F.R. Gouin, and F.C. Stark. 1981. Composted digested sludge medium for growing annuals. *J. Amer. Soc. Hort. Sci.* 106:45-49.

43

BUILDING MARKETING INTO FACILITY PLANNING STAGE

Brian R. Golob

WHENEVER a composting project is considered, the question always asked is: "What are you going to do with the end product?" That question is so important that it must be addressed early in the planning phase. Unfortunately, marketing too often is addressed last—after siting, collection and processing.

In developing a realistic strategy, overall market structure and trends must be understood. Initial steps involve assessing consumer demand; competition; social, economic and technical developments; and estimated sales. All data lead to target market selection—the well-defined set of customers you seek.

To illustrate the process, staff responsible for managing the yard waste composting program in Ramsey County, Minnesota selected two target markets—private residential and public agencies. The former was chosen because the general public brought leaves to compost sites, and staff wanted them to use the end product. The public works and parks department were contingency users if compost supply exceeded the public's demand.

The next step in the process involves developing an effective marketing mix strategy for the target market. "Marketing mix" is defined as the particular blend of controllable marketing variables that an organization uses to achieve its objective in the target market. There are actually a great number of marketing mix variables. Fortunately, they can be classified into what are commonly known as the four P's: product, price, place, and promotion.

Product—What quality does the product need to be to meet your customers' needs? In Ramsey County, Minnesota, staff wanted the compost to be earth-like in appearance so it could be easily used in different residential applications. How will you ensure a reliable supply? Staff accomplished this through a publicity campaign which encouraged people to drop off material at multiple sites located throughout the county. Do you need to do product testing? County staff and a soil science professor at the University of Minnesota devised a sampling procedure to test for heavy metals. This was done to alleviate concerns about heavy metal concentration before distribution.

Price—What is the appropriate list price? Even though the county did not sell compost, if your organization plans to do so you should consider items such as the quality of your product, competition, and supply and demand in establishing your list price. Does your organization intend to give discounts for volume or early payment? You can also consider discounting the price initially to establish yourself in the market.

Place—This raises questions about distribution methods and sales channels. The county's distribution method used eight sites. Compost was distributed by people coming to the sites and taking as much material as they wanted on a "first-come, first-served" basis. The residents had to provide their own storage containers and fill them. At a couple of sites, the Public Works Department also came and hauled away material mixed with soil. How should the product be transported to the customer? In this case, the county did not provide any transportation.

Promotion—One must consider and assess different types of advertising vehicles and publicity instruments to determine which will best convey your message. The county's campaign served two purposes—informational and educational. The informational aspect addressed what, where, and when, and the educational aspect focused on how and why. The specific message depended on the instrument. For example, Public Service Announcements (PSAs) and Community Calendar Announcements (CCAs) were strictly informational due to the 20- or 30-second time limit. Newspaper ads, news articles, posters, brochures, and media events were educational. Staff developed a slogan and logo which was used with all the promotional activities. The public eventually came to associate the program with the slogan, "Lend Us Your Leaves."

MARKET ACTION PLAN

After a target market has been chosen and the marketing mix has been considered, your organization is ready to develop the last step—the market action plan. A marketing plan should consist of the following items: objectives and goals, a situational analysis, a marketing strategy, a budget, and control mechanisms. Objectives and goals typically indicate the direction management intends to proceed. Situational analysis involves examining several items which will affect your operation such as background data, normal forecast of market size, opportunities and threats, and strengths and weaknesses. The marketing strategy represents the game plan; it involves the target market, the marketing mix, and expenses. Budgets are essential because without any financial resources, programs cannot be initiated.

The last item to consider is a control mechanism. It is very important to monitor the progress of any project in terms of goals or dollars. Staff monitored the program using three different methods. First, the program was controlled through the budget. Second, the goal of distributing all the collected material was achieved. Finally, staff surveyed customers coming to the sites to determine which publicity instruments were most effective. Staff determined that most people learned of the program through newspaper articles and a door-to-door distribution of brochures.

Brian Golob is with DPRA, Inc. of St. Paul, Minnesota and previously had been coordinating the Ramsey County, MN leaf composting project.

44

RECYCLING LEAVES: THE MULTI-USE APPROACH

WHAT EVERY SUBURBAN area needs are farmers like Tom Williams of Dauphin County, Pennsylvania, who makes use of all the tree leaves his township hauls out to his farm. The wetter leaves he spreads on his fields to build humus and add fertility; the dry ones he uses either for field spreading or as bedding for his 120 cow dairy. He prefers dry leaves. "Wet ones are a pain in the neck in a way," he says. "They are easier to handle than wet manure, but not much."

On the fields, he spreads the leaves out roughly six inches thick, then plows them under or disks them into the soil in the fall. "I'm still experimenting," he says. "As the leaves decay to humus, they use nitrogen, causing a temporary shortage of this nutrient to the crop. I put the leaves on the poorest parts of the field planted to corn this year, and I think I can see a little nitrogen deficiency showing up (in July). But when the leaves finish decaying, they will return the nitrogen to the soil. It's too early to tell the final outcome on the corn crop but over the long haul organic matter and fertility both will be increased."

Williams is a recycler's dream come true. He also used shredded wastepaper for bedding, applying it over a layer of old tires filled with dirt. "I rely on urban pressure to make money," says Williams, only half jokingly. "Every free load of leaves or paper is just one more load of urban pressure for me. I've tried convincing industrial parks and big office buildings to let me pasture their extensive lawns. They don't see it that way, of course, even though I point out my cows mow and fertilize at the same time." He does however get loads of old asphalt macadam and limestone chip sweepings from their parking lots, which he uses to pave his farm lanes.

Williams notes some cautions about using leaves. "Our township sweeps the streets right before leaf pickup. This is very important for a farmer who wants to use the leaves for sheet composting or especially bedding. Otherwise, you get too much trash, especially cans and bottles, mixed in with the leaves." He also points out that homeowners sometimes mix hedge clippings with the leaves. Yew is poisonous and any larger amount should be kept out of the bedding as much as possible. Cows will eat a few leaves, and they would sample things like yew too, if given the chance. "If a farmer is feeding his livestock well, most of this problem is avoidable, but cows always want to try something different in their diet just like we do.

"There's a lot more experimentation to be done using leaves on cropland," he continues. "I think for some larger seeded crops or for transplants, it may be possible to plant right into the layer of leaves on top of the soil. But you would still have to till the soil periodically, because leaves are usually full of tree seeds which easily root and grow in the leaves."

In Dublin Township, Ft. Washington, PA, park superintendent Kevin O'Donnell has taken on the responsibility of overseeing and encouraging yard waste disposal in his area out of a commitment to environmental concern. He has achieved significant success by pursuing multiple uses for yard wastes. Upper Dublin has for six years composted leaves at a central location but has turned to other options too.

"We encourage home composting first of all, since that is the most logical and simplest way to use yard wastes," says O'Donnell. "We can't realistically hope for more than 10 percent of the people to compost their own leaves for their own land-scaping uses, but that many would be a big help. Gardeners almost always can be motivated to compost leaf piles or spread leaves on their gardens for sheet composting." Also some homeowners not aesthetically committed to a perfect rug-like lawn can sometimes be persuaded to try special mulching attachments now made for mowers that grind or shred leaves fine enough so they can be left on the lawn without affecting the grass adversely.

"Actually, we can compost leaves at a central location more efficiently than many of our home-owners can," says O'Donnell. "Many of the homes in this area are on rather large lots with many trees, and the sheer volume of leaves is more than can be conveniently handled on the property."

At the central composting location, O'Donnell says the secret to success in composting leaves (currently about 12,000 cu. yds. every year) is com-mitment to detail. "You can't just dump them in a pile and forget them. The leaves have to be turned periodically—every three weeks in our case—and watched carefully so temperature does not get too high. "We don't add water or anything else. Our compost is 100 percent leaves. No lime, no sludge." A front end loader does the turning. A nearby community, where O'Donnell is also in-volved, builds smaller piles, uses a Wildcat wind-row turner, and turns every week. "That makes compost a little faster, but also is more expensive."

A third way O'Donnell gets rid of some leaves is by spreading them in parkland forest. "We don't advise using leaves for mulch in home landscaping because they do have weed seeds and tree seeds in them. But a limited amount of leaves work out all right in woodland."

A fourth outlet for Upper Dublin is agricul-ture and horticulture. "We've used leaves in large volumes to stem erosion in field gullies. Farmers disk or more often plow leaves into crop fields in the fall. If you have a layer of leaves on the ground in spring, the soil under them will not dry early enough for spring cultivation." O'Donnell also notes one instance where leaves were used effec-tively to regenerate an old asparagus bed.

"We have tried large scale sheet composting," says O'Donnell. "The leaves compost well in this way without the work and attention necessary for windrow composting. At the end of a year, you can push the compost in a pile and put down another layer of leaves. But this method takes longer, and requires too much space. It is not practical for us although it very well could be a way for a farmer to regenerate old fields depleted of organic matter."

Another outlet is a local nursery which applies the leaves directly to nursery beds and fields and tills them in with a rotary tiller. "There's also been successful experiments in growing sod for land-scaping on leaf compost," says O'Donnell. "This way, not so much topsoil is lost with the removal of successive sod crops. Growing sod on compost also appears to be effective where topsoil has been removed by previous sod crops. But for growing sod, leaf compost is spread at only about 130 cu. yds. per acre, not much in terms of getting rid of a lot of leaves."

One of the most unusual new uses for leaves and grass clippings is one Germaine Heise is try-ing on her ginseng farm near Wausau, Wisconsin. She and her husband are taking yard wastes from Wausau, composting them, then spreading the compost on land that will become ginseng beds next year. "It's a pilot program to convert farm-land into rich humusy soil like forest soil where ginseng grows naturally. We want to grow our gin-seng as organically as possible." The Heises have been growing ginseng commercially for 32 years, and experimenting with organically grown meth-ods for 10 years. "We hope that by rotating our beds every four years or so on composted, clean soils, we can avoid phytopthera root rot, which has become a serious problem in commercial ginseng beds." Research has been done on how compost combats soil-borne diseases, including various root rots (see *BioCycle*)—diseases which do not seem to show up as seriously in natural stands of ginseng. Both the effects of rotation and of compost itself will avoid the problem, the Heises hope.

They get about a truckload of yard waste a week, which they compost in piles for two weeks, turning the mixtures of grass clippings and leaves every day with a tractor and bucket fork. Then they load the compost on a manure spreader and spread it on the land. The first application is plowed into the soil, and subsequent applications are worked only about 3 inches into the soil with a disk. Total application might amount to 10 tons per acre so far, but Mrs. Heise says they would really like to get more yard waste so that more of the land could be enriched faster. New beds, in in-crements of 2 acres a year, are formed for the gin-seng plants, and old beds are rotated to grain or legumes after being in production 4 to 6 years. As now planned, the beds would then be enriched with another charge of yard waste compost and the cy-cle repeated. Altogether the Heises have 160 acres, with only a fraction of it in ginseng at one time. "Ginseng is a gamble, and although we've been growing it a long time, there is so much more we need to know," says Germaine. "When we began our pilot composting project, there were fears in the neighborhood that we were going to be a dumping ground for town wastes. But things are better now. Popular opinion is changing as people understand what composting is and does. It cer-tainly seems to me that water filtering through our organic compost will be purer and safer than what seeps down to groundwater from a conventional, pesticide treated cornfield."

At the University of Wisconsin, soil scientist Art Peterson has been studying the effects of applying yard wastes to cropland for going on three years. His experiments so far indicate that leaves can be spread at a 20 ton to 40 ton per acre rate with beneficial results. "In fact, in the severe drouth last year," he says, "some of the experimental plots where leaves were applied in large quantities made the best yields of all my corn plots around the state. Those plots were on a north slope, so I think there was more moisture than at other sites, but still I have to wonder." There were other surprises too. Although the corn appeared to be paler where leaves were applied without additional fertilizer, indicating possible nitrogen deficiency because of the high C/N ratio of the leaves, the corn produced as well as any. "And this year, all the corn has a good deep green color, even with leaves and no fertilizer. We are just not seeing nitrogen deficiency even where leaves were spread at the 40 ton per acre rate. I am quite surprised. I don't want to say too much until I get three complete years of data completed. I'm old enough so it doesn't bother me to say I just don't know how to explain this. According to the book, we should be getting N deficiency while all those leaves are decaying into humus."

Adding fertilizer to the leaf applications increased yields in most applications, but not dramatically so, and in some cases not at all. The nitrogen content of ear leaf and grain was about the same on all plots whatever the application rates of leaves and fertilizer or none of either. Heavy metal content was also about the same on all plots. Bottom line: Considerable increases in organic matter and moisture retention can be gained from heavy leaf applications with no adverse affects and indeed with good yields. The biggest problem, says Peterson, is spreading the raw leaves and incorporating them. A manure spreader proved to be the best tool for application but transferring the leaves from truck to spreader took considerable time. An offset disk did not work very well for incorporation, so a rotary tiller was used instead. On the heavier 40 ton per acre applications, incorporation was still difficult even with a tiller. "If you are applying only 5 to 10 tons of leaves per acre, you can handle that just about any way you wish, but higher rates, especially 30 to 40 tons, are difficult," says Peterson. "It is better to spread the leaves on partially worked soil rather than sod. We learned that raw leaves are very difficult to incorporate into sod, and I hesitate to suggest plowing leaves under—inverting that layer of leaves to the bottom of the plow depth could create anaerobic conditions in the soil not conducive to plant growth." He also thinks, from the standpoint of labor efficiency, that he believes farmers should spread leaves immediately rather than compost them in piles and then spread them. "I don't think on a conventional farm, the farmer has time to compost leaves before using them. Incorporate the leaves right away and let nature do the work"—a viewpoint that farmer Tom Williams, in Pennsylvania, agrees with.

Peterson, a life-long soil scientist, is enthusiastic about the role yard wastes and other wastes can play in soil fertility. "We are certainly not making any discoveries we didn't already know. Organic matter is extremely valuable to soil, and whether you get it from manure, green manure, sludge, yard wastes or whey, the results in our tests are good. It's a sin to be sending this stuff to the landfill."

45

EXPANDING MARKETS FOR YARD WASTE COMPOST

Kathryn A. Cox

THE PRIMARY MARKETS for yard waste compost depend upon whether the composting operation is publicly or privately run, the existence of a profit-making incentive, the quality of the compost, the quantity of available compost and the local industries. The markets are usually restricted to local areas due to the high cost of transportation relative to the cost of the compost. In general, residents use a great portion of all yard waste compost, as do the nursery and landscaping industries, construction firms, public agencies, private institutions, soil amendment retailers and wholesalers, sod dealers, landfill operators and farmers.

Several means exist of distributing yard waste compost to users. In the Illinois Department of Energy and Natural Resources document entitled *Landscape Waste Compost: Distribution and Marketing Strategies,* the following choices are outlined:

1) Direct retail free distribution or sale of bulk compost (truckload, on-site or at central distribution center).

2) Direct free distribution or sale of bagged compost (on-site or at a special distribution center).

3) Direct free distribution or sale to wholesalers for processing and resale in bulk or bags to retailers.

Any of these choices could include free delivery, which is particularly useful when the supply exceeds the demand or when there is little storage space. Producers planning to sell the compost could do so with either the goal of covering costs or of making a profit.

While public and private yard waste composting operations could be found to illustrate all the above possibilities, some patterns emerge. Most composting operations that rely on giving away compost as the means to fully distribute their product are publicly owned, perhaps because their goal is to avoid the costs of landfilling yard waste and not necessarily to make a profit.

Residents and public agencies such as public works departments are often the primary users of yard waste compost in municipally-owned composting operations. In many cases, such as in Wellesley, Massachusetts, where the compost goes to residents and the public works department; in San Mateo, California where it is used to landscape city parks; and in Palo Alto, California where it is used as a landfill cover, the compost is given away.

The perception that this is the only way to fully distribute the product is untrue, however, as many operations do sell their compost. Unless they have a contract with a public agency, it is likely that all commercial composting facilities choose to sell their compost. Occasionally a public composting operation sells its product. For example, Lane County, Oregon sells its compost to the general public and to local nurseries.

Several innovative arrangements have been established to distribute compost to users. "Composting Concepts" in Woodbury, Minnesota trades finished compost in exchange for the use of a nursery's land for their operation. A private farm in Westfield, New Jersey accepts yard waste, composts it and applies it on-site as a soil amendment and fertilizer supplement, thereby saving significantly on fertilizer costs.

INCREASING UTILIZATION

Means of increasing the use of yard waste compost (or expanding the markets for yard waste compost) are numerous and varied. They can focus on increasing the use of all yard waste compost in general or on increasing the marketability of a facility's specific compost. Any entity hoping to market compost could target possible markets—either those which were expanding or those which might accept yard waste compost as a substitute for the soil amendments they were currently using. Most state and regional offices recommend that a market analysis be done at the local level prior to attempting to sell yard waste compost, as transportation costs generally restrict compost markets to the local area.

Preferential procurement by government agencies of recycled products can serve to increase the market for yard waste compost in general. Laws in Illinois, New Jersey, Michigan and Pennsylvania require state agencies to purchase recycled products, including yard waste, when available. An executive order in Minnesota does the same. Oregon is currently developing similar laws for state and local agencies.

Another way to develop demand for yard waste compost is through educational programs. These usually focus on informing the public both on the importance of adding organic material to inferior soils and on the safety of yard waste compost as a soil amendment. They can be carried out through literature, media, school programs and trade shows.

In Portland, the Metropolitan Service District has created a markets assistance program for commercial composting operations, with education and quality assurance testing of the compost as two major components of the program. Testing criteria have been developed for evaluation of compost quality. Quarterly testing of the compost following these criteria is recommended by Metro in order to guarantee a consistent, high quality product and thereby overcome any negative perceptions of compost by potential consumers. Florida has begun a process to establish regulations for quality control of compost and for coding according to the level of quality.

While the marketing of compost by a specific yard waste composting operation can be positively affected by state or local preferential procurement requirements, market analyses and education, a composting entity can take further steps to insure full use of its product. For example, Ann Gatlin of the Maryland Environmental Service (which produces and sells a leaf compost, "Leafgro"™) asserts that a consistently high quality compost is the primary requirement. High quantity users of organic soil amendments, such as landscapers, must be able to depend upon receiving a consistent product which meets their specifications. Furthermore, she recommends targeting all potential customers in the area—focusing on high quantity users of organic soil amendments such as nurseries, golf courses, landscapers and farmers, and speaking to them about the product. Participation in annual trade shows can facilitate contact. Literature explaining the merits and uses of the compost, as well as samples are often helpful in informing potential buyers.

Ed Janesz of the Greater Cleveland Ecological Association which runs a non-profit leaf composting operation, states that experience has taught him the best ways to market the finished product:

1) **Bag and Bushel Program:** Small scale gardeners bring their own containers and pay $.75 per generous bushel.

2) **Bulk Load Pickup:** The customer's truck is loaded and he is charged by the cubic yard.

3) **Home Delivery:** The minimum load is 2 cubic yards, maximum is 10 cubic yards. Also semi truckloads are delivered to landscapers and commercial growers.

Apparently the home delivery program is the most popular, accounting for 60 percent to 70 percent of the compost sold. Janesz believes the popularity of the program is due both to their very active publicity program on TV and in the newspaper, and to word of mouth from satisfied customers and observing neighbors. Like Ann Gatlin, Janesz agrees that the primary reason for the successful marketing of the Association's compost is its consistent high quality. They are now considering producing an even higher quality compost in order to develop new markets.

**Section
IX**

COSTS AND
ECONOMICS

46

COST COMPARISONS OF COMPOSTING VS. LANDFILLING YARD WASTES

Richard M. Kashmanian and Alison C. Taylor

THE AUTHORS recently completed an EPA-funded study characterizing 8 yard waste composting programs in the U.S. to provide information about the options available for designing such programs. (See the chapter, "EPA Analysis of Yard Waste Composting Programs," in the section on Case Studies.)

The following communities were selected: Davis, California; East Tawas, Michigan; Montgomery County, Maryland; Omaha, Nebraska; Seattle, Washington; Wellesley, Massachusetts; Westfield, New Jersey; and Woodbury, Minnesota. This paper provides estimates on the total, total net, and full costs (defined below) of yard waste composting for these communities.

General information about these communities and their composting programs is provided in Tables 1 and 2, respectively. Since Wellesley and Westfield are each served by 2 composting facilities, there are a total of 10 facilities represented (Wellesley has 1 for resident drop-off and 1 for landscaper drop-off; Westfield sends its leaves and grass clippings to 2 separate private composting facilities (Middlebush Compost, Inc. and Woodhue Ltd., respectively), while its brush and other woody materials are sent to another private facility (Alternate Disposal Systems Inc.) for shredding. Davis, Seattle, and Woodbury's composting are done by private facilities (Davis Waste Removal Co., Pacific Topsoils, Inc., and Composting Concepts, respectively).

Assessing and comparing the costs and benefits of a composting program or of individual composting steps can determine their net impact in economic terms. As for any waste management practice, there are various costs to consider. With respect to yard waste composting, there are typi-

cally costs for: collection, transportation, and processing; compost storage and marketing; and program administration, public education, and technical assistance. Benefits received from composting include: revenues received from selling the finished compost; avoided costs (rather than earned revenues) from using the finished compost instead of purchasing a substitute product; and avoided tip fees from not landfilling (or incinerating) the yard wastes. These economic variables are discussed in greater detail below.

It is important to recognize that in many cases it may not be appropriate to directly compare program costs between communities because their program designs, cost estimation, accounting, and/or financial procedures may be quite different (i.e., like "comparing apples and oranges"). In some cases, capital and operation and maintenance costs are directly attributed to composting or associated with rental payments or cost contracts with a private contractor and therefore are more easily and likely to be accounted for. In other cases, costs may be shared with other public works operations or with other communities and are therefore more difficult to estimate.

In this paper, costs not included in some of the estimates are specified. In general, costs for administration, public education, and technical assistance were *not* obtained. The following costs and benefits are those which were obtained (or estimated) from the 8 communities (see Chapter 30 for more detailed information on these communities and their yard waste composting programs and facilities, especially data which relate to the costs of composting). In order to estimate the net total and full costs of composting, the costs are added and the revenues and avoided costs are subtracted.

yard waste collection and transport costs
plus
yard waste processing costs
(including reject material disposal costs)
minus
compost revenues
minus
avoided costs

1. Yard Waste Collection and Transport Costs

Collection costs for dropoff programs (e.g., Wellesley's yard waste collection and Westfield's grass and brush collection) are zero to the community. However, households pay to transport their yard wastes to the appropriate area. There are, therefore, tradeoffs between convenience and participation rates for the households, costs to the households and community, and the amounts and types of yard wastes diverted from landfills to be composted. If dropoff occurs at a transfer station, the cost of transport from the station to the final destination is paid by the community. Costs and revenues reported by these yard waste composting programs are provided in Table 3. Footnotes to Table 3 indicate what costs are and are not included in these cost estimates.

2. Yard Waste Processing Costs

Each step included in the composting process influences the costs of composting. For example, (1) pre-processing steps, such as debagging or removal of unwanted materials, may be needed prior to forming windrows; (2) pre-processing and processing steps, such as grinding and shredding,

may be used to reduce particle size and accelerate the composting process; (3) monitoring of windrows is a useful indicator of their turning frequency; (4) post-processing steps, such as shredding and screening, are used to improve the quality and appearance of the end product; and (5) testing of the finished compost can determine its quality and appropriate market use. In general, processing costs are much lower than the collection and transport costs.

Reject material, i.e., non-compostable material, is separated manually or mechanically and typically sent to a landfill for disposal (and this is a cost which is directly or indirectly paid) or used on-site. On average, reject material represents approximately 5 percent of the yard waste stream received *for the facilities studied.*

Costs of landfill disposal of rejects were estimated by multiplying their tonnage by the landfill disposal fee, and then dividing by the tons of yard wastes received. These calculations were only made for the publicly operated facilities under the assumption that these costs when incurred by the privately operated facilities were included as part of their tip fee charged or revenues earned; this assumption avoided double-counting this cost. Among the publicly operated facilities, Wellesley provided an estimate for the amount of reject material generated. On the other hand, East Tawas' cost for this disposal is included in their cost for yard waste processing; Omaha did not have an available estimate for the amount of reject material. Montgomery County's cost for disposal of reject material for its public/private facility was esti-

---

TABLE 1:
Background Information on Cities/County Selected

City/County	State	Total Pop.	Total Households	Total Yard Waste Stream (tons/yr)	Year of Data
Davis	CA	44,000	10,000	5,475[a]	1987
East Tawas	MI	2,600	1,350	350	1987
Montgomery Co.[b]	MD	633,000	244,000	110,000	1987
Omaha	NE	350,000	100,000	48,000	1988
Seattle	WA	500,000	229,000	92,000[a]	1988
Wellesley	MA	27,000	8,500	8,000	1987/1988
Westfield	NJ	30,000	10,400	n/a	1987/1988
Woodbury	MN	13,520	4,790	1,092[c]	1987

Source: Taylor and Kashmanian (1988)
Notes: [a]estimate of total yard waste stream does not include amount generated and collected by lawn service companies and public work crews
[b]population and household estimates based on 1986 data
[c]yard waste esitmate does not include brush
n/a: not available

mated to be $2.30-$3.45 per ton of yard wastes received (depending on the conversion factor, or an average of $2.88 per ton). Wellesley's disposal of this material was calculated to cost $2.46-$8.66 per ton of yard wastes received (depending on the conversion factor, or an average of $5.56 per ton).

3. Other Costs

There are also indirect costs associated with composting. These costs are often less tangible than the direct costs and more difficult to estimate, but should at least be recognized in a qualitative manner. As an example, indirect costs can include: the time spent by households in separating their yard wastes into specified containers; the impact of the separation method on yard waste collection, the composting process, and the value of the finished compost; and impacts by the composting facility on the environment and neighborhood. These costs are *not* included in this analysis.

4. Compost Revenues

One of the benefits of composting (in addition to the avoided costs) is the ability to earn revenues by selling the finished compost, or avoid the cost for purchasing a substitute product. The revenues (or values) of the end products from the facilities studied are influenced by the level of technology, processing, and post-processing steps followed. In addition, there may be avoided costs by not having to purchase substitute products, as in the case of using compost: (1) as a landfill cover material and soil amendment for county parks (at Omaha, a savings of $6.30 per ton of yard wastes received as a substitute for topsoil); (2) as a soil amendment (at Wellesley, a savings of $4.05 per ton of yard wastes

received); (3) for private use as a supplement to fertilizer (at Woodhue Ltd., $35-$65 per acre savings at their adjacent farm); or (4) in exchange for use of another facility's land (at Woodbury, with a nursery's land). For the same reasons stated above, these avoided costs are only included in the cost calculations for the publicly operated facilities.

When revenues are reported as the price received per ton of *finished compost sold*, and costs are reported as expenditures per ton of *yard wastes received*, a conversion is needed so that these individual per ton estimates are compatible to estimate the net per ton cost of composting. The conversion is as follows: multiply the ratio of tons of finished compost sold to tons of yard wastes received, by the revenue earned per ton of finished compost. This revenue figure can now be subtracted from the cost of composting, per ton of yard wastes received, to estimate the net cost of composting, per ton of yard wastes received. As in the approach taken in calculating costs for disposal of reject material, only revenues received from selling finished compost, or information provided on avoided cost from using finished compost, by publicly operated facilities were included in these calculations, to avoid their double-counting.

5. Avoided Costs

One of the main benefits of composting yard wastes is the avoided cost of not landfilling (or incinerating) these materials. Other avoided costs include postponement of using a higher-cost replacement facility, and the reduction of potential environmental problems by not landfilling (or incinerating) yard wastes; however, these avoided

TABLE 2:
Composting Program Effectiveness

City/County	Total Pop. Served by Compost.	Total Households Served by Compost.	Total Yard Waste Stream Composted (tons/yr)	% of Total Yard Waste Stream Comp.
Davis	44,000	10,000	500	9
East Tawas	2,600	1,350	138[a]	39[a]
Montgomery Co.	282,000	75,000	15,600	14
Omaha	3,735	830	500	1
Seattle	500,000	229,000	3,600	4
Wellesley	27,000	8,500	6,500	81
Westfield	30,000	10,400	4,687[a]	n/a
Woodbury	2,329	825	116	11[a]

Source: Taylor and Kashmanian (1988)
Notes: [a] does not include amount of brush chipped or shredded
n/a: not available

TABLE 3:
Costs and Revenues of Yard Waste Composting[a]

City or County	Collect. & Trans. Cost for Yard Wastes ($/ton rec'd)	Process. Cost for Yard Wastes[b] ($/ton rec.'d) (+)	Total Compost. Cost ($/ton rec'd) (=)	Revenues for Compost ($/ton rec'd) (−)	Net Total Compost. Cost[c] ($/ton rec'd) (=)	Local Landfill Tip Fee ($/ton rec'd) (−)	Full Compost. Cost[d] ($/ton rec'd) (=)
Davis[e]	n/a	n/a	n/a	$ 0.00	n/a	$ 8.00	n/a
East Tawas[f]	$10.00	<$10.00	<$20.00	$ 0.00	<$ 20.00	$ 5.25	<$ 14.75
Mont Co.[g]	$83.33	$18.60	$101.93	$ 4.31	$ 97.62	$ 46.00	$ 51.62
Omaha	$40.16	$ 3.60	$ 43.76	$ 6.30[h]	$ 37.46	$ 6.40	$ 31.06
Seattle	$12.00[i]	$22.50	$ 34.50	$10.00	$ 34.50	$ 31.50	$ 3.00
Wellesley[j]	$ 0.00	$16.67	$ 16.67[j]	$ 4.05[k]	$ 12.62[j]	$ 52.00	−$ 39.38[j]
Westfield[lm]	$70.69	$31.58	$102.27	$ 6.54	$102.27	$137.00[n]	−$ 34.73
Westfield[lo]	[p]	$33.33	$33.33[p]	AC[q]	$ 33.33[p]	$137.00[n]	−$103.67[p]
Woodbury	$43.00	$15.00	$ 58.00	AC[r]	$ 58.00	$ 30.00	$ 28.00

Source: *Taylor and Kashmanian (1988)*

Notes: [a]*costs for Davis, East Tawas, Montgomery County, and Wellesley programs are based on 1987 $; costs for Omaha, Seattle, and Westfield programs are based on 1988 $; costs for Wellesley program are based on 1987-88 $*

[b]*processing costs for Seattle, Westfield, and Woodbury programs represent payments made to privately operated facilities (Montgomery County's facility is public/private); cost for disposal of reject material is not included for private facilities; Montgomery County's and Westfield's facilities use windrow turning machines—the other facilities use front end loaders*

[c]*net total cost of composting represents summation of costs for collection, transport, and processing, including cost for disposal of reject material (i.e., the total cost of composting), minus revenues for compost; revenue for private facilities is not included in calculating net total cost*

[d]*full cost of composting represents net total cost minus landfill tip fee (other avoided costs, e.g., avoided garbage collection cost, are not included); negative sign implies a benefit*

[e]*cost charged to Davis residents for collection, transport, and composting of yard wastes is $3.46/month/household*

[f]*cost for equipment shared with Department of Public Works not included in composting costs; no information available on avoided cost from using finished compost*

[g]*processing cost does not include cost for land nor amortized capital cost*

[h]*derived from an avoided cost of $8-$10/ton of landfill cover and soil amendment not purchased*

[i]*collection cost not included in 1988 estimate, $56/ton in 1989*

[j]*yard wastes are dropped off at 2 composting facilities; therefore, collection and transport costs are $0/ton; processing cost does not include cost of land; $52/ton tip fee includes transport cost to landfill*

[k]*derived from selling price of $0.00-$0.50/ton sold and avoided cost of $15/cu yd of loam not purchased*

[l]*Westfield pays $10/cu yd (3.3 cu yds/ton) to Alternate Disposal Systems Inc. (ADSI) to receive and shred its brush and other woody materials (not included in the cost estimates in the table; 1,423 tons, 1988); ADSI sells fine mulch ($12/cu yd), coarse mulch ($10/cu yd), topsoil ($10/cu yd), and boiler fuel ($3-$4/cu yd) ($/outgoing cu yd sold)*

[m]*Middlebush Compost Inc. composts leaves from Westfield ($3,287 tons, 1988); conversion factor used is 475 lbs/cu yd for leaves received*

[n]*$137.00/ton is tip fee at the transfer station*

[o]*Woodhue Ltd. composts grass clippings from Westfield (1,400 tons, 1988); conversion factor used is 600 lbs/cu yd*

[p]*collection cost of grass clippings (and brush) for Westfield is $0/ton with resident drop-off; cost for transport to Woodhue (and ADSI) was not estimated by Westfield*

[q]*avoided cost of $35-$65/acre for on-site use on farm as fertilizer supplement*

[r]*avoided cost of use of nursery's land by exchanging compost (no estimate available)*

AC: avoided cost;   n/a: not available

costs are *not* estimated in this paper.

In addition, composting tends to "even out" the peaks in MSW generation and dampen the impact on the household garbage collection cost. Although it is true that yard wastes collected en route to a composting facility do not need to be picked up for regular garbage collection, it is not fully evident how garbage collection costs will be affected, at least in the short term.[1] For example, private garbage collection services may be subject to contracts which are not likely to change in the short term. However, when these contracts are rebid, total garbage collection costs will likely drop, especially if they are based on tons of garbage collected. On the other hand, reductions in garbage collection costs are likely, even in the short term, if collection is publicly operated and, as well, if any overtime collection costs can be avoided during the peak generation seasons for yard wastes. These avoided collection costs were *not* included in this analysis due to the lack of supported data and information in the literature.[2] However, they may be significant and should not be ignored. In fact, costs for yard waste collection may be the same as the savings from the avoided costs for garbage collection; if this were the case, the net costs of yard waste collection would be $0 per ton. A key factor in deciding whether, and to what extent, garbage collection costs are avoided is to determine whether the *total* costs for garbage collection have changed.

As stated above, cost savings due to the diversion of yard wastes from landfills, i.e., avoided tip fees, can be subtracted from the total net cost of composting to estimate the "full" cost of composting. Of course, this assumes that the cost of landfilling (and composting) reflects its full cost. To avoid double-counting costs, the full cost of composting should not be compared to the cost of landfilling since both cost measures include estimates of landfill disposal costs, whether in the form of avoided costs or the price paid for landfill disposal.

6. Total/Net Total/Full Costs of Composting

As explained in the footnotes to Table 3, the total cost of composting is calculated by adding yard waste collection, transport, and processing (including reject disposal) costs. The net total cost of composting is calculated by subtracting compost revenue (or avoided cost) from the total cost. Finally, the full cost of composting is derived by subtracting the landfill tip fee from the net total cost of composting. A negative full cost of composting would result when the net total cost is less than the landfill tip fee (i.e., the cost of the alternative yard waste management method for the communities studied). Estimation and inclusion of other avoided costs (e.g., avoided garbage collec-

tion costs) would, at a minimum, bring the costs of composting and landfilling closer together.

CONCLUSION

As discussed above, direct cost comparisons between these 8 community composting programs studied by Taylor and Kashmanian (1988) may not be appropriate because their cost figures may be based on their different program designs, accounting, estimation, and/or financial procedures used. For example: (1) East Tawas' cost estimates only reflect costs solely applicable to composting, i.e., costs for equipment shared with their DPW were not estimated; (2) Montgomery County's estimate for its processing cost does not include the opportunity cost for land nor amortized capital costs, the latter being paid in single lump sums; (3) Wellesley's processing cost estimate does not include the cost of land; and (4) Westfield does not include the cost of shared equipment, only rented equipment (as well as labor and fuel), in its processing cost estimate. Furthermore, cost per ton estimates for composting can be highly variable over time, depending on, among other things, annual fluctuations in the amount of yard wastes generated.

This can make cost comparisons between communities and regions, and over time, difficult and oftentimes misleading. For the most part, the data presented in this paper are *not* generalizable to other communities and should *only* be considered in light of the information provided here. However, it is evident in Table 3, as landfill tip fees continue to soar, *reflecting their own full costs*, yard waste composting will continue to become a more preferred solid waste management alternative for communities on *economic grounds alone*.

Future data collection, estimation, and reporting efforts should document the methods used in accounting of costs, what costs are and are not included, and the avoided costs (including avoided garbage collection costs). Only when there is an understanding of the cost accounting methods used and a consensus on cost estimation procedures can cost data become generalizable.

---

[1] *Per ton* garbage collection costs for these communities are: Montgomery County, $54.00; Omaha, $30.30; Seattle, $71.50; Wellesley, $0.00; Woodbury, $65.00. For Davis, households are charged $5.64 per month for garbage collection. No data were available for East Tawas and Westfield.

[2] In addition, in New Jersey, there is a tonnage grant for recycling. The state will pay communities $1-$2 per ton of MSW diverted from landfills as a recycling incentive as well as a tracking mechanism for the level of recycling activity. This subsidy is *not* included in Table 3 for Westfield.

ACKNOWLEDGEMENTS

The authors would like to thank Tapio Kuusinen, U.S. Environmental Protection Agency; Donn Derr, Rutgers University; Luis Diaz, Cal Recovery Systems; Edward Gottko, Town of Westfield; Joseph Hayes, Woodhue Ltd.; Patrick Kennedy, Alternate Disposal Systems, Inc. (formerly with Middlebush Compost Inc.); Ellen McShane, New Jersey Department of Environmental Protection; James Opaluch, University of Rhode Island; John Schaal, Energy Systems Research Group; and Keith Wolff, New York City Department of Sanitation for their review and comments on an earlier draft.

The views and opinions expressed in this paper are those of the authors and are not to be taken as official policy of the U.S. Environmental Protection Agency or any other public or private entity.

REFERENCES

Taylor, A.C. and R.M. Kashmanian. 1988. *Study and Assessment of Eight Yard Waste Composting Programs in the United States.* Project funded by U.S. Environmental Protection Agency through Fellowship Number U-913010-01-0. EPA/530-SW-89-038. December.

Richard Kashmanian is in the Office of Policy, Planning and Evaluation of the U.S. EPA in Washington, DC. Alison Taylor is at the School of Public Health, Harvard University.

47

MINIMIZING THE COST OF LEAF COMPOSTING

Donn A. Derr and Pritam S. Dhillon

ALTHOUGH a great deal is known about the physical and biological aspects of leaf composting, there is only limited knowledge about the economic aspects of this waste-handling system. Economic issues that need to be addressed are the comparative costs of alternative composting arrangements for municipalities and the economies of size in leaf composting. In other words, what kind of ownership and at what scale of operation are costs per cubic yard of leaves minimized and how might small communities keep their costs to a reasonable level?

Since municipalities vary in size, location, quantity of leaves generated, availability of suitable land for compost sites and distance, one can expect the "best" approach or strategy to leaf composting to vary also. In terms of size and ownership, at least three types of compost facilities may be needed to serve the varied municipalities: Small farmer-operated facility (5,000 cubic yards or less); Medium municipal operated facility (20-30,000 cubic yards); and Large private commercial facility (80,000 cubic yards or more).

ON-FARM COMPOSTING

The intent of this alternative is to recycle leaves at a very low cost near the source. Small communities that are rural in character, with agricultural open space nearby, should consider subcontracting with local farm operators and encouraging them to engage in leaf composting as a supplemental activity. The leaves would be transported only a short distance and there would be no need to market the end product as it could be in-corporated into the soil. There is equipment available to handle small volumes of leaves on farms without incurring a large start-up expenditure. For example, a $14,000 investment for a new compost turner, where a farm tractor and front end loader are already owned, can enable a small farmer to get into this business.

The resulting compost when applied directly to the farmland would reduce some of the agricultural chemical inputs used. Such an initiative would be consistent with the Agricultural Productivity Act passed by Congress in 1985 to encourage the reduction in purchased chemical inputs, lower environmental hazards, and develop "a more sustainable agriculture" over the long term (USDA, 1988). Financially, farmers can realize savings in terms of reduced expenses on chemical fertilizers by substituting compost in their place (Madden, 1988).

At the same time, tipping fees paid by the municipality for leaf composting would be an additional source of revenue for the farm operator. For many farm operators who produce field and vegetable crops, December through February is a slow time of the year, so composting would offer an opportunity to utilize family labor. A potential problem may be posed by the presence of nonbiodegradables such as aluminum cans, tree branches, stones, tennis balls, broken pavement, wrappers, etc. in the leaves.

Estimates indicate that for a 5,000 cubic yard operation, composting costs would be less than $4.00 per cubic yard. Included in this cost is (1) a land charge for the site, (2) site improvement costs, (3) equipment depreciation, (4) equipment operating costs, (5) labor cost, (6) watering cost,

(7) disposal costs for nonbiodegradables, (8) insurance, (9) operating fees, (10) contingencies, (11) return to management, and (12) interest on investment (Dhillon and Latimer, 1986).

It's assumed that the finished compost would not be screened as it would greatly add to the costs and would defeat the purpose of this approach. However, manual separation of nonbiodegradable materials from leaves would be necessary and the municipality would have to attempt to minimize debris by promptly picking up leaves. About 135-150 hours of labor would be required for windrow construction, windrow turning, separation of debris, and wetting of leaves. Compost turners have large capacities so labor requirements would be low for this activity. With high-level technology, composting would be completed in less than 150 days (Strom and Finstein, 1985).

Total composting costs would be low because of small site development and equipment costs. About two acres of land would be sufficient for the operation. Since this is an "add on" activity, it's not necessary to purchase a tractor, front end loader, or a pick-up truck. Thus, only a portion of the overall costs of this equipment actually used for composting would be charged to composting. The largest cost components would be depreciation and interest for the new compost turner and site improvements. A given municipality may have to contract with two or three farm operators since processing a larger volume at one site may become a concern for the state environmental protection agency in charge of recycling and monitoring composting sites.

MUNICIPALLY OWNED COMPOSTING OPERATION

For municipalities that are not highly developed, and have open land remaining, a medium-sized facility handling 20,000-30,000 tons of leaves would be feasible. It will require a higher initial investment in site preparation and equipment, and operating expenses for labor, fuel, utilities, etc. The leaves could be hauled to this facility by a carter or by the municipality itself. It is assumed that the Strom/Finstein low-level technology composting method would be used for this operation (Strom and Finstein, 1985). In this method, two side-by-side windrows would be formed and a month later, combined. The windrows would be turned in the spring and during late summer moved to form curing piles at the edge of the site. This would permit the preparation of the site for the next composting cycle.

Estimates for this size of operation, including costs for land, land improvements, windrow construction, windrow turning, wetting of leaves, curing pile formation, shredding and screening, disposal of nonbiodegradable screened materials,

insurance, supplies, contingency costs, and overhead are a minimum $4 per cubic yard for 1989. Higher costs, however, are being reported for some operations around the country (Glenn, 1989). This cost would be higher if (1) the site is operating at less than design capacity, (2) there is extensive downtime at the site when leaves are initially being windrowed, or when leaves are being turned, and (3) shredding/screening small quantities of leaves at one time.

The largest cost components would be for shredding/screening, land, and overhead, accounting for over half the total costs. Equipment other than the screener/shredder would be shared with other municipal departments and no buildings would be constructed at the compost site. Further, these costs reflect only the cost of leaf composting and do not include the disposal of wastewood and tree and grass clippings. Marketing costs would be minimal in that the finished compost would be used by the municipality, picked up by local residents, and some sold to local landscapers. Overall, offsetting some of the costs via compost sales would not be of concern to the municipality.

An alternative approach for municipalities could include a countywide program whereby county government purchases the equipment and composts the leaves (turns the leaves with a windrow turner) at local municipal sites. Equipment would be transported instead of leaves. This would be appropriate for a situation where local sites are available but the leaves from each municipality are relatively small in volume. The county would then prorate the cost over the annual volume of leaves composted and establish fees for the individual municipalities. This approach would minimize transport costs which would be higher if a centralized county facility was constructed.

Other options include the establishment of a common compost site that a consortium of nearby municipalities could use and operate. Each would make contributions to the labor and/or equipment time required. Coordination and increased labor costs may be a concern in that personnel and equipment will have to be moved between the site and the municipalities' public works facilities. Alternatively, one municipality could accept the leaves of one or two neighboring municipalities for a fee and in turn lower unit costs.

COMMERCIAL COMPOSTING OPERATION

For municipalities that are highly developed (high population densities per acre), there would be difficulty in finding suitable composting sites (affordable acreage located away from housing to avoid conflicts over odors). For these situations, leaves will have to be transported and composted several miles from the point of origination in which private commercial operators may be employed to handle the flow. These sites would be relatively large (80,000 cubic yards or more) and would handle leaves from several sources. In time, they would have to devote resources to the marketing of the end product which could generate revenue to offset the cost of leaf composting.

This type of facility would be more capital intensive than the 5,000 or 30,000 cubic yard operation in order for the leaves to be properly composted. Windrow turners would be used so that leaves could be turned frequently and composted quickly, buildings would be required to house personnel and equipment, and more resources would be devoted to marketing because of the large volume of finished compost produced. Since this would be high technology composting, the process would take less than 150 days.

More time and effort would go into the overall management because of the size and arrangements with several municipalities. This would involve more office work—weighing, billing, etc. Preliminary estimates indicate that a minimum cost would be about $6.00 per cubic yard for 1989. Again, operating at less than design capacity would raise costs significantly. This cost would include land, site improvements, buildings, equipment, screening, engineering, maintenance, labor supplies, insurance, disposal costs, contingencies, and return to management. The largest cost component would be labor, depreciation, and interest on investment in equipment and land, accounting for two-thirds of the total costs. A slightly higher return on resources is allowed for because of risk to private capital as compared to a municipal operation.

The composting costs for this alternative are higher because a substantial up-front investment is required as compared to the on-farm or the municipal operations which are "add-on" activities. Further, unlike the seasonal nature of the first two alternatives, this is a year round operation bearing substantial overhead costs. Also, personnel would be full-time and not part-time. Operating at less than design capacity, expensive and lengthy design approval costs by county and state agencies, and changing recycling regulations would increase total composting costs still further. On the other hand, establishing markets for compost could lower these costs over the long term, as a dependable flow of leaves develops for the operator.

ECONOMIES OF SCALE

So far, only the costs of operating a compost site have been considered. Composting costs per cubic yard of leaves are highest for the larger commercial operation and lowest for the smaller on-farm operation, with the medium sized municipal operation being inbetween. Obviously, this implies that the composting operations are subject to diseconomies of scale which is contrary to the economic theory.

According to the economic theory, normally economies of scale are expected for larger sizes because of the better organization of labor force and possibilities of using larger pieces of equipment. However, this apparent contradiction is explained by the very different nature of the three operations considered here. The operations differ not only in size, but more importantly in the mode of ownership and scope as well. The on-farm and the municipal operations are seasonal in nature and represent add-ons to large existing farm and public works departments, respectively. As a result, the equipment and labor services are obtained at a modest cost without the involvement of new investments and overhead. On the other hand, the larger commercial operation is a year round activity requiring major new investments and full-time staff which contribute to relatively higher costs.

The economies or diseconomies of scale are subject to further modification when costs of collecting and transporting leaves to the site are considered. Although leaves do have to be picked up, transported and disposed of either at the landfill or the compost site, transport costs do not remain neutral when considering the economies of size over the full range of compost sites. As the size of any facility increases, leaves must be transported a greater distance, resulting in a higher transport cost.

The rise in cost would not necessarily be that large because a significant portion of the costs would be due to the loading and unloading of the truck, which would not change with distance. For the 5,000 and 30,000 cubic-yard sites previously discussed, distance would not be that great—say 15 miles at the maximum for a one-way distance. On the other hand, for the larger site (80,000 cubic yards or more), transportation costs could be significantly higher in that distance would increase rapidly, perhaps three to four times. This is likely to further accentuate the diseconomies of scale seen in the composting phase of this operation. However, if nearby farms or open lands are not available, municipalities may not have much choice except to bear the higher costs of a commercial operation.

SUMMARY

While the technical aspects of municipal leaf composting have been largely worked out, the economic and political dimensions are still being debated. Some of these latter issues include: (1) What is the optimum size of a composting facility in terms of minimizing costs per cubic yard? (2) What is the best form of ownership—public or private? and (3) Will the size and location influence both the ownership and the level of technology?

Municipalities that are still rural in character but generate less than 15,000 cubic yards annually, should consider sub-contracting with local farm operators. Today, windrow turners are available in a wide range of sizes. For an on-farm composting facility, equipment purchase could be limited to a small windrow turner powered by a farm tractor. Costs can be kept to a minimum because of lower overhead due to reduced land and site costs.

Several options are available for medium sized municipalities. One is where they compost their own leaves using low-technology. Composting costs, though higher than the on-farm composting costs, will be reasonable. The major expense would be for the composting site since equipment costs could be minimized by utilizing equipment from the public works department. Sharing of a common site by a consortium of municipalities whereby personnel and equipment are transported to the site to complete the composting is another option. Or, a county may consider purchasing and operating a windrow turner to service several small municipal sites for a fee.

More developed communities, however, may have to look outside their municipal boundaries because of the lack of local suitable sites. Large facilities which are privately owned and operated may serve these communities. Not only will transport costs be higher in this case, but also composting costs will be higher as full-time personnel, large equipment and high overhead costs will be involved. Out of all these alternatives available to municipalities, local circumstances will dictate the most feasible alternative.

REFERENCES

Derr, D.A. 1988. Economics of Leaf Composting. *Waste Age*, December.

Dhillon, P.S. and R.G. Latimer. 1986. Costs of Producing Market Vegetables in Southern New Jersey. P-02131-1-86. Rutgers University Department of Agricultural Economics and Marketing.

Glenn, J. 1989. Private Management of Yard Waste. *BioCycle, Journal of Recycling*. Vol. 31, No. 1, pp. 26-28.

Madden, P. 1988. Policy Options for a More Sustainable Agriculture. Proceedings, 38th National Public Policy Education Conference, September 2-15, 1988, Cincinnati, Ohio, pp. 134-142.

McMahon, J. 1986. A Development Project Outline. *Waste Age*. December. p. 68.

Office of Recycling. 1982. How to Obtain a Composting Permit. New Jersey Department of Environmental Protection, State of New Jersey.

Strom, P.F. and M.S. Finstein. 1985. Leaf Composting Manual for New Jersey Municipalities. Rutgers University Department of Environmental Science.

USDA. 1988. Low-Input/Sustainable Agriculture. Research and Education Program. Cooperative State Research Service and Extension Service, United States Department of Agriculture, Washington, D.C.

Donn A. Derr and Pritam S. Dhillon are Associate Professors in the Department of Agricultural Economics and Marketing, New Jersey Agricultural Experiment Station, Cook College, Rutgers, the State University of New Jersey, New Brunswick, New Jersey 08903. Paper of the Journal Series No. D-02513-01-89 of the New Jersey Agricultural Experiment Station.

48

CALCULATING COSTS OF LEAF COMPOSTING

AFTER New Jersey enacted its leaf composting law, Morris County expanded its composting facility to assist neighboring towns. The Shade Tree Commission accepted the responsibility of managing the composting operation and set a goal to provide a program that would be self-sustaining at the lowest possible cost to participating municipalities. Clarence Peterson, the County Forester and Alan Little, Assistant County Forester, have published a report which shows how they arrive at a tipping fee per load that they charge the municipalities to meet this goal.

Leaves are composted in windrows and turned periodically, with compost matured in 120 days. Participating municipalities can pick up compost at no cost. Non-participating municipalities can buy compost at $1/cu. yd. Residents can get compost at no cost other than delivery, which runs $40/ 7 yd. load. Any surplus compost is offered to private contractors; the minimum is 100 cu. yds. at $1.50/yd.

To figure operating costs, Peterson and Little first calculated the Commission's "Hourly Production Rate" which is based on man hours, equipment, and operating expenses. The average man hour production rate (total hours divided by 19 employees, from forester at $70,621 including fringe benefits to tree trimmer at $27,872 with benefits) is $21.27.

Next Peterson and Little calculated an "hourly equipment cost" based on depreciation and replacement schedules. They used a straight line method of depreciation for a given period of time and based replacement cost per year on a 70 percent increase over the original equipment purchase price minus the salvage value divided by the equipment life. Purchase value of all equipment was $324,277; salvage value, $64,861.20; annual depreciation, $25,944.48; and annual replacement $48,645.90. The average hourly equipment rate therefore equalled the total replacement cost plus the total depreciation divided by 32,300 total production manhours (1,700 production hours per employee times 19), or $2.31.

Other expenses incurred—office budget, equipment maintenance, fuel, rent, equipment rental—amounted to $115,000, divided by 32,300, giving the average hourly operating expense rate of $3.56. Adding together the average man hour production rate, average equipment rate and average operating expense rate gave an hourly production rate total of $27.14.

A site maintenance cost was set at 25¢/cu. yd., with the site's capacity at 25,000 cu. yd. or $6,250.00.

Development of 75 acres of combined compost facilities was calculated at an in-house cost of $6,000 per acre or $450,000. Distributed over 10 years on the basis of one million cu. yds. of leaves equals $.45/cu. yd.

Adding the facility costs and then dividing by the facility capacity brought a base rate of $4.16/ cu. yd.

Current charge is $4.10, or a deficit of 6¢ per cu. yd.—$1500 on a capacity of 25,000 cu. yd. "We think we can reduce that by the sale of surplus compost after county and municipal demands are met," says Little.

49

ECONOMICS
WORKSHEET

AS SET FORTH by the staff of the Compost Program, Massachusetts Department of Environmental Protection, composting offers municipalities four economic benefits:

If disposal fees are calculated by tonnage, composting reduces tonnage by as much as 18 percent;

If a municipality owns a landfill, diverting leaf and yard waste transfers into a minimum savings of $50 per ton for each ton diverted;

Soil amendment purchases can be reduced or even eliminated;

Income from sale of finished product can reduce costs.

To assist towns and cities in Massachusetts to assess costs of start-up and operation of projects, the state's composting group prepared an Economics Worksheet which included figures for three communities (Newton, Springfield and Holden) as well as a format for cost calculations: The staff cautions that the sampling should not be taken as a standard against which to measure your costs. "Figures for each community vary greatly due to the many variables involved in starting up and operating a municipal leaf and yard waste composting facility," note the staff. The worksheet was prepared with the assistance of Lawrence Galkowski, P.E.

Following is the worksheet and general instructions for use:

START-UP (CAPITAL) COSTS

If you are able to pay for both site preparation and equipment using existing funds, they are a one-time expense and should be recorded on the worksheet in the space for total one-time start-up costs.

However, in order to incorporate these costs into the annual cost of composting, you must also annualize separately the costs of site preparation and equipment.

To annualize site preparation costs, divide them by 10 (years). To annualize equipment costs, divide cost of each piece of capital equipment by its estimated life span. (Front end loaders, other types of trucks and collection vehicles typically need replacement in 7 years; shredders, windrow turners, chippers, and screeners in 10 years.) The sum of the annualized site preparation and annualized equipment costs equals the total amortized start-up costs/yr.

If you will need to borrow or issue a bond for part or all of the start-up costs, the principal and interest will be amortized over the loan payback period.

Site Preparation: The cost of engineering design is the cost of the engineer's or planner's time. If an in-house employee is used, remember to include the cost of fringe benefits in hourly rate.

Equipment: Several types of equipment may be used. The cost of any equipment not used solely for the compost project should be multiplied by the percentage of time per year it is used in the compost operation. In order to determine this percentage, you must decide whether your operation will be open year-round or fall only, for how many days/year and for how many hours/day.

Typically, the only heavy equipment needed is a front end loader. It may be needed almost full-time during the fall but only infrequently for the rest of the year. Its use will vary according to the drop-off schedule, the volume of material received, and whether any other heavy equipment is used to perform the same function.

In order to simplify the worksheet, the existence of specific conditions in your community has been presumed (see below). If your community differs, include any additional start-up costs under "other".

The presumptions:
1. Site is on municipally-owned land.
2. Site already has an access road.
3. A municipal employee is available who can draw up a simple site plan to scale (e.g., engineer, planner, highway superintendent).
4. A front end loader is available.
5. Water is accessible at the site (piped or trucked in).

OPERATIONAL COSTS

Labor: The smallest operation requires two people—one to operate the front end loader and one to double as site overseer and waterer. This person can serve both functions if drop-offs are relatively small and staggered throughout the day.

Very large or continuous drop-offs require a separate overseer and waterer.

Remember to perform separate calculations for each individual if personnel are paid at different rates.

Some communities have reduced their labor costs by using volunteers for site monitoring.

Fuel and maintenance: These costs for each piece of equipment (and labor, if you lease equipment and operator at a flat rate) should be multiplied by the percentage of time per year that each piece is used in the compost operation.

Use the following formula to calculate labor, fuel and maintenance costs. Remember to include fringe benefits in the hourly rate for labor.

$$(\$ \quad /hr) \times (\quad hrs/wk) \times (\quad wks/yr) = \$_____$$

Related costs: These will be minimal if you intend to use the end product for DPW projects and give away the balance to residents. However, if you want to sell the end product, you will need to maintain a higher level of quality control. Paying customers demand a consistently high quality product.

COST PROFILE FOR THREE COMMUNITIES

	Newton	*Springfield**	*Holden**
Year of Start-up	86-87	88-89	88-89
Population	83,000	159,000	14,000
Turning Equipment	Front End Loader	Windrow Turner (Scarab)	Front End Loader
Collection System	Street bulk & small scale curbside	curbside in bags & drop-off	drop-off
YEAR 1			
Tons Composted	925	4,040	150
Cost/Ton	$10.36	$47.00	$70.60
YEAR 2			
Tons Composted	3,000	5,000	500
Cost/Ton	$4.17	$29.00	$13.60
Tipping Fee	$80	$30	$25
NET COSTS AND SAVINGS			
Avoided Disposal Cost	$240,000	$150,000	$12,500
Avoided Soil Purchases	$27,000	$50,000	$4,500
TOTAL NET SAVINGS:	**$254,000**	**$55,000**	**$10,200**

Springfield and Holden figures are estimated.

EQUIPMENT AND SUPPLIES PRICE LIST
(updated August 1989)

Roll-off Open Container:

20 cu yd	$ 2,800
30 cu yd	$ 3,000
40 cu yd	$ 3,600

Packer Truck:

20 cu yd capacity	$ 63,000 - $ 84,000
31 cu yd capacity	$115,000 - $168,000

Water Tank Truck:

new	$ 52,000 - $ 68,000
used (surplus)	$ 10,000 - $ 15,000

Front End Loader:

1-2 cu yd bucket	$ 40,000 - $ 60,000
3-4 cu yd bucket	$115,000 - $168,000

Tractors with Creeper Gear:

116 HP	$ 93,000
177 HP	$109,000
225 HP	$132,000
300 HP	$150,000

Windrow Turner:

Tractor Attachment	$ 12,000 - $ 25,000
Self-Propelled	$104,000 - $157,000 - $262,000
Tractor with Augor	$105,000 - $155,000

Vacuum Pick-up:

Tow Behind	$ 9,300 - $ 10,500
Chassis Mount	$ 15,700 - $ 17,700
Vacuum Truck	$ 57,700 - $ 63,000

Shredder/Screener:

45 cu yd/hr	$ 27,000 - $ 33,000

Screen:

30 HP, 6 cu yd hopper capacity	$ 68,000
70 HP, 8 cu yd hopper capacity	$131,000 - $136,000

Tub Grinder:

Mobile	$ 63,000 - $157,000
Stationary	$147,000 - $294,000

Hose:

2" high pressure	$2.83 - $3.78/foot
1½" construction grade	$ .94 - $1.15/foot

Water Pump:

1½" to 2" discharge	$800 - $1,000

6" Water Line (installed)	$26.88/foot
Paper Leaf Bags:	$262/thousand

Note: All prices are rounded off and will vary depending on manufacturer.

COST BENEFIT WORKSHEET FORMAT

START-UP (CAPITAL) COSTS

Site Preparation
    Engineering Design   _____
    Grading, drainage & pad prep.   _____

Equipment
    Thermometers (2)   _____
    Other   _____
    TOTAL ONE-TIME START-UP
        COSTS: $_____
TOTAL AMORTIZED START-UP
        COSTS/YR: $_____

OPERATIONAL COSTS

Labor
    Monitoring incoming materials and
    directing vehicles: _____
    Forming windrows (loader operator) _____
    Turning windrows (loader operator) _____
    Watering windrows: _____
    Monitoring temperature: _____

Fuel and Maintenance
    Front end loader   _____

Related Costs
    Lab analysis of compost   _____
    Marketing/distribution compost   _____
        TOTAL OPERATIONAL
        COSTS/YR: $_____

MISCELLANEOUS COSTS
    Public Education   _____
    Bags (optional)   _____
        TOTAL MISCELLANEOUS
        COSTS/YR: $_____

OPTIONAL OPERATIONAL COSTS

Equipment, Related Labor and O & M

	AMORTIZED PRICE OF EQUIPMENT	LABOR	O & M
Separator/shredder	_____	_____	_____
Chipper	_____	_____	_____
Windrow turner	_____	_____	_____
Screener	_____	_____	_____
Water truck	_____	_____	_____
Subtotal:	_____ +	_____ +	_____ = _____

Other Optional Labor
Debagging   _____
Manual leaf separation and shredding   _____
Site maintenance   _____
        Subtotal: _____

OPTIONAL COLLECTION COSTS *(continued)*

Equipment, Related Labor and O & M

	AMORTIZED PRICE OF EQUIPMENT	LABOR	O & M
Compactor truck	_____	_____	_____
Loader w/claw	_____	_____	_____
Vacuum truck	_____	_____	_____
Dump truck	_____	_____	_____
Catch basin cleaner	_____	_____	_____
Subtotal:	_____ +	_____ +	_____ = _____

TOTAL OPTIONAL COLLECTION COSTS/YR: $_____

COST EFFECTIVENESS ANALYSIS: COMPOSTING VS. CURRENT METHOD

TOTAL COSTS

   A. Total amortized start-up costs/yr $_____

   B. Total operational costs/yr $_____

   C. Total miscellaneous costs/yr $_____

   D. Total optional operational costs/yr $_____

   E. Total optional collection costs/yr $_____

   F. (A + B + C + D + E) Total Costs/Yr $_____

TOTAL BENEFITS

   G. Avoided disposal cost/yr $_____

   H. Avoided purchases of soil amendments/yr $_____

   I. Projected income from sale of compost/yr $_____

   J. (G + H + I) Total Benefits/Year $_____

TOTAL NET SAVINGS OR COST

   K. (J − F if J > F) *Net Savings/Year* $_____

   L. (F − J if F > J) Net Cost/Year $_____

OPTIONAL OPERATIONAL COSTS

Equipment: For some large scale operations, or those with a highly specific market for the end product, it may be advisable to purchase or lease a specialized piece of equipment.

Labor, fuel and maintenance: See data for approximate costs.

Other optional labor: Debagging costs range from $13 to $26 per hour (.82 tons/person hour). Some communities save money by using volunteer labor for debagging.

OPTIONAL COLLECTION COSTS

If you already pick up yard wastes separately from other MSW, your collection costs will not increase unless your composting site is further away than your current disposal site.

Labor, fuel and maintenance: Some communities use two people per collection vehicle—a driver and a collector. Some are able to get by with only one.

COST EFFECTIVENESS ANALYSIS: COMPOSTING VS. CURRENT METHOD

Items A through E should be copied from the Section totals in boldface.

Items G through I should be calculated using the following formulas.

Current disposal cost = hauling cost/ton + tipping cost/ton

Line G:
Avoided disposal cost/yr = current disposal cost × projected volume to be composted

Line H:
Avoided purchases of soil amendments/yr = annual cost of soil purchases as long as your fall composting operation remains open as much as the volume demands

Projected volume of end product = volume of L&YW composted × .33

Line I:
Projected income from sale of compost/yr = (projected volume of end product - volume of avoided soil purchases) × $8/cu yd

Section
X

COMPOSTING YARD WASTE WITH OTHER MATERIALS

50

COCOMPOSTING GREEN WASTES

G.R. van Roosmalen and J.C. van de Langerijt

IN THE NETHERLANDS, there are 64 auctions (produce terminals) where vegetables and fruits are sold. To protect farmer interests, merchandise which does not receive a minimum price is taken off the market. As a result, each year 50,000 tons of vegetables and 21,000 tons of fruit are mostly dumped in landfills.

Since these materials have a high water content and produce odors, landfills either increasingly refuse to accept these wastes or charge premium fees. The auction C.V.V. Grubbenvorst in the southeastern province of Limburg generates 7,000 tons of waste annually, mainly from June to October. A research composting project was begun to find an alternative disposal method, undertaken in cooperation with the Waste Management Program of Tilburg and Eindhoven Universities.

The objectives of the experiments were to study the possibility of composting auction waste in combination with other green wastes which arise in large quantities in the Province of Limburg. If the results were positive, a composting plant would be designed for the composting of the selected wastes. This article describes the pilot experiments where auction waste was composted in combination with chipped wood from public gardens and where auction waste was composted in combination with separately collected vegetable, fruit and garden wastes from households.

The public garden waste was selected as a bulking agent because it takes up water and because it gives a desirable structure in the composting material. Public garden waste arises in an estimated quantity of 28,000 tons in the province of Limburg each year. The separately collected vegetable, fruit and garden waste was selected because

the policy of the Dutch government and of the province of Limburg is to introduce large scale collection systems where the separate collection and composting of the organic waste of households stands central.

MATERIALS AND METHODS

In the pilot experiments, the method of composting is with forced aeration. The mixture of auction waste with bulking agent was composted on a pile situated over a perforated plastic pipe (diameter pipe 185 mm, aeration area 16.8 cm2/m pipe). The pipe was connected to a ventilator (capacity 950 m3 air/hr by a static pressure of 1000 Pa) which was installed in such a way that it could either extract air or blow air through the pipe. The extracted air was not filtered to get an impression of the arising odors.

Due to the high water content of the starting material, aeration quantity had to be adjusted carefully on the conditions in the pile. Therefore the ventilator was linked with a temperature sensor in the compost pile. When the temperature in the pile exceeded 58°C, the ventilator was switched on. Below 53°C, the ventilator was switched off. In addition to this automatic adjustment, a base aeration was continuously regulated by a time switch. The total time of aeration was registered by a time clock, the pile was situated under a roof which protected it from rain, and the underground consisted of a stone floor.

Composting of the mixture of auction waste and chipped wood started in July, 1988. The auction waste consisted of salad, tomatoes, cucumbers and French beans. The wood was pruned from public gardens and roughly cut in pieces. Both materials were mixed in a ration of 1:1 (on weight basis) with a mechanical shovel, but mixing was not carried out intensively. The mixture was put on a pile over the perforated pipe. The length of the pile was 11m, the width at the base 3.4m, and at the top 1.5m. The volume of the pile was 32 m3. It contained 5.8 tons of auction waste and 6.2 tons of chipped wood.

The composting of the mixture of auction waste and separately collected organics from households started in November, 1988. The auction waste consisted of cabbage, carrots, capsicums, French beans and salad. The separately collected organics were a mixture of vegetable, fruit and garden wastes which contained many leaves. To prevent leaching of percolation water, 0.5 tons of chipped wood from the former experiment and a small part of the organics were put over the perforated pipe as a relatively dry underlayer. The auction waste and the organics were now mixed in a ratio of 1:1.5 (weight basis) with the mechanical shovel. This mixture was put on the underlayer. To obtain equal composting conditions throughout the pile, 6.3 tons of compost from the former experiment were put over the pile as a cover layer. The dimensions of the pile were 9.2m × 4.6m × 1.8m (l × w × h). The volume of the pile was 36 m3. It contained 7.4 tons auction waste, 12.3 tons separately collected organics, 0.5 tons of chipped wood and 6.3 tons of compost.

During the composting of the auction waste the following measurements were carried out: *Daily:* temperature in the pile; aeration time; air velocity in the pipe during aeration. *Weekly:* water content in the pile; height of the pile. *Other:* weight of the pile (start and end of the composting); chemical analyses (starting material and final products); sieve fractions of the final products.

Temperature of the composting waste was measured daily at three different places in the pile. Air velocity in the pipe during aeration was measured daily with a digital air velocity meter. Together with the total time of aeration, which was readable on the time-clock, the total amount of air used to aerate the composting material was calculated. Every week the water content of the pile was determined from the weight loss of samples after drying 24 hr at 105°C. Final products were first sieved at 70mm then the small fractions were sieved again at 18mm. After the sieving, all fractions were weighed. Samples from the starting material and the final products were analyzed for water content, organic content, nitrogen, extractable organic halides and heavy metals.

Chemical analyses of the fresh auction waste were carried out on a composite sample which contained parts of all vegetables which were present in the waste. Parts were also taken for chemical analyses from the chipped wood and separately collected organics. The water content in the pile was determined on samples which were taken at three different places in the pile at a height of 0.6m above the ground. In addition, parts of the sieve fraction smaller than 18mm were taken from the final products, for the chemical analyses.

COMPOSTING AUCTION WASTE AND CHIPPED WOOD

The mixture of auction waste and chipped wood was aerated by air extraction with the ventilator. During the composting, no annoying odors were detected. A very limited amount of percolation water was generated (180 ltr.) which was intercepted and spread over the pile. Figure 1 shows the temperature, the aeration quantity, and the water content of the pile during composting.

The temperature in the pile increased in four days to 60°C. Above 58°C, the ventilator was switched on by the sensor in the pile and extracted more air. The temperature now decreased and stabilized at 50/55°C. After two weeks, the upper layer of the pile was relatively dry with regard to the underlayer. To dry the underlayer the ventilator was switched from air extraction to blowing at day 15. Due to a higher air capacity of the ventilator during blowing, the time-clock regulated aeration quantity now doubled. This caused a rapid temperature decrease in the pile. At this moment, the composting conditions of the pile had become less favorable. The volume of the pile had decreased from 32 m3 at the start of the composting to 20 m3 at day 22. The surface area of the pile was too small to hold enough warmth for optimal composting. Even switching off the ventilator could (in this case) not raise the temperature in the pile.

At day 27, the pile was turned and reformed with a smaller surface area. The new dimensions of the pile were 5.3m × 4m × 1.5m (l × w × h). After turning, the temperature quickly rose to 50°C. The fresh compost was sieved 43 days after the start of the composting. The starting material contained 68 percent water (weight basis) which rapidly decreased during composting. After turning, an increase in water content was measured because the wet underlayer was mixed with the relatively dry upper layer. The fresh compost contained 48 percent water.

COMPOSTING AUCTION WASTE AND COLLECTED ORGANICS

The mixture of auction waste and separately collected organics was aerated by air extraction with the ventilator. During the composting, no annoying odors were detected and no percolation water was generated. Figure 2 shows the temperature, the aeration quantity and the water content of the pile during composting. The temperature in the pile rose quickly to 65°C and then stabilized at 55°C. In the following weeks, the temperature slowly decreased to 45°C at the moment of turning (day 27). The volume of the pile had decreased from 36 m3 at the start of the composting to 25 m3 at day 27. In this time, the water content had decreased from 78 percent to 53 percent.

After turning, almost no air was extracted through the pile because the aeration area of the perforated pipe was blocked by compost from the cover layer. Switching the ventilator from air extraction to blowing at day 38 could not solve this problem. The lack of aeration caused an increase in water content in the underlayer of the pile. The fresh compost was sieved at day 46 and contained 58 percent moisture.

TABLE 1:
Mass balance of auction waste and chipped wood and particle size of fresh compost

	Total (kg × 1000)	Water (kg × 1000)	Dry weight (kg × 1000)
Input			
auction waste	5.8	5.5	0.3
chipped wood	6.2	2.5	3.7
Total	12.0	8.0	4.0
Output			
Total	7.7	3.7	4.0
>70mm	0.2		
18-70mm	1.2		
<18mm	6.3		

TABLE 2:
Mass balance of auction waste and separately collected organics and particle size of fresh compost.

	Total (kg × 1000)	Water (kg × 1000)	Dry weight (kg × 1000)
Input			
auction waste	7.4	6.8	0.6
organics	12.2	8.5	3.7
pruned wood	0.5	0.2	0.3
compost	6.3	3.1	3.2
Total	26.4	18.6	7.8
Output			
Total	17.9	10.3	7.6
>70mm	1.4		
18-70mm	1.6		
<18mm	14.9		

MASS BALANCE

During composting, 4.2 tons of water were evaporated. This is 53 percent of the water in the starting material; 82 percent of the fresh compost was smaller than 18mm. This compost can be used in different applications (agricultural, public gardens, gardens, etc). The larger sieve fractions have to be cut in pieces before use. The mass balance of the composting of auction waste in combination with separately collected organics, and the particle size distribution of the so obtained fresh compost is given in Table 2. The starting material contained 18.6 tons of water. During composting, 8.3 tons of this water (44.6 percent) were evaporated; 83 percent of the fresh compost was smaller than 18mm.

CHEMICAL ANALYSIS

The results of the chemical analysis of starting materials and of the final products are given in Table 3. This table contains the standards for the use of compost in agricultural applications that will be used by the Dutch government after 1992.

The values of Table 3 show that the produced compost is of an excellent quality. The heavy metal concentrations in the compost are only a fraction of the standards that will be applied after 1992. The EOX concentration, which is indicative for remainders of insecticides, pesticides etc. is very low and will not influence the use of the composts.

From the results of the analysis, it can be calculated that the C/N value of the final products is about 12. This indicates that the final products are well stabilized. The compost produced from auction waste and pruned wood contained some germinative weed seeds. In the second experiment when a cover layer was used, no germinative seeds were detected in the compost.

The water content of the composts is relatively high. This was caused by aeration problems during composting. These problems can be solved which will result in lower water content in the final products.

CONCLUSION

It is possible to compost the very wet auction waste in combination with chipped wood from public gardens (ratio 1:1) and in combination with separately collected organics from households (ratio 1:1.5). During the composting of these very wet mixtures, no annoying odors were detected and no percolation water problems arose.

During composting of these wastes, it is important to get an efficient control of the composting conditions. This can be achieved by using forced aeration whereby the aeration quantity must be adjusted to the temperature in the pile.

The final products were of an excellent quality

FIGURE 1:
Temperature, aeration quantity and water content during composting of auction waste with chipped wood.

FIGURE 2:
Temperature, aeration quantity and water content during composting of auction waste with separately collected organics.

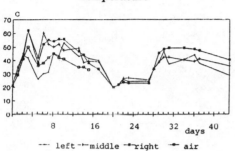

Auction waste and organics
Temperature

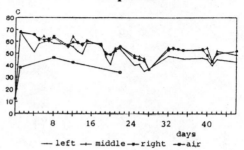

Auction waste and chipped wood
Temperature

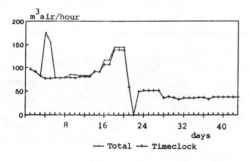

Auction waste and organics
Aeration

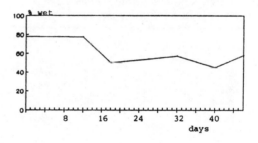

Auction waste and chipped wood
Aeration

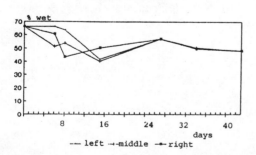

Auction waste and organics
Water Content

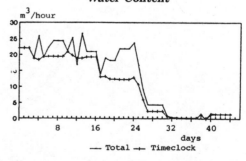

Auction waste and chipped wood
Water Content

and will easily meet the future Dutch standards for the use of compost. The results of these experiments have led the Gewest Northern Limburg and the Province of Limburg to prepare for the design and construction of a plant for the composting of different green wastes which arise in the Dutch Province of Limburg.

TABLE 3:
Chemical analysis of starting materials and final products, and governmental standards for compost use after 1992.

	auction waste 1	chipped wood 2	organics 3 3	compost from 1 and 2	compost from 1 and 3	standards after 1992
water content	92.8	40	69.7	48	60	
organic content	73	51	74	27	25	
Nitrogen	29	21	20	12	15	
EOX	6.2	1.9	5.8	1.7	2.5	
Cd	0.34	0.58	1.5	0.97	0.55	2
Cr	2.6	25	21	36	32	200
Cu	10	30	18	28	23	300
Pb	4	28	25	42	38	200
Ni	2.6	5.2	6	7.1	10	50
Zn	54	160	280	170	135	900
Hg	0.07	0.32	0.05	0.08	0.06	2

- *water content in % wet weight*
- *organic content in % dry weight*
- *Nitrogen in g/kg dry weight*
- *EOX = extractable organic halides in mg/kg dry weight*
- *heavy metals in mg/kg dry weight*

LITERATURE

1. Finstein, M.S., e.a. Composting ecosystem management for waste treatment. *Biotechnology,* June 1983, Vol 1, Number 4.
2. Heidemij Reststoffendiensten B.V., Waste Management Programm. Verwerking Groenafval Noord-Limburg, January, 1989.

G.R. van Roosmalen is with the Waste Management Program of Tilburg University—Eindhoven University. J.C. van de Langerijt was with Heidemij Reststoffendiensten during the experiments.

51

YARD WASTE AS BULKING AGENT

WOOD CHIPS or sawdust have been commonly used as a bulking agent in sludge composting projects. Recently as the price of wood chips has climbed to $10 per cubic yard, yard waste — specifically shredded tree trimmings and brush — is being used as an alternative bulking agent.

"We should be able to recycle daily around 25 tons of yard waste plus Christmas trees, logs cleared from local streams and leaves," reports Dan Chlebanowski, manager of the sludge composting facility operated by the DuPage County Public Works Department in Woodridge, Illinois. As part of a pilot project last year, the facility used a stump chipper to reduce 18,000 Christmas trees collected in Naperville. The chips worked well as a bulking agent in the aerated static pile system which composts 10 dry tons per day.

Logs that were up to 48 inches in diameter were handled by the chipper. "It's all part of our effort to reduce the amount of material going to the landfills," says Chlebanowski who has also been testing leaves (up to 25 percent) in the bulking agent mix. Last summer, the facility bought 5,000 cubic yards of woodchips, but with the flow of material coming in from tree services plus what is collected by county crews. The finished product (about 14,000 cubic yards a year) is mainly marketed to nurseries and greenhouses at $4/cu yd. "This year about half of our total production has been 'specified' in landscape projects," adds Chlebanowski. The world-famous Morton Arboretum in nearby Lisle is also a big user of the compost. The yard waste bulking agent is mixed with sludge at a ratio of three to one, sometimes as low as two to one.

CREATING PRODUCT FOR COUNTY TREE NURSERY

When the sludge composting facility in Broward County, Florida first began, the wood chips used as the bulking agent were supplied by Streets and Highways Division tree trimming crews. In 1982, when the amount of sludge received by the facility increased, the need for a greater amount of bulking agents also increased. Explains Bill Farrell, Nursery Supervisor:

"A readily available source of wood chips is now supplied by private tree-trimming companies who are happy to deliver their waste to the compost facility because tipping fees at the public and private landfills are $60 to $80 a load. Over 25,000 cubic yards of wood material that would otherwise be wasted is delivered each year.

"At the time of delivery, sewage sludge is placed on a bed of wood chips 18″ to 24″ thick. The front-end loader mixes the wood chips with the sewage sludge until a good uniform mixture is achieved. It is then placed in the first position, making a windrow about 12' high and 24' across at the bottom, eventually making a windrow 200' long. After windrow number one is completed it is aerated by turning it over into the next position with the front-end loader. This process is repeated every ten days for a total of three aerations.

"After the last aeration, the compost is moved by truck to the storage area for curing. If the compost is to be used as a top dressing or artificial top soil, it can be applied after three months of curing. When the compost is to be used as a soilless potting medium, it is generally allowed to cure for at least six months."

Although the Broward County facility is no longer operational, a nearby project in Fort Lauderdale started using tree trimmings and brush as a bulking agent to cut costs and increase recycling capability. The Fort Lauderdale Compost Facility is designed to handle 32 tons of sludge per day. The dewatered sludge ranges from 16 to 18 percent solids.

According to Glenn Cunningham, a civil engineer with Hazen and Sawyer who helped to design the facility, bulking agent requirements to attain the desired feed moisture is about a 3:1 ratio of bulking agent to sludge cake based upon an aerated pile compost system. The quantity and dryness of recycled product can reduce this ratio. At maximum design, 35 tpd (dry) or 250 cubic/yards of sludge cake will be processed on a daily basis. The aerated pile compost system would require about 750 cy/day of wood chips. Even recovering 80 percent of the chips, about 150 cy/day of make-up bulking agent are required. Cost to purchase wood chips was estimated to range from $800 to $1,200 per day depending upon the source and quality in Florida.

In-vessel compost mass balance calculations indicated that typical volume requirements of the waste streams are as follows:

Volume Ratio	Material	Moisture Content Percent
1	Sludge cake	16-18%
1	Bulking agent	50-60%
1	Recycle	35-40%

Yard waste and tree trimmings make up a large percent of the solid waste stream in south Florida. Florida has recently deemed that yard waste must be removed from the solid waste stream and not be placed in sanitary landfills. In 1983/84 the decision was made by the City staff and consultants to capture a part of the yard waste stream and use it as a bulking agent. Compost vendors were given an anticipated volume of yard waste to be delivered to the site and processed as bulking agent. Quantities were specified at a minimum of 500 to a maximum of 1,200 cubic yards per week.

Currently about 1,000 to 1,500 cy per week of yard waste is delivered to the site. The City accepts good material at no charge. Tipping fees at the landfills are about $7 per cubic yard. In the future, the facility may charge a nominal $1 to $2 per cubic yard fee to cover handling cost.

The vendor was responsible to design a system that could shred the yard waste, so that the final compost product would consist of material in which 90 percent of product is less than 1/2 inch.

Two shredders with 250 hp drives were installed to mulch the yard waste. Continuous problems have occurred due to the mixed consistency of the yard waste. Certain types of native tropical brush (i.e., palm fronds) bound the shredders. Modifications to the shredders coupled with more selective brush feed practices reduced plugging problems. The City and consultant have taken the following steps to enhance the shredding operation.

1. Purchase a tub grinder and a drop spout wood chipper to chip bulky yard waste.

2. Design a screen to segregate bulky sized materials from the yard waste stream.

52

COCOMPOSTING SLUDGE AND YARD WASTE

THE INGREDIENTS for composting success were apparently properly blended to select, design, and build a facility for composting sewage sludge, leaves, and yard waste from the town of Fairfield, Connecticut. This organic waste recycling project, which began in August, 1989, is also processing street sweepings and muck from drainage catch basins.

The plan to initiate a sludge composting system was developed by Richard White, Chief Operating Engineer of the wastewater treatment plant, as well as the composting program. His staff conducted an engineering feasibility study of sludge disposal, and in 1987 issued a request for proposals for an in-vessel sludge composting system which the town would own and operate. After International Process Systems (IPS) of Glastonbury, Connecticut, had been selected, the state announced plans to ban leaf disposal in landfills and incinerators, so Fairfield decided to increase the capacity of the proposed system to compost yard waste. Although the town had been composting leaves for a number of years at the landfill, as well as burning brush and clean wood waste, a decision was made to stop those activities at the landfill and convert it to a park. A committee charged with closing the landfill supported the construction of the composting facility since it would eliminate the use of the landfill site for composting leaves, and provide a soil material to use in reclaiming the landfill.

COMPOSTING 26 PERCENT OF FAIRFIELD SOLID WASTE

The Fairfield facility is designed to treat 6,000 wet tons of sludge per year, although 4,000 wet tons are currently produced. The dewatered sludge is approximately 20 - 22 percent solids as it comes off the filter press.

Annually, Fairfield produces 45,000 tons of municipal solid waste; 12,200 tons of yard waste, stumps, logs and clean waste wood; and 4,000 tons of anaerobically digested sewage sludge. By cocomposting these wastes the town will be recycling 26 percent of this waste stream.

However, according to K.C. Alexander, Senior Environmental Analyst with the Connecticut Department of Environmental Protection, this 26 percent does should not be interpreted as Fairfield achieving the state recycling goal of 25 percent since sewage sludge is considered a "special waste", and leaves are only one of the nine items which state law will require to be 100 percent recycled by January 1, 1991. The mandatory recylables list includes cardboard, metal food containers, glass food containers, scrap metal, leaves, storage batteries, newspaper, office paper, and waste oil.

COMPOSTING PROCESS

IPS describes its process as an "automated multi-bay" composting system which is based on a Japanese technology that has operated for more than 20 years. Modifications to the system during operation since 1986 at the first IPS facility are the basis for pending patent applications for the company's combination of vessel, agitator, and computerized temperature monitoring. Its first facility is located at Lebanon, Connecticut, where EarthGro, Inc., a division of IPS, operates two composting plants which recycle a variety of organic wastes, primarily animal manures. IPS also has a sludge composting facility operating at the Anheuser-Busch brewery in Baldwinsville, N.Y.

The Fairfield facility utilizes a series of six concrete bays inside a building, with each bay 6 feet wide by 6 feet high and 220 feet long. The bays have an automatic agitator which runs on rails on top of the bay walls, mixing the waste material while moving it down the bay. At the end of the bay, the agitator is automatically transferred to the next bay on a trolley.

Composting takes place within a building next door to the treatment plant and across the street from the landfill. Only one person is required to operate the composting building, which requires loading the bays, monitoring temperatures, testing moisture content and housekeeping. Another employee operates the mixer truck, and two persons operate the yard waste processing.

Fiberglass panels in the wall of the building provide natural lighting, and the heat of the composting process will be used to keep the facility warm in winter. Large garage doors on three sides of the building provide access for vehicles as well as fresh air for employees. White pointed out that offensive odors have been so minimal that the garage doors have been left open on warm days.

Six ventilation blowers exhaust air, dust and moisture either to the outside atmosphere, or to a bio-filter built into the ground between the composting building and the treatment plant. The filter media consists of a 5,600 square foot mixture of leaf compost, shredded brush and topsoil. White has used the filter only one time when an unusually smelly batch of sludge was delivered to the plant. According to White, exhaust air from one of the six blowers is being circulated through the filter to maintain sufficient moisture to sustain the bacterial populations living in the filter.

After picking up 3,000 pounds of sludge from the dewatering building (the truck has a built-in scale), a mixer truck picks up chipped yard waste, and blends the material as it is transported to the facility. When the mixer truck is being repaired, the yard waste and sludge are mixed on the tipping floor of the composting facility with a front-end loader. Operators want to achieve a mixture which has a solids content of 40 percent. During the first two months of operation four of the six bays composted chipped brush and sewage sludge at a 1:1 ratio. As the leaf season's annual deluge hit in October, the two additional bays were used to compost 100 percent shredded leaves, and leaves replaced chipped brush as a bulking agent for sludge in ratios ranging between 2:1 and 1:1 leaves to sludge. Other ratios of leaves and sludge are also being tested this fall.

A front end loader deposits the raw waste material into the front of a bay, where it starts a 21 day journey to the other end of the 220 foot long vessel. The agitator machine starts at the back end of the bay by removing the finished compost and moving towards the front, mixing, agitating, and moving the material 12 feet down the bay every day, thus creating space for a new load of waste (each bay has capacity for up to 14 cubic yards per day).

As now operated, the agitator is sent through the sludge compost five times per week. If the bays are mixed seven days a week then the retention time in the bay can be shortened to 18 days, and even less with multiple turnings each day. In order to process as many leaves as possible, the two bays being used for leaves are agitated as much as twice each day. Since an entire batch of leaves had not been processed as of November, it is not yet known if moisture will have to be added during the composting process. So far, it has not been necessary to add moisture to the sludge compost, although, if required, a hand held hose would be utilized. The sludge and chipped brush compost has been coming out of the bays with approximately 60 percent dry solids content.

Within each composting bay, the objective is to achieve the desired temperature of 55 degrees C within approximately three days, and maintain it for at least six days to assure pathogen destruction. Temperature records indicated that one bay of sludge compost maintained at least 55 degrees for 15 consecutive days. Operators try to keep temperatures below 65 degrees C, but have on occasion hit 70 degrees.

Each of the five aeration zones has a blower and a thermocouple in the wall of the bay. The blowers suck air from inside the building and push it up through the bottom of the bays into the pile. The plant operator can program temperatures into the computer which will not be exceeded in each of the five aeration zones since the blowers cool the compost. The blowers can also be set to activate at regular intervals rather than on the basis of temperature.

During these start-up months plant operators have been manually measuring temperatures inside the pile at 10 foot intervals. Since the temperatures measured by the thermocouples in the side walls of the bay are generally lower than temperatures deeper within the piles, White wants to correlate side wall temperatures with the temperatures within the pile. This will allow him to determine optimum "set" temperatures which are entered into the computer. The computer also provides a printed record of the temperatures for each batch of compost and can plot temperatures on a graph.

OPERATING VARIABLES

White observed that the composting system is much more responsive to changes in operating variables than his wastewater treatment plant where it can take several days before an operating change is noticed in the process. Some of the variables which affect the rate of composting at the Fairfield composting facility include: particle size of shredded leaves and brush; mixture ratio of organic material; moisture content of yard waste, which is affected by precipitation; outside air temperature; activation of building ventilation blowers; activation of the five blowers in each bay; frequency which the agitator is run through each bay; the speed which each agitator is run through each bay (10 speed options); and the temperatures in adjoining bays (more rapid heat loss if adjacent bay is empty).

IPS provided the town with an operating manual for the composting plant, but White explained that he will obviously be learning "the art" of operating this particular facility during its first year. During these first months of operation, White said that the six bays can be considered six different experiments as they vary operating conditions and waste inputs.

YARD WASTE AS BULKING AGENT

Leaves are collected curbside by a waste hauler contracted by the town. The yard waste processing operation takes place on the landfill across the street from the sludge composting operation, and is operated by the public works department, which is separate from White's department. White emphasized the importance of coordination between the two departments to ensure a constant flow of ground yard waste for mixing with sludge.

Fairfield will periodically rent a stump grinder to process stumps, trees and clean wood waste too large for the two tub grinders. Along with wood chips from the stump grinder, brush is processed twice, with the first tub grinder using a four inch diameter screen, and the second grinder using a one inch screen to produce inch long slivers of wood. According to Geoffrey Kuter, Senior Vice President of IPS, it is preferable to produce such a small particle size from wood wastes for use in the composting process. By producing small wood chips, it is not necessary to screen the finished compost at this time, although the town is evaluating screening of finished compost for some uses. Since much of the wood particles are not biodegraded in the process, White is currently testing a cellulose enzyme in one bay to see if the wood can be further degraded by composting.

Leaves which are collected in plastic garbage bags are processed just once in a tub grinder. Having two tub grinders also allows processing to continue while one grinder is being repaired.

For this year residents are allowed to put leaves in plastic bags, but use of degradable bags will probably be mandated next year. Besides the presence of plastic in the compost, another problem with outdoor shredding of leaves in plastic bags is the pieces of plastic blowing around the processing site.

White wants the town to conduct an education program so that residents will not put debris other than leaves in bags. Rocks and other large solid objects increase maintenance of the tub grinders and can also jam the compost agitator if it encounters such objects in the composting bay.

A portion of the leaves will be ground up and stockpiled for use as bulking agent during the winter. If all leaves and brush chips are used before the start of the spring yard waste season, White says that compost can be recycled as the bulking agent for sludge. Kuter explained that IPS has successfully tested the use of shredded magazines and glossy paper as a bulking agent for sludge, and Fairfield may utilize these wastes as bulking agents in the future.

APPROVAL PROCESS

The composting facility is permitted by the Connecticut Department of Environmental Protection (DEP) as a modification to Fairfield's sludge disposal process at the wastewater treatment plant and is regulated as a component of the wastewater treatment plant. Although there are no plans to compost other solid wastes at the facility, to do so would require a permit modification.

Instead of preparing an environmental impact statement for the proposed composting facility, Fairfield and IPS submitted a detailed management plan to the DEP which addressed major environmental concerns of leachate, air emissions, odor control, etc. In addition, an extensive approval process was required from numerous town boards on two different occasions; first for funding the design, and then to approve use of municipal bonds to finance construction.

COSTS FOR THE FACILITY

The capital costs for the facility are approximately $3,250,000, which includes a new filter press for sludge dewatering, the mixing truck, two tub grinders, and the building and composting system equipment. The annualized capital costs are $330,000, financed through a 7.25 percent interest rate bond over 20 years. Annual operating and maintenance costs are estimated at approximately $180,000, for a total annual cost of $510,000. The tub grinders are the largest operating expense, estimated at $120,000 per year.

According to Kuter, if the composting facility had not been built, it would have cost Fairfield $398,000 this year to incinerate sludge. White further explained that even though it is costing more to compost the leaves in the facility than it did to compost them on the landfill as they had been doing for a number of years, the value of the landfill space as park land will offset the increased cost of composting their yard waste in the facility. Future cost savings are expected to be substantially greater due to the inevitable escalation of avoided sludge disposal costs at distant incinerators or landfills. Another cost saving is the value of the compost product as a replacement for topsoil.

The town charges $40 per ton to take unchipped wood and brush brought by landscapers and contractors, but does not charge for leaves or chipped brush.

COMPOST MARKETS

The town is taking full responsibility for utilizing and marketing the compost. Compost which is removed from the bays will be stockpiled on the landfill property for future use. The first major use will be to reclaim the landfill as a public park. It is expected that other parks and public works projects will utilize compost, thereby eliminating the need for purchasing screened topsoil at a cost of $30-$40 per ton.

Residents will probably be allowed to pick up small loads of compost for home use, but the town hopes to sell the compost in bulk.

WASTE REDUCTION VIA BACKYARD COMPOSTING

53

THE COMPOST HEAP THAT NEVER STOPS GROWING

Clarence G. Golueke

IN THESE DAYS when so much research involves the use of highly sophisticated and expensive instruments, it is surprising how many advances are made in science with the benefit of simple and makeshift tools. In my own career, some of my best accomplishments were made on a budget that consisted of little more than my salary. An example is the research on composting carried on about 37 years ago at the University of California's Sanitary Engineering Research Laboratory (University of California, Richmond Field Station) and which led to the development of the 14-day compost method.

It began in 1951 when the University received a grant of $5,000 from the State of California to investigate the feasibility of reclaiming municipal refuse through composting. My part in the work came about a year after the grant had been made, and unfortunately, after the grant money had been depleted. At that critical juncture, armed with a brand-new Ph.D. diploma, I was placed in charge of the project, and because of the non-existent budget, I simultaneously became the entire project staff. Happily, I inherited the use of a pick-up truck, a John Deere silage chopper, saw, hammer, nails, and some second-hand lumber, a pair of work-gloves, and a sturdy 4-tined pitchfork which is still in my possession. I did have access to laboratory glassware, chemicals, and basic laboratory apparatus (e.g., balances, drying oven, combustion furnace) and a chemist who did the phosphorus and nitrogen analyses. Also available was a "hot shack," i.e. an 8-by-15-foot frame structure in which the temperature was kept at 120°F., and a few 50-gallon drums.

As is so often the case with apparent disadvantages, those that I encountered proved to be highly useful. For one thing, they led to the adoption of certain constraints, the most important of which is that the simplest workable approach is the one to be sought. The simplest approach obviously is the least expensive and most reliable since there are fewer parts to buy or to fail.

So much for the history, now to describe the research. The description which follows is not a technical one in the sense of a scientific paper, but rather it deals with the rationale behind the work and with the measures taken to compensate for a meager budget. Obviously, with the type of equipment available at the time, it was not feasible to use municipal refuse as the raw material in our first experiments. Moreover, it also made sense to determine in a scientific manner the basic principles involved in composting. The problem then became one of settling upon a waste, the composition of which would be so like that of the compostable material in municipal refuse as to enable findings made with it to be directly applicable to composting the latter. I decided that the vegetable trimmings discarded by grocery stores would be suitable as the main ingredient. Because vegetable trimmings are very moist, and tend to become compacted, it became necessary to find another waste to serve as an "absorbent." (In practice, the "absorbent" also is the principal source of carbon.) In refuse, paper would serve that purpose, although it does become compacted when wettened. My concern about compaction was that the more compacted the material, the fewer the air spaces in the composting pile, in other words it would not be as porous as would be desirable. Since early in the study, I had concluded that aerobic composting was the best type, I wished to keep the composting material as porous as possible. Not being set up to use paper in the first part of the study, I decided to use other wastes, such as dry bones, straw, and sawdust. Towards the end of the pilot-scale studies, I did use paper, since I felt that it would be an appropriate step before moving to large-scale work with municipal refuse.

Inasmuch as composting is a biological process, the logical thing to do would be to evaluate those factors which influence the activity of living organisms—in this case, bacteria, actinomycetes (actually a higher form of bacteria), and fungi. Since in reality a large number of factors can affect biological processes, and my resources were limited, I decided to confine my attention to the more important factors, namely, moisture content, temperature, aeration, pH (acid vs. alkaline), and nutrient availability. I would have liked to have identified the organisms responsible for the activity, if for no other reason than to determine their needs. However, I did not indulge that desire other than to cursorily "key down" (identify) the more prominent groups. In passing, it should be noted that "prominence" does not necessarily imply "most active." In the long run, except from a purely academic point of view, it would have been a "luxury" undertaking, the results of which could be interpreted in terms only of the material and conditions applied in my experiments. The reason is that microbial populations differ with type of material being composted, and even with the locale of a compost operation. Another reason is that in a real-life situation, the total compost process is a function of the *collective* and *integrated* activity of a wide range of organisms; and therefore, the sensible thing to do is to provide those conditions which benefit the process as a whole, and not merely one segment of it.

The subject of microorganisms brings up that of inoculums. Early in the study, the matter of inoculums came up. From the reasoning given in the preceding paragraph I knew that there would be no omnipresent microbe, or even collection of particular microbes, that could be dumped into a pile of raw material and lo-and-behold, convert it to compost! Nevertheless, to be objective about the matter, I did procure samples of several inoculums on the market at the time of the study and tested their effectiveness. In every case, the controls (piles with no inoculum) did just as well as did the inoculated piles. One thing I noticed was that if the directions given with the inoculums were followed, a successful compost operation with or with*out* the inoculum could be accomplished.

Before describing the experiments on environmental conditions, it would be a good idea to say something about the sequence of the study.

In keeping with the scientific approach, I began with bench-scale experiments (using 5-gallon jars) to get a "feel" for the boundary conditions. Then I expanded the scale to 50-gal. drums to test

findings made with the jars. Seeing that my results continued to be applicable, I stepped up to the small scale pilot stage—for me the more interesting phase since it more closely duplicated real-life applications. Toward the end of the study, the City of Berkeley, by providing the necessary equipment and manpower, made it possible to work with municipal refuse, and to do so at the Berkeley landfill site.

The time devoted to the bench-scale experiments was only a few months. The experiments showed that the composting material could be kept sufficiently aerobic to prevent the production of bad odors simply by stirring the contents of a jar each day or even every other day. There was an important condition, however. It was that the material must be neither too wet nor too finely ground. I found the ideal moisture content to range from about 70 to 85 percent when straw, leaves, or sawdust was the absorbent. (A simple way to determine moisture content for the home composter is to remove a sample of raw material and weigh it—about a pound should do. After weighing, place the sample in an oven heated to about 180°F and leave it there for 6 to 8 hours, and then weigh it again. The heat bill can be cut down somewhat by spreading the material in a thin layer and allowing it to dry overnight. Then place the sample in the oven for an hour or two. The loss in weight over the original weight times 100% equals the moisture content. For example, the original weight is 1 lb. (16 oz.) and the final weight is 1/2 lb. (8 oz.), then the percent moisture is the moisture content. Generally, if the material glistens somewhat like dew on the grass, it is sufficiently moist.) When vegetable trimmings constituted the "green" portion, then a particle size of about an inch across was about as small as would be desired. Because of the small volume of the containers and lack of insulation, heat rise in the jars containing the composting material was slight. Of course, the usual chemical tests were run on the samples.

$$\frac{16 \text{ oz.} - 8 \text{ oz.}}{16 \text{ oz.}} = \frac{8}{16} \times 100\% = 50\%$$

For the small pilot studies, I constructed two bins side-by-side (i.e. one wall common to the two bins) in an abandoned building. Because some old $4'' \times 4''$ were on hand, I used them as the corner posts, and some scrap $1'' \times 8''$ to $12''$ boards for the sides. The fronts of the bins were made removable by devising slots on the front $4'' \times 4''$ such that the boards could be slipped up and removed. Incidentally, each bin had a floor area of about $40'' \times 40''$ and was about $60''$ high.

The pick-up truck was especially handy for the bin tests because of the volumes and weights involved. When filled to the full 5-ft. level, each bin held on the order of 1,100 lbs. This meant visiting a number of grocery stores to collect the necessary supply of vegetable trimmings. During the autumn months, I used fallen leaves as the absorbent and principal carbon source. To collect them, I simply parked the truck and took out a rake and proceeded to collect the amount of leaves needed. When the study called for manure, I would persuade a nearby feedlot operator, dairyman, stable operator, or chicken rancher to give me the amount needed, and then transport the manure to the bins.

To provide a uniform basis with respect to time, all material was processed and the experiment started on the day of the collection. Accomplishing this allowed no time for dilly-dallying inasmuch as from 1 to $1\frac{1}{4}$ tons of material were involved. Usually, the materials were gathered by noon. The time from noon until 4:00 or 5:00 p.m. was spent in passing the material through the silage chopper. Setting up the chopped material in the bins could be done within an hour.

The factors of interest in the bin studies included those in the laboratory studies with a few additions. The rise and fall of temperature within the composting material could now be followed because volumes involved were large enough to ensure self-insulation. Required frequency of turning as a function of moisture content was another point, since again, the volume involved was large enough to make findings directly applicable to full-scale operations.

Generally, the moisture content of the mixtures was adequate. When the experiment called for a high moisture content, water was added at the start and during the process in the amounts required. The carbon-nitrogen ratio (C/N) was adjusted to the desired level by varying the proportion of "green" wastes such as fresh plants, vegetable trimmings (rich in nitrogen) to dry wastes (absorbent and mostly carbonaceous). Low C/N's were obtained by the addition of manure. In the experiments calling for pH adjustment, lime was added to keep the mixture at or around 7.0 (neutrality), when it was acid (lower than 7.0). Nothing was done when the pH rose above 7.0. A number of other variables were tried in the bin tests, however, it would be too space consuming to describe them in detail. I determined the temperature of the piles with the use of 12 to 18 inch laboratory glass thermometers. The temperature of the interior of a pile was determined by inserting the thermometer (with a string attached to it) into a hole poked with a stick to the desired depth. The hole was filled around over the thermometer, leaving the string accessible for pulling out the thermometer to read.

Turning was done by muscle power and with the aforesaid 4-tined fork. A fork is ideal for turning because the material can be "sifted" between the tines, thereby fluffing it thoroughly and promoting maximum aeration. In these and in later experimental runs with dairy and pig-farm bedding at the San Quentin State Prison, I found that a well-motivated man moving briskly can turn about 5 to 10 tons of composting material in a 6-hour day.

Generally, the pungent odor of the fresh material disappeared within a couple of days and was replaced by a "cooking" odor. After 5 or 6 days, an earthy odor would become noticeable. At the same time the color would be turning from a dingy gray to a deep brown. These early changes in color and the attainment of the earthy odor bring to mind an important warning, namely, do not jump to the conclusion that the composting process is finished simply because the material has begun to look and smell like compost. Actually, if the material were to receive no further attention beyond this stage, it would become extremely smelly. A more reliable indicator of the completion of the process in terms of safe storage or usage is the final drop in temperature. If all conditions are appropriate, the temperature in a pile rises rapidly, reaching 110 to 120°F. in two or three days, and 150°F. in four or five days. Turning brings about only a temporary drop in temperature. In my experiments, the temperature was back to its prior level within three to four hours after turning—providing no delay ensued in reconstituting the pile. After a couple of weeks (or less), depending upon the nature of the material, the temperature will go down inexorably regardless of optimum conditions. I found that when the temperature had dropped to 100 to 110°F., the process was finished for practical purposes. The problem of establishing techniques for determining when the process has reached completion has been explored extensively. Thus far, no test more reliable than the final drop in temperature has been found. The drop occurs because all of the readily decomposable material has been decomposed. Further decomposition will take place, but it will be slow and the end-products will not be malodorous.

My biggest surprise came when I switched from the "structurally strong" absorbents to paper. On the mistaken assumption that the 70 to 80 percent moisture found to be excellent in preceding experiments would be equally suitable with paper, I adjusted content of the first two batches of material to that level. The first shock came the morning after setting up the bins. What had been a 5-ft. mass, had compacted to about $1\frac{1}{2}$ ft. More mixture was added to bring the pile back to 5 ft. This was repeated on the third day. At the first turning, I noticed that the odor, instead of resembling that of cooking mincemeat, was more like that of a "rotting meat." By the fourth and fifth days, only those strong of stomach could venture near the bins when the contents were being turned. However, remaining unwavering in the face of adversity, I turned the pile twice each day, and by the end of the week the stench of rotting cadavers began to be replaced by that of a good loam, and within a couple of weeks an excellent compost was produced. What had happened was that the compaction of the paper reduced the volume of the interstices (pores) to a point at which air was excluded, and the pile became anaerobic. In other words, the moisture content was too high. In succeeding experiments, I found that the maximum permissible moisture content was from 55 to 60 percent when paper was the principal carbon source.

During the course of the bin studies, I conducted an experiment in which were duplicated the conditions to be encountered by a backyard gardener who did not have a grinder. In this run, the only size reduction applied was that needed to break up over-long plant stalks into pieces that would fit within the bin. The raw material was a mixture of garden debris, dry leaves, and enough vegetable trimmings to bring the volume to somewhat more than a cubic yard. The mixture was composted within two weeks and with only four turnings.

About the time the bin tests were coming to an end, officials of the City of Berkeley approached the University with an invitation to conduct experiments at the City's landfill site. Since the City would meet all expenses it was an invitation that could hardly be refused. The study ran an eminently successful course. It not only provided useful information on composting, but also on the compostion of municipal refuse and the relation between economic level of a population group and the nature of the waste it generated. An opportunity was afforded for including experiments on the composting of raw sewage sludge, of digested sludge, and of cannery wastes with municipal refuse. It also was possible to explore a wide-range of C/N ratios. This was done by selecting materials from certain parts of the City and by pulling out varying amounts of paper from the pile during the sorting process. Experiences at the landfill were many, enough to constitute an article solely about them. Suffice it to state here that the findings made in the laboratory and the bin studies were corroborated by the results of those conducted at the Berkeley site.

Among the findings which might interest the reader, in addition to those mentioned in the preceding paragraphs of this rambling account, are the following: 1) There is no need to worry about acidity or alkalinity. Although a drop in pH takes place at the start, it is not a serious one, and the pile will soon become alkaline. Moreover, when lime is added to raise the pH, it also promotes loss of nitrogen to the atmosphere. 2) Other things being equal, speed of composting is a function of aeration—i.e. frequency of turning. However, with bin composting and hand-turning, nothing is gained by turning more frequently than once every other day, *provided* the moisture content is not too high. An excessively high moisture content can be remedied by turning the pile frequently—once or twice a day. If one is in a hurry and doesn't mind a bit of physical effort, he can compost his garden debris within two weeks by turning the material every other day for a total of about four turnings and *without* additives of any kind. 3) The nose, eyes, and thermometer are the best instruments for monitoring the compost operation in home composting, and perhaps even for large-scale composting. Inadequate aeration leads to the production of foul odors. Failure of the temperature to rise when it should do so means something is wrong. 4) There is no magic and hence no short-cuts in composting. It is a natural, biological process. All we can do is to endeavor to provide optimum conditions.

54

INTEGRATING THE BACKYARD INTO MUNICIPAL PROJECTS

WHILE TREMENDOUS activity is taking place in the collection and centralized composting of yard waste, many municipal and county programs are simultaneously encouraging residents to do backyard composting. The age-old compost heap is taking on new significance in the Age of Waste Reduction.

Notes Doreen Cantor of the Montgomery County, Maryland Division of Environmental Planning: "While the County prefers composting of yard waste to landfilling or incineration, its greatest preference is backyard composting, primarily because it avoids the cost of transportation. We actively encourage backyard composting and will include incentives to backyard composters in any large-scale program."

In this regard, an interesting effort is underway in Texas where Dr. Bill Knoop, a turfgrass expert with the Texas Agricultural Extension Service, urges a shift in traditional lawn care practices. Knoop's "Don't Bag It" Lawn Care Plan recommends that clippings be left on the lawn. Mowing can be done every five days (instead of the usual weekly), with no more than a third of the leaf surface removed at any one time. No thatch problems result, reports Knoop. A similar program in Plano, Texas several years ago saved that city $60,000 in collection costs despite a 12 percent growth in number of households served.

As part of its long-term strategy to manage solid wastes, Seattle has established an aggressive support program for home composting. In 1985, the City contracted with a regional nonprofit group (Tilth) to promote ecologically-sound gardening, which soon led to a composting education and "Master Composter" program. Originally, vol-

unteers were given a pitchfork, compost thermometer, materials to build a compost bin and a training manual. Each year, the public education effort for backyard composting has been greater.

In Bothell, Washington, high school students were trained to go from door-to-door distributing information "to promote home composting and other waste reduction techniques."

TRANSFERRING BASIC KNOW-HOW

Franklin Flower, now retired, and Peter Strom of the New Jersey Cooperative Extension Service concentrated most of their efforts in building successful municipal composting programs. They also focused on how individuals can manage successful *Backyard Leaf Composting*, which was the title of a report they co-authored. It included these simple instructions:

Leaves may be composted by piling them in a heap. Locate the pile where drainage is adequate and there is no standing water. The composting pile should be damp enough that when a sample taken from the interior is squeezed by hand a few drops of water will appear. A shaded area will reduce moisture evaporation from the surface, but tree roots may grow into the pile. If the surface of the pile becomes excessively dry, it will not compost, and those leaves may blow away.

The leaf pile should be at least 4 feet in diameter and 3 feet in height. If it is too small, it is difficult to maintain adequate temperatures for rapid decomposition. The maximum size should be about 5 feet in height and 10 feet in diameter. If the pile is too large, the interior will not obtain the oxygen needed for adequate, odor-free decomposition. If more material is available, lengthen the pile into a rectangular shape while keeping it 10 feet wide and 5 feet high. If there is sufficient space and material, two or three piles will provide greater flexibility. One pile can contain compost for immediate use; the second is actively composting; and the third receives newly fallen leaves. If there is space for only one pile, new material may be added gradually to the top while removing the decomposed product from the bottom.

The pile should be periodically turned or mixed. The main objectives of turning are to shift materials from the outer parts of the pile closer to the center for better decomposition, and to incorporate oxygen. During warm weather, turn the pile once a month. In cool weather frequent turning is not recommended because it allows too much heat to escape. Piles should be turned immediately if ammonia or other offensive odors are detected. If space is available, turn by shifting the entire pile to an adjacent area or bin.

A publication, *Composting in Your Backyard*, prepared by Maryland's Montgomery County begins with a description of its 47-acre asphalt pad where over 80,000 cubic yards of leaves from county residents are composted each year. "We sell all the compost that we produce, mainly to nurseries and landscapers. Its price was $7.50/cubic yard in 1989," explains the report which them makes this most logical statement to residents:

"So where does backyard composting fit in with all these large-scale programs? Well, when you think about it, it's silly to have the county pick up your yard wastes, haul them across the county to compost them, and then sell the product back to you and your neighbors! Yard waste is a valuable raw material if you're willing to put in the work necessary to convert it. You'll be rewarded with rich, sweet-smelling compost—back gold! And you'll be taking one more step towards helping your community deal with its solid waste problem. For those of you who are especially dedicated to the art of composting, you may even want to consider becoming a "Master Composter" and showing your fellow county residents how to begin and improve their piles."

TIPS ON A NATURAL ROUTINE

In his poem, *This Compost*, Walt Whitman gave this quality to the process:

"Behold this compost! behold it well!
Perhaps every mite has once form'd part of a
    sick person—yet behold!
The grass of spring covers the prairies,
The bean bursts noiselessly through the mould
    in the garden,
The delicate spear of the onions pierces upward,
The apple-buds cluster together on the
    apple-branches,
The resurrection of the wheat appears with pale
    visage out of its graves.
What chemistry!
That the winds are not really infectious,
That all is clean forever and forever,
That the cool drink from the well tastes so good,
That blackberries are so flavorous and juicy,
That the fruits of the apple-orchard and the
    orange-orchard, that melons, grapes, peaches,
    plums, will none of them poison me,
That when I recline on the grass I do not catch
    any disease
Now I am terrified at the Earth, it is that calm
    and patient,
It grows such sweet things out of such
    corruptions,
It turns harmless and stainless on its axis, with
    such endless succession of diseased corpses,
It distils such exquisite winds out of such
    infused fetor,
it gives such divine materials to men, and
    accepts such leavings from them at last."

As a garden practice, composting goes back a long way—always making good sense and always a practice that could be done simply—and naturally. As the final pages of this book were being assembled, we came across this traditional and useful backyard composting advice in an early November issue of *The New York Times*. It was offered by Joan Lee Faust, under the traditional title, Nature's Black Gold.

"Now that landfills are running out of space and burning leaves adds to air pollution, the best way to handle garden debris is to recycle it as compost. Here are seven steps to the perfect compost pile:

- Select an out-of-the-way site and make the pile at least five feet wide. Chicken wire or cinder blocks can be used to contain it, but this is not necessary.
- For the base of the pile, make a loose aeration layer about six inches high using twigs, brush and tree prunings.
- Pile leaves on top, up to about two feet high. All tree leaves are suitable to supply carbonaceous material.
- Add a smaller layer of flower and grass clippings and vegetable tops, six inches or so high. These supply nitrogen; a roughly 3-to-1 ratio of carbonaceous to nitrogenous material is necessary.
- Wet the pile to help decomposition.
- Continue this sandwich layering of leaves and clippings. The pile can be built as high as it is wide.

● Without turning, the compost should be ready for use—in garden soil or as mulch around plants—in about six months. To speed decay, turn the entire pile. In cold climates, the pile will freeze and decomposition will be delayed until spring.

Like all significant recycling efforts, yard waste composting has a full scope and full cycle of its own.

COLLECTION
EQUIPMENT

Section
XII

COLLECTION
AND COMPOSTING
EQUIPMENT

57

COLLECTION EQUIPMENT

G ENERALLY, yard waste either can be collected from the home loose or in some form of container. The type of equipment that is utilized in collection varies with the method chosen.

LOOSE COLLECTIONS

There are two basic types of collection equipment used to accomplish a loose collection — mechanical scoops and vacuums.

The most predominant mechanical scoop is the front end loader. These loaders with the standard bucket attachment are not particularly efficient at performing a loose collection, but they are used because of their ready availability in most public works agencies. Several firms make a special "pincer" type bucket that can be attached to front end and skid steer loaders that are well suited for collecting leaves and other yard waste. Davis and San Jose, California perform year round yard waste collections with such equipment and other communities such as Bridgewater, New Jersey and Columbia, South Carolina use them to collect leaves. The capacity of pincer buckets ranges from 1/4 to 2 cubic yards, with one cy bucket costing between $4,000 and $7,500 and two cy buckets costing between $10,000 and $11,000.

Generally, standard and pincer buckets are used in conjunction with dump trucks or garbage packers. The buckets scoop the yard waste from the streets and load it into the available trucks. Another mechanical scoop is the Kolman-Athey Force-Feed Loader. This self-contained unit uses a series of paddles to scoop material onto a conveyor which then dumps into trailing dump trucks. The unit which is used in Olean and Jamestown, New York costs between $85,000 and $100,000.

Manufacturers of mechanical scoops are Ag-Bag Corporation; Kolman-Athey; Tink, Inc.; and Walluski Western Ltd.

The other type of equipment used for loose collection are vacuum machines. These machines suck leaves from the street through a nozzle or hose and blow the leaves into a collection unit. A related machine, manufactured by Ford-New Holland uses a brushing action to collect the leaves and propel them into the collection unit.

Vacuum equipment comes in two types of configurations. Vacuum collectors are "self-contained" units that include both the vacuum machine and a self-dumping collection unit. Generally, the collection units do not offer any compaction capability, but one company, Athey, does have 14 and 18 cy capacity compactor units. The capacity of the collector ranges from 12 to 25 cy. Collectors can be either trailer or chassis mounted and cost between $15,000 and $40,000 for the body or body and trailer.

Vacuum loaders do not include a collection unit, instead load into enclosed containers that are usually built onto dump trucks. Vacuum loaders are usually trailer-mounted so that they can be detached from the truck while it is being dumped, but some manufacturers do make a vacuum loader that can be mounted on the front of a truck. The cost of vacuum loaders is between $6,000 and $25,000, with most in a $10,000 to $15,000 range.

Manufacturers of vacuum collectors are American Road Machinery, Inc.; Athey Products Corporation; Giant-Vac Manufacturing, Inc.; and Haul-All Equipment Systems.

Manufacturers of vacuum loaders are American Road Machinery; Ford - New Holland; Giant-

Vac Manufacturing; Gledhill Road Machinery and Vac-All Div., Leach Co.

CONTAINERIZED COLLECTION

With containerized collection, yard waste is either placed in a bag or plastic bins by the householder and placed at the curb for collection. In this type of system the collector uses standard garbage compactor trucks to pick up the material and take it to the composting site.

With a bagged collection program, at least three different types of bags can be utilized — standard plastic bags, degradable plastic bags or heavy duty paper bags. By using standard plastic bags, a community does not have to become involved in changing the buying habits of its citizens. However, at some point in the composting process, it has to remove the plastic from the yard waste. A number of communities have begun to use either photodegradable or biodegradable plastic bags so that the bags don't have to be removed. Unfortunately, in many cases, while the plastic does in fact degrade, some of the bag manufacturers use a formulation that degrades at a rate less than the composting rate, or in the case of photodegradable plastics bags, of not degrading in the compost pile, thus leaving plastics remaining in the composted material. Additionally, there is some concern about the residue that remains after the plastic degrades and what effect if any it has on compost quality.

Another option available to those who wish to use a bagged collection is paper bags. Unfortunately, special wet strength paper bags cost from 30 to 35 cents each, or approximately three times that of either standard or degradable plastic bags.

Manufacturers of degradable plastic bags are Amko Plastics, Inc.; Colonial Bag Co.; Commercial Plastics; Guardian Poly Industries, Inc.; Home Plastics; Manchester Packing; North American Plastics; Petoskey Plastics, Inc.; Poly-Tech, Inc.; Rollpak and Webster Industries.

Manufacturers of paper bags are International Paper; Stone Container (Dano Enterprises); and Union Camp Corp (Set Point).

For those communities that prefer to not use bags but still want containerized collection, an option would be to utilize plastic bins. As with the collection of recyclable materials, the use of reusable plastic bins is becoming increasingly popular. Their use in communities like Barrington, Illinois and Huntington Woods, Michigan have met with great success.

To collect yard waste using reusable plastic bins, a community can utilize either manual rear or side loading packers or automated side loaders. The size of the containers needed is generally based on the expected amount of yard waste to be collected, with 30 to 90 gallon containers used mainly for single family residences. Containers up to 400 gallons can be shared by neighborhoods. One of the drawbacks to utilizing bins is when the amount of yard waste exceeds the capacity of the bin. In those instances, some form of bag is generally used to hold the overflow.

The cost of containers varies with capacity as well as other factors. Thirty to 32 gallon plastic trash cans range in price from $10 to $15 each. The price of wheeled containers range from $18 to $38 each for 32 gallon units, to $63 to $75 each for 90 gallon. Multi-family units of 300 to 400 gallons cost from $160 to over $200 each.

Manufacturers of plastic yard waste containers are Bonar Plastics; Greif Brothers Corp.; Heil Rotomold; Kirk Manufacturing; Master Cart; Otto Industries; Pawnee Products; Refuse Removal Systems; Reuter, Inc.; Rotational Molding; Rubbermaid; Snyder Industries; SSI Schaeffer; Sulo of America, Inc. and Zarn, Inc.

56

COMPOSTING EQUIPMENT

Although most yard waste composting projects in this country have a simple design and utilize little equipment other than a standard front end loader, projects are becoming both more sophisticated in design and larger in size. At the composting site, there is potential for three separate processing functions - materials preparation, composting and finishing.

Materials preparation, the first step in the process, takes the raw yard waste from the collection program and readies it for composting. The process depends largely on the way yard waste is collected. For instance, if yard waste is collected in standard plastic bags this is the point where the bags are removed. Another activity that can be accomplished in the materials preparation phase is shredding leaves and/or grass and chipping brush or other woody material, as well as blending of any two or more of these materials.

● **Bag Breaking Equipment**—As the size of projects grow, the need for a system other than the manual opening of bags has increased. Today there are several manufacturers that produce bag breaking or ripping units to separate yard waste from the bags. There are two general bag breaker designs. First is a system that utilizes widely spaced flails to slice the bag followed by a trommel screen that actually separates the yard waste from the bag. In the other system, only a trommel is used, but the trommel contains hooks or barbs that cut the bags as they pass through it.

The capacity of bag breaking systems ranges from 10 to 50 tons per hour with the systems costing from $60,000 to $180,000.

Manufacturers of bag breaking systems are Heil Engineered Systems; Lindemann Recycling Equipment, Inc. and Recomp, Inc.

● **Shredding Equipment**—Shredding during the materials preparation phase of a yard waste composting project is used to reduce the volume of the incoming material and thus the space needed for windrows. The shredding operation can also be used to mix or blend various types of yard waste prior to composting. This may be particularly important if grass is to be composted. Although there are merits to the initial shredding, at least several sources including Peter Strom at Rutgers and the Michigan DNR Yard Waste Composting Manual caution against the practice. Strom suggests in some of his work, that shredding at the materials preparation stage speeds up the composting process and thus requires the site operator to increase the frequency of turnings beyond what is normally suggested for the "Rutgers" Low Technology Method. The Michigan manual states that it's better to wait until after the first six to eight weeks of composting so that debris such as bottles can be removed by hand and because the material is "drier and crumbles easier and it blends better after the initial composting phase."

The most widely used type of shredding system is the "tub grinder." This is a hammermill type shredder that has a rotating cylindrical hopper. Some tub grinder units have the capability of processing materials of up to two inches in diameter while others can process material to 12 inches.

Tub grinders that utilize a PTO for a power source cost between $15,000 and $35,000, while self-powered units cost from $36,000 to $131,000.

Manufacturers of tub grinders are Farmhand; Fuel Harvester; and Jones Manufacturing.

Other types of shredding systems beyond tub grinders are being increasingly used at yard waste composting sites. These shredders are generally either hammermill units or slow speed shredders. On the whole, the majority of those systems are capable of processing more material than tub grinders, up to 50 tons per hour, but the cost of the units ranges $75,000 to $400,000.

Manufacturers of other yard waste shredders are Iggesund Recycling, Inc.; Jacobson, Inc.; Recycling Systems, Inc.; Shredding Systems, Inc.; Stumpmaster, Inc. and Universal Engineering.

● **Brush and Wood Chippers**—In projects that plan to collect woody materials, a chipper is a must to reduce the volume of material included in the composting system or set aside as mulch. The infeed capacity of most chippers ranges from 6" to 12" although some whole tree chippers do have larger capacities. In some models of chippers, the chip size can be adjusted through a range of 1/2" to 3" and above, depending upon the size of product that is desired. Some chippers can be powered with a PTO, while others come with self-contained power. The cost of chippers ranges from $10,000 to $50,000.

Manufacturers of chippers are Bandit Industries, Inc.; Lindig Manufacturing Corp.; Olathe Manufacturing, Inc.; Promark Products, Inc.; Recycling Systems, Inc. and Valby Woodchippers.

Composting of yard waste in the United States is done almost exclusively using windrow technology, where the yard waste can be piled to various heights and widths in rows of virtually any length. The material is then turned periodically until the material has become compost.

In most yard waste composting projects, that ubiquitous public works tool—the front end loader—is used to do the turning. However, increasingly project managers are relying on specially-designed compost turners to perform the mixing function. Compost turners are becoming popular because they provide a more complete mixing action than front end loaders, as well as speed both processing and composting time when compared to front end loaders.

● **Compost Turners**—Most compost turners utilize a series of tines placed along a horizontal drum to move through the composting material, turning, mixing, aerating and reforming the pile as it moves along the windrow. As a variation on this action, one company, Kolman-Athey, uses a paddle system to move through and work the material. A new type of turner, developed by Scat Engineering, uses a moving elevating face, equipped with sharp teeth to turn the pile.

Compost turners are designed as self-contained units that straddle the windrow or push the composting material to one side as they operate. Other units are powered by a PTO and either pushed or pulled by a tractor. The PTO powered units move the material to the rear of the machine similar to machines that straddle the windrows. Depending upon the design of the equipment, windrow turners are capable of handling windrows up to 7' high and 18' wide, with production rates up to 3,000 tons per hour. The cost of self-contained units ranges from $100,000 to $200,000. PTO-powered systems range in price from $35,000 to $70,000.

Manufacturers of self-contained windrow turners are Brown Bear Corp.; Eagle Crusher Co. (Cobey); Kolman-Athey; Resource Recovery Systems of Nebraska, Inc.; Scarab Manufacturing; and Scat Engineering.

Manufacturers of PTO-powered windrow turners are Scat Engineering and Wildcat Manufacturing Co.

● **Finishing Process**—The final phase of a yard waste composting system is the finishing of the composted material. The finishing process is designed around the intended market for the compost. If a finishing step is utilized, the material can be screened to remove rocks, plastic and other debris. A shredding process can also be added prior to the screening.

● **Screening equipment**—Most screens on the market that are used for yard waste composting are rotating or trommel screens although vibrating screens are also used. Screening equipment can be purchased with throughput capacities of up to 350 cy per hour. The cost of screens ranges from $60,000 to $135,000.

Manufacturers of Screening Equipment are Heil Engineered Systems; Hobbs-Adams Engineering Co.; Lindemann Recycling Equipment; Parker Manufacturing; Powerscreen of America; Recycling Systems, Inc.

● **Shredder/Screens**—Combined shredder/screens provide an opportunity to reduce the particle size of the compost prior to screening. These combined units are particularly well suited for yard waste composting projects that use front end loaders to turn the material, because the composted material may not be as homogenized as when compost turners are used.

Shredder/screens come in a variety of capacities from 15 to 250+ cy per hour. The cost of the systems are equally varied, with prices ranging from $25,000 to $180,000.

Manufacturers of Shredder/Screeners are Lindig Manufacturing; Powerscreen of America; Resource Recovery Screens; Resource Recovery Systems; and Royer Industries.

DIRECTORY

COMPOSTING EQUIPMENT

● **Materials Preparation**

Bandit Industries
6750 Millbrook Rd.
Remus, MI 49340
517-561-2270

Farmhand, Inc.
6421 Hazeltine Blvd.
Excelsior, MN 55331
612-474-1941

Fuel Harvester Equipment
12759 Loma Rica Dr.
Grass Valley, CA 95945
916-272-7664

The Heil Co.,
Engineered Systems Div.
P.O. Box 593
Milwaukee, WI 53201
414-647-3333

Iggesund Recycling
P.O. Box 380
Nisswa, MN 56468
218-963-4343

Jacobson, Inc.
2445 Nevada Ave. North
Minneapolis, MN 55427
612-544-8781

Jones Manufacturing Co.
Route 1, Box 80
Beemer, NE 68716
402-528-3861

Lindemann Recycling
500 Fifth Ave., Suite 1234
New York, NY 10110
212-382-0630

Lindig Manufacturing
Box 106
St. Paul, MN 55113
612-633-3072

Olathe Manufacturing, Inc.
100 Industrial Parkway
Industrial Airport, KS 66031
913-782-4396

Promark Products, Inc.
330 9th Ave.
Industry, CA 91746
818-961-9783

Recomp, Inc.
1500 East 79th St., Suite 102
Bloomington, MN 55420
612-854-6211

Recycling Systems
P.O. Box 364
Winn, MI 48896
517-866-2800

Shredding Systems, Inc.
P.O. Box 869
Wilsonville, OR 97070
503-682-3633

Stumpmaster, Inc.
P.O. Box 103
Rising Fawn, GA 30738
404-462-2445

Universal Engineering, Div.
of Pettibone Corp.
800 First Ave., NW
Cedar Rapids, IA 52405
319-365-0441

Valby Woodchippers
Northeast Implement Corp.
Box 402
Spencer, NY 14883
607-589-6160

West Salem Machinery Co.
P.O. Box 5288
Salem, OR 97304
503-364-2213

● Compost Turners

Brown Bear Corp.
P.O. Box 148
Lenox, IA 50851
515-333-4551

Eagle Crusher Co., Inc.
(Cobey Composter)
4250 S.R. 309
Galion, OH 44833
419-468-2288

Kolman/Athey
P.O. Box 806
Sioux Falls, SD 57101
605-336-2610

Resource Recovery Systems
of Nebraska, Inc.
Route 4
Sterling, CO 80751
303-522-0663

Scarab Manufacturing
Route 2, Box 40
White Deer, TX 79097
806-883-7621

Scat Engineering
P.O. Box 266
Delhi, IA 52223
319-922-2981

Wildcat Manufacturing Co., Inc.
Box 23
Freeman, SD 57029
605-925-4512

● Finishing Equipment

The Heil Co.,
Engineered Systems Div.
P.O. Box 593
Milwaukee, WI 53201
414-647-3333

Hobbs-Adams Engineering
1100 Holland Rd.
Suffolk, VA 23434
804-539-0231

Lindemann Recycling
500 Fifth Ave.
'New York, NY 10110
212-382-0630

Lindig Manufacturing
Box 106
1877 West County Rd.
St. Paul, MN 55113
612-633-3072

Parker Manufacturing, Inc.
18012 Bothell Highway, S.E.
Bothell, WA 98012
206-486-3547

Powerscreen of America
11300 Electron Dr.
Louisville, KY 40299
502-255-5330

Recycling Systems
P.O. Box 364
Winn, MI 48896
517-866-2800

Resource Recovery Screens
P.O. Box 32035
Detroit, MI 48232
519-977-9852

Resource Recovery Systems
P.O. Box 32965
Detroit, MI 48232
519-736-5481

Royer Industries
P.O. Box 1232
Kingston, PA 18704
717-287-9624

● Thermometers

Reotemp Instrument Corporation
11568 Sorrento Valley Road #10
San Diego, CA 92121
(619) 481-7737

Omega Engineering, Inc.
1 Omega Drive
Stamford, CT 06907

Meriden Cooper Corporation
112 Golden St. Park
Box 692
Meriden, CT 06450
(203) 237-8448

Walden Instrument Supply Company
910 Main Street
Wakefield, MA 01880
(617) 245-2944

YARD WASTE COLLECTION
EQUIPMENT

● **Loose Collection**

Ag-Bag Corporation
P.O. Box 418
Astoria, OR 97103
503-325-2488

American Road Machinery, Inc.
401 Bridge St.
Minerva, OH 44657
216-868-7724

Athey Products Corporation
P.O. Box 669
Raleigh, NC 27602
919-556-5171

Ford - New Holland
500 Diller Ave.
New Holland, PA 17557
717-355-1121

Giant-Vac Manufacturing, Inc.
South Windham, CT 06266
203-423-7741

Gledhill Road Machinery Co.
P.O. Box 567
Galion, OH 44833
419-468-4400

Haul-All Equipment Systems
4115-18 Ave. North
Lethbridge, Alberta,
Canada T1H 5G1
403-328-7719

Tink, Inc.
2361 Durham-Dayton Hwy.
Durham, CA 95938
916-895-0897

Vac-All Div., Leach Co.
P.O. Box 2608
Oshkosh, WI 54903
414-231-2770

Walluski Western Ltd.
P.O. Box 642
Astoria, OR 97103
503-325-5187

● **Containerized Collection - Bags**

Colonial Bag Co.
205 East Fullerton
Carol Stream, IL 60188
312-690-3999

Commercial Plastics Co.
2322 East 13 St.
Ames, IA 50010
515-233-2268

Dano Enterprises, Inc.
(Stone Container)
75 Commercial St.
Plainview, NY 11803
516-349-7300

Guardian Poly Industries, Inc.
238B Ste-Rose Boulevard
Ste-Rose, Laval, Quebec,
Canada H7L 1L6
514-663-9943

Home Plastics
5250 N.E. 17th
Des Moines, IA 50313
515-265-2562

International Paper
International Place I
6400 Poplar Ave.
Memphis, TN 38197
800-321-0293

Manchester Packing
2000 East James Blvd.
St. James, MO 65559
314-265-3569

North American Plastics
921 Industrial Dr.
Aurora, IL 60506
312-896-6200

Petoskey Plastics, Inc.
U.S. 31
Petoskey, MI 49770
800-999-6556

Poly-Tech, Inc.
1401 West 94th St.
Bloomington, MN 55431
612-884-7281

Rollpak
1413 Eisenhower Dr., South
Goshen, IN 46526
219-533-0541

Set Point (Union Camp Corp)
69 Elm St.
Foxboro, MA 02035
508-543-3800

Webster Industries
58 Pulaski St.
Peabody, MA 01960
508-532-2000

● **Containerized Collection - Bins**

Bonar Plastics
1 Valleywood Dr.
Markham, Ontario,
Canada L3R 5L9
416-475-6980

Greif Bros. Corp.
P.O. Box 796
Hebron, OH 43025
614-928-0070

Heil Rotomold
P.O. Box 8676
Chattanooga, TN 37411
615-899-9100

Kirk Manufacturing, Inc.
4052 Highway 56
Houma, LA 70363
504-868-9975

Master Cart
P.O. Box 12543
Fresno, CA 93778
209-233-3277

Otto Industries
P.O. Box 410251
Charlotte, NC 28241
601-922-0331

Pawnee Products
P.O. Box 751
Goddard, KS 67052
316-794-2213

Refuse Removal Systems
P.O. Box 2258
Fair Oaks, CA 95628
800-231-2212

Reuter, Inc.
410 11th Ave., South
Hopkins, MN 55343
612-935-6921

Rotational Molding
17038 South Figueroa St.
Gardena, CA 90248
213-327-5401

Rubbermaid
3124 Valley Ave.
Winchester, VA 22601
703-667-8700

Snyder Industries
P.O. Box 4583
Lincoln, NE 68504
402-467-5221

SSI Schaeffer
666 Dundee Rd., Suite 1501
Northbrook, IL 60062
312-498-4004

Sulo Of America, Inc.
700 Larkspur LDG Cr.,
Suite 199
Larkspur, CA 94939
415-461-8528

Zarn, Inc.
P.O. Box 1350
Reidsville, NC 27320
919-349-3323